PBIS Principal Investigators

Janet L. Kolodner is a Regents' Professor in the School of Interactive Computing in Georgia Institute of Technology's College of Computing. Since 1978, her research has focused on learning from experience, both in computers and in people. She pioneered the Artificial Intelligence method called *case-based reasoning*, providing a way for computers to solve new problems based on their past experiences.

Her book, *Case-Based Reasoning*, synthesizes work across the case-based reasoning research community from its inception to 1993.

Since 1994, Dr. Kolodner has focused on the applications and implications of case-based reasoning for education. In her approach to science education, called Learning by Design™ (LBD), students learn science while pursuing design challenges. Dr. Kolodner has investigated how to create a culture of collaboration and rigorous science talk in classrooms, how to use a project challenge to promote focus on science content, and how students learn and develop when classrooms function as learning communities. Currently, Dr. Kolodner is investigating how to help young people come to think of themselves as scientific reasoners. Dr. Kolodner's research results have been widely published, including in *Cognitive Science, Design Studies,* and *The Journal of the Learning Sciences*.

Dr. Kolodner was founding Director of Georgia Techs' EduTech Institute, served as coordinator of Georgia Techs' Cognitive Science program for many years, and is founding Editor in Chief of *The Journal of the Learning Sciences*. She is a founder of the International Society for the Learning Sciences (ISLS), and she served as its first Executive Officer. She is a fellow of the American Association of Artificial Intelligence (AAAI).

Joseph S. Krajcik is a Professor of Science Education and Associate Dean for Research in the School of Education at the University of Michigan. He works with teachers in science classrooms to bring about sustained change by creating classroom environments in which students find solutions to important intellectual questions that subsume essential curriculum standards and use learning technologies as productivity tools. He seeks to discover what students learn in such environments, as well as to explore and find solutions to challenges that teachers face in enacting such complex instruction. Professor Krajcik has authored and co-authored over 100 manuscripts and makes frequent presentations at international, national and regional conferences that focus on his research, as well as presentations that translate research findings into classroom practice. He is a fellow of the American Association for the Advancement of Science and served as president of the National Association for Research in Science Teaching. Dr. Krajcik co-directs the Center for Highly Interactive Classrooms, Curriculum and Computing in Education at the University of Michigan and is a co-principal investigator in the Center for Curriculum Materials in Science and The National Center for Learning and Teaching Nanoscale Science and Engineering. In 2002, Professor Krajcik was honored to receive a Guest Professorship from Beijing Normal University in Beijing, China. In winter 2005, he was the Weston Visiting Professor of Science Education at the Weizmann Institute of Science in Rehovot, Israel.

Daniel C. Edelson is director of the Geographic Data in Education (GEODE) Initiative at Northwestern University where he is an Associate Professor of the Learning Sciences and Computer Science. Trained as a computer and cognitive scientist, Dr. Edelson develops and studies software and curricula that are informed by contemporary research on learning and motivation. Since 1992, Dr. Edelson has directed a series of projects exploring the use of technology as a catalyst for reform in science education and has led the development of a number of software environments for education. These include My World GIS, a geographic information system for inquiry-based learning, and WorldWatcher, a data visualization and analysis system for gridded geographic data, both of which have been recognized by educators for their contributions to Earth science education. Dr. Edelson is the author of the high school environmental science text, *Investigations in Environmental Science: A Case-Based Approach to the Study of Environmental Systems*. Dr. Edelson is currently engaged in research on professional development and implementation support for schools that have adopted *Investigations in Environmental Science*.

Since 1995, he has been the principal investigator on more than a dozen NSF-funded educational research and development grants, and he is a member of the leadership team of the NSF-funded Center for Curriculum Materials in Science. His research has been widely published, including in the *Journal of the Learning Sciences, The Journal of Research on Science Teaching, The Journal of Geoscience Education*, and *Science Teacher*.

Brian J. Reiser is a Professor of Learning Sciences in the School of Education and Social Policy at Northwestern University. Professor Reiser served as chair of Northwestern's Learning Sciences Ph.D. program from 1993, shortly after its inception, until 2001. His research focuses on the design and enactment of learning environments that support students' inquiry in science, including both science curriculum materials and scaffolded software tools. His research investigates the design of learning environments that scaffold scientific practices, including investigation, argumentation, and explanation; design principles for technology-infused curricula that engage students in inquiry projects; and the teaching practices that support student inquiry.

Professor Reiser also directed BGuILE (Biology Guided Inquiry Learning Environments) to develop software tools for supporting middle school and high school students in analyzing data and constructing explanations with biological data. Reiser is a co-principal investigator in the NSF Center for Curriculum Materials in Science. He recently served as a member of the NRC panel authoring the report *Taking Science to School*. Professor Reiser received his Ph.D. in Cognitive Science from Yale University in 1983.

TEACHER'S PLANNING GUIDE

Project-Based Inquiry Science™

DIVING INTO SCIENCE

IT's ABOUT TIME®

333 North Bedford Road, Mount Kisco, NY 10549
Phone (914) 273-2233 Fax (914) 273-2227
www.its-about-time.com

President
Tom Laster

Director of Product Development
Barbara Zahm, Ph.D.

Creative Director, Design
John Nordland

Project Development Editor
Ruta Demery

Editorial Coordinator
Sarah V. Gruber

Writers/Editors
Heide M. Doss
Jake Gillis

Assistant Editor
Rhonda Gordon

Production/Studio Manager
Robert Schwalb

Layout and Production
Kadi Sarv

Production
Sean Campbell

Creative Artwork
Dennis Falcon

Technical Art
Marie Killoran

Photo Research
Michael Hortens

Content and Safety Reviewer
Edward Robeck

The 2nd printing of *Diving Into Science* was completed by Courier Kendallville, Inc. in
Kendallville, IN in March 2012.

ISBN 978-1-58591-605-4

2nd Printing

2 3 4 5 CK 15 14 13 12

This project was supported, in part, by the **National Science Foundation**
under grant nos. 0137807, 0527341, and 0639978.
Opinions expressed are those of the authors and not necessarily
those of the National Science Foundation.

Acknowledgements

Three research teams contributed to the development of Project-Based Inquiry Science (PBIS): a team at Georgia Institute of Technology headed by Janet L. Kolodner, a team at Northwestern University headed by Daniel Edelson and Brian Reiser, and a team at University of Michigan headed by Joseph Krajcik and Ron Marx. Each of the PBIS units was originally developed by one of these teams and then later revised and edited to be a part of the full three-year middle-school curriculum that became PBIS.

PBIS has its roots in two educational approaches, Project-Based Science and Learning by Design™. Project-Based Science suggests that students should learn science through engaging in the same kinds of inquiry practices scientists use, in the context of scientific problems relevant to their lives and using tools authentic to science. Project-Based Science was originally conceived in the hi-ce Center at University of Michigan, with funding from the National Science Foundation. Learning by Design™ derives from Problem-Based Learning and suggests sequencing, social practices, and reflective activities for promoting learning. It engages students in design practices, including the use of iteration and deliberate reflection. LBD was conceived at Georgia Institute of Technology, with funding from the National Science Foundation, DARPA, and the McDonnell Foundation.

The development of the integrated PBIS curriculum was supported by the National Science Foundation under grants no. 0137807, 0527341, and 0639978. Any opinions, findings and conclusions, or recommendations expressed in this material are those of the authors and do not necessarily reflect the views of the National Science Foundation.

PBIS Team

Principal Investigator
Janet L. Kolodner

Co-Principal Investigators
Daniel C. Edelson
Joseph S. Krajcik
Brian J. Reiser

NSF Program Officer
Gerhard Salinger

Curriculum Developers
Michael T. Ryan
Mary L. Starr

Teacher's Edition Developers
Rebecca M. Schneider
Mary L. Starr

Literacy Specialist
LeeAnn M. Sutherland

NSF Program Reviewer
Arthur Eisenkraft

Project Coordinator
Juliana Lancaster

External Evaluators
The Learning Partnership
Steven M. McGee
Jennifer Witers

The Georgia Institute of Technology Team

Project Director:
Janet L. Kolodner

Development of PBIS units at the Georgia Institute of Technology was conducted in conjunction with the Learning by Design™ Research group (LBD), Janet L. Kolodner, PI.

Lead Developers, Physical Science:
David Crismond
Michael T. Ryan

Lead Developer, Earth Science:
Paul J. Camp

Assessment and Evaluation:
Barbara Fasse
Daniel Hickey
Jackie Gray
Laura Vandewiele
Jennifer Holbrook

Project Pioneers:
JoAnne Collins
David Crismond
Joanna Fox
Alice Gertzman
Mark Guzdial
Cindy Hmelo-Silver
Douglas Holton
Roland Hubscher
N. Hari Narayanan
Wendy Newstetter
Valery Petrushin
Kathy Politis
Sadhana Puntambekar
David Rector
Janice Young

The Northwestern University Team

Project Directors:
Daniel Edelson
Brian Reiser

Lead Developer, Biology:
David Kanter

Lead Developers, Earth Science:
Jennifer Mundt Leimberer
Darlene Slusher

Development of PBIS units at Northwestern was conducted in conjunction with:

The Center for Learning Technologies in Urban Schools (LeTUS) at Northwestern, and the Chicago Public Schools
Louis Gomez, PI;
Clifton Burgess, PI
for Chicago Public Schools.

The BioQ Collaborative
David Kanter, PI.

The Biology Guided Learning Environments (BGuILE) Project
Brian Reiser, PI.

The Geographic Data in Education (GEODE) Initiative
Daniel Edelson, Director

The Center for Curriculum Materials in Science at Northwestern
Brian Reiser,
Daniel Edelson,
Bruce Sherin, PIs.

The University of Michigan Team

Project Directors:
Joseph Krajcik
Ron Marx

Literacy Specialist:
LeeAnn M. Sutherland

Project Coordinator:
Mary L. Starr

Development of PBIS units at University of Michigan was conducted in conjunction with:

The Center for Learning Technologies in Urban Schools (LeTUS)
Ron Marx, Phyllis Blumenfeld,
Barry Fishman,
Joseph Krajcik,
Elliot Soloway, PIs.

The Detroit Public Schools
Juanita Clay-Chambers
Deborah Peek-Brown

The Center for Highly Interactive Computing in Education (hi-ce)
Ron Marx,
Phyllis Blumenfeld,
Barry Fishman,
Joe Krajcik,
Elliot Soloway,
Elizabeth Moje,
LeeAnn Sutherland, PIs.

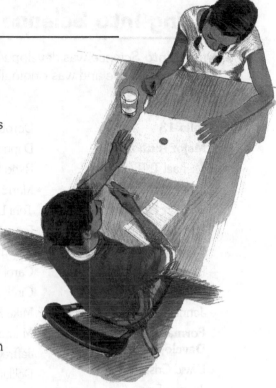

Field-Test Teachers

National Field Test
Tamica Andrew
Leslie Baker
Jeanne Bayer
Gretchen Bryant
Boris Consuegra
Daun D'Aversa
Candi DiMauro
Kristie L. Divinski
Donna M. Dowd
Jason Fiorito
Lara Fish
Christine Gleason
Christine Hallerman
Terri L. Hart-Parker
Jennifer Hunn
Rhonda K. Hunter
Jessica Jones
Dawn Kuppersmith
Anthony F. Lawrence
Ann Novak
Rise Orsini
Tracy E. Parham
Cheryl Sgro-Ellis
Debra Tenenbaum
Sara B. Topper
Becky Watts
Debra A. Williams
Ingrid M. Woolfolk
Ping-Jade Yang

**New York City
Field Test**
*Several sequences of PBIS
units have been field tested
in New York City under the
leadership of Whitney Lukens,
Staff Developer for Region 9,
and Greg Borman, Science
Instructional Specialist,
New York City Department of
Education*

6th Grade
Norman Agard
Tazinmudin Ali
Heather Guthartz Aniba
Asher Arzonane
Asli Aydin
Joshua Blum
Filomena Borrero

Shareese Blakely
John J. Blaylock
Tsedey Bogale
Zachary Brachio
Thelma Brown
Alicia Browne-Jones
Scott Bullis
Maximo Cabral
Lionel Callender
Matthew Carpenter
Ana Maria Castro
Diane Castro
Anne Chan
Ligia Chiorean
Boris Consuegra
Careen Halton Cooper
Cinnamon Czarnecki
Kristin Decker
Nancy Dejean
Gina DiCicco
Donna Dowd
Lizanne Espina
Joan Ferrato
Matt Finnerty
Jacqueline Flicker
Helen Fludd
Leigh Summers Frey
Helene Friedman-Hager
Diana Gering
Matthew Giles
Lucy Gill
Steven Gladden
Greg Grambo
Carrie Grodin-Vehling
Stephan Joanides
Kathryn Kadei
Paraskevi Karangunis
Cynthia Kerns
Martine Lalanne
Erin Lalor
Jennifer Lerman
Sara Lugert
Whitney Lukens
Dana Martorella
Christine Mazurek
Janine McGeown
Chevelle McKeever
Kevin Meyer
Jennifer Miller
Nicholas Miller
Diana Neligan

Caitlin Van Ness
Marlyn Orque
Eloisa Gelo Ortiz
Gina Papadopoulos
Tim Perez
Albertha Petrochilos
Christopher Poli
Kristina Rodriguez
Nadiesta Sanchez
Annette Schavez
Hilary Sedgwitch
Elissa Seto
Laura Shectman
Audrey Shmuel
Ragini Singhal
Katherine Silva
C. Nicole Smith
Gitangali Sohit
Justin Stein
Thomas Tapia
Eilish Walsh-Lennon
Lisa Wong
Brian Yanek
Cesar Yarleque
David Zaretsky
Colleen Zarinsky

7th Grade
Mayra Amaro
Emmanuel Anastasiou
Cheryl Barnhill
Bryce Cahn
Ligia Chiorean
Ben Colella
Boris Consuegra
Careen Halton Cooper
Elizabeth Derse
Urmilla Dhanraj
Gina DiCicco
Lydia Doubleday
Lizanne Espina
Matt Finnerty
Steven Gladden
Stephanie Goldberg
Nicholas Graham
Robert Hunter
Charlene Joseph
Ketlynne Joseph
Kimberly Kavazanjian
Christine Kennedy
Bakwah Kotung

Lisa Kraker
Anthony Lett
Herb Lippe
Jennifer Lopez
Jill Mastromarino
Kerry McKie
Christie Morgado
Patrick O'Connor
Agnes Ochiagha
Tim Perez
Nadia Piltser
Chris Poli
Carmelo Ruiz
Kim Sanders
Leslie Schiavone
Ileana Solla
Jacqueline Taylor
Purvi Vora
Ester Wiltz
Carla Yuille
Marcy Sexauer Zacchea
Lidan Zhou

Diving Into Science

Diving Into Science was developed at the Georgia Institute of Technology as part of the Learning by Design™ initiative and was originally titled *Apollo 13: The Launcher Unit.*

Apollo 13

Major Authors
Michael T. Ryan
Janet L. Kolodner
Jennifer Holbrook
David Crismond

Contributing Authors
Paul J. Camp
Jackie Gray
Jennifer Turns

Formative Development
David Crismond
Joanna Fox
Jackie Gray
Cami Heck
Jennifer Holbrook
Susan McClendon
Kristine Nagel
Lindy Wine
Janice Young

Pilot Teachers
Barbara Blasch
Audrey Daniel
Pam Davis
Carmen Dillard
Yvette Fernandez
Joyce Gamble

Dorothy Hicks
Daphne Islam-Gordon
Rudo Kashiri
Marni Klein
Toni Laman
Paige Lefont
Susan McClendon
Carol Pennington
Cindy Rhew
Mike Ryan
Maureen Shalinski
Jeffrey Slater
Delilah Springer
Lindy Wine
Avis Winfield
Mary Winn

Diving Into Science

PBIS Development Team
Michael T. Ryan
Mary L. Star
Janet L. Kolodner

Contributing Field-test teachers
Asher Arzonane
Suzy Bachman
Greg Borman
Matthew Carpenter

Anne Chan
Lizanne Espina
Enrique Garcia
Steven Gladden
Greg Grambo
Lillian Arlia Grippo
Dani Horowitz
Nicole Shiu Horowitz
Stephan Joanides
Verneda Johnson
Sunny Kam

Crystal Marsh
Kristin McNichol
Melissa Nathan
Tim Perez
Christopher Poli
Nadiesta Sanchez
Caitlin Van Ness
Melanie Wenger
Cesar Yarleque
Renee Zalewitz

Development of *Diving Into Science,* previously called *Apollo 13: The Launcher Unit,* was supported in part by the National Science Foundation under grants no. 9553583, 9818828, and 0208059 and by grants from the McDonnell Foundation, the BellSouth Foundation, the Woodruff Foundation, and the Georgia Tech Foundation.
Any opinions, findings, and conclusions or recommendations expressed in this material are those of the authors and do not necessarily reflect the views of the National Science Foundation.

Diving Into Science Teacher's Planning Guide

Learning Set 1
The Book-Support Challenge

Collaboration, building on the work of others, iteration, criteria and constraints, design process, keeping good records, science of support.

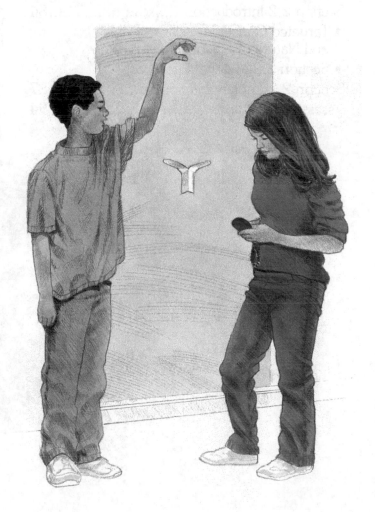

Learning Set 2
The Sandwich-Cookie Challenge

Recording information, graphing results, factors that lead to variation, reliability, inexactness and uncertainty in science.

Learning Set 3

The Whirligig Challenge

Factors that lead to variation, manipulated (independent) and responding (dependent) variables, designing experiments, reliability, fair tests, physics of falling objects, using evidence to support claims, explanation, collaboration.

Learning Set 4
The Parachute Challenge

Fair tests, independent and dependent variables, designing experiments, keeping good records, graphing, physics of falling objects, using evidence to support claims, explanation, collaboration, iteration, applying science knowledge.

4.0 Learning Set Introduction

Welcome to Project-Based Inquiry Science!

Welcome to Project-Based Inquiry Science (PBIS): A Middle-School Science Curriculum!

This year, your students will be learning the way scientists learn, exploring interesting questions and challenges, reading about what other scientists have discovered, investigating, experimenting, gathering evidence, and forming explanations. They will learn to collaborate with others to find answers and to share their learning in a variety of ways. In the process, they will come to see science in a whole new, exciting way that will motivate them throughout their educational experiences and beyond.

What is PBIS?

In project-based inquiry learning, students investigate scientific content and learn science practices in the context of attempting to address challenges in or answer questions about the world around them. Early activities introducing students to a challenge help them to generate issues that need to be investigated, making inquiry a student-driven endeavor. Students investigate as scientists would, through observations, designing and running experiments, designing, building, and running models, reading written material, and so on, as appropriate. Throughout each project, students might make use of technology and computer tools that support their efforts in observation, experimentation, modeling, analysis, and reflection. Teachers support and guide the student inquiries by framing the guiding challenge or question, presenting crucial lessons, managing the sequencing of activities, and eliciting and steering discussion and collaboration among the students. At the completion of a project, students publicly exhibit what they have learned along with their solutions to the specific challenge. Personal reflection to help students learn from the experience is embedded in student activities, as are opportunities for assessment.

The curriculum will provide three years of piloted project-based inquiry materials for middle school-science. Individual curriculum units have been defined that cover the scope of the national content and process standards for the middle-school grades. Each unit focuses on helping students acquire qualitative understanding of targeted science principles and move toward quantitative understanding, is infused with technology, and provides a foundation in reasoning skills, science content, and science process that will ready them for more advanced science. The curriculum as a whole introduces students to a wide range of investigative approaches in science (e.g., experimentation, modeling) and is designed to help them develop scientific reasoning skills that span those investigative approaches.

Technology can be used in project-based inquiry to make available to students some of the same kinds of tools and aids used by scientists in the field. These range from pencil-and-paper tools for organized data recording, collection, and management to software tools for analysis, simulation, modeling, and other tasks. Such infusion provides a platform for providing prompts, hints, examples, and other kinds of aids to students as they are engaging in scientific reasoning. The learning technologies and tools that are integrated into the curriculum offer essential scaffolding to students as they are developing their scientific reasoning skills and are seamlessly infused into the overall completion of project activities and investigations.

Standards-Based Development

Development of each curriculum Unit begins by identifying the specific relevant national standards to be addressed. Each Unit has been designed to cover a specific portion of the national standards. This phase of development also includes an analysis of curriculum requirements across multiple states. Our intent is to deliver a product that will provide coverage of the content deemed essential on the widest practical scope and that will be easily adaptable to the needs of teachers across the country.

Once the appropriate standards have been identified, the development team works to define specific learning goals built from those standards, and takes into account conceptions and misunderstandings common among middle-school students. An orienting design challenge or driving question for investigation is chosen that motivates achieving those learning goals, and the team then sequences activities and the presentation of specific concepts, so that students can construct an accurate understanding of the subject matter.

Inquiry-Based Design

The individual curriculum Units present two types of projects; engineering-design challenges and driving-question investigations. Design-challenge Units begin by presenting students with a scenario and problem and challenging them to design a device or plan that will solve the problem. Driving-question investigations begin by presenting students with a complex question with real-world implications. Students are challenged to develop answers to the questions. The scenario and problem in the design units and the driving question in the investigation Units are carefully selected to lead the students into investigation of specific science concepts, and the solution processes are carefully structured to require use of specific scientific reasoning skills.

Pedagogical Rationale

Research shows that individual project-based learning units promote excitement and deep learning of the targeted concepts. However, achieving deep, flexible, transferable learning of cross-disciplinary content (e.g., the notion of a model, time scale, variable, experiment) and science practice requires a learning environment that consistently, persistently, and pervasively encourages the use of such content and practices over an extended period of time. By developing project-based inquiry materials that cover the spectrum of middle-school science content in a coherent framework, we provide this extended exposure to the type of learning environment most likely to produce competent scientific thinkers who are well grounded in their understanding of both basic science concepts and the standards and practices of science in general.

Evidence of Effectiveness

There is compelling evidence showing that a project-based inquiry approach meets this goal. Working at Georgia Tech, the University of Michigan, and Northwestern University, we have developed, piloted, and/or field-tested many individual project-based units. Our evaluation evidence shows that these materials engage students well and are manageable by teachers, and that students learn both content and process skills. In every summative evaluation, student performance on post-tests improved significantly from pretest performance (Krajcik, et al., 2000; Holbrook, et. al., 2001; Gray et. al. 2001). For example, in the second year in a project-based classroom in Detroit, the average student at post-test scored at about the 95th percentile of the pre-test distribution. Further, we have repeatedly documented significant gains in content knowledge relative to other inquiry-based (but not project-based) instructional methods. In

one set of results, performance by a project-based class in Atlanta doubled on the content test while the matched comparison class (with an excellent teacher) experienced only a 20% gain (significance $p < .001$). Other comparisons have shown more modest differences, but project-based students consistently perform better than their comparisons. Most exciting about the Atlanta results is that results from performance assessments show that, within comparable student populations, project-based students score higher on all categories of problem-solving

and analysis and are more sophisticated at science practice and managing a collaborative scientific investigation. Indeed, the performance of average-ability project-based students is often statistically indistinguishable from or better than performance of comparison honors students learning in an inquiry-oriented but not project-based classroom. The Chicago group also has documented significant change in process skills in project-based classrooms. Students become more effective in constructing and critiquing scientific arguments (Sandoval, 1998) and in constructing scientific explanations using discipline-specific knowledge, such as evolutionary explanations for animal behavior (Smith & Reiser, 1998).

Researchers at Northwestern have also investigated the change in classroom practices that are elicited by project-based units. Analyses of the artifacts students produce indicate that students are engaging in ambitious learning practices, requiring weighing and synthesizing many results from complex analyses of data, constructing scientific arguments that require synthesizing results from multiple complex analyses of data (Edelson et al, 1998; Reiser et al, 2001). Students are engaged in planning, performing, monitoring and revising their investigations, and reporting on their investigation processes as well as their results (Loh et al, 1998). In general, the classrooms engaging in project-based activities reveal substantial moves toward a scientific discourse community in which students focus on arguing from evidence, critiquing ideas, and conjecturing, rather than simply reporting on what they have read or been told (Tabak & Reiser, 1997).

Introducing PBIS

What Do Scientists Do?

1) Scientists...address big challenges and big questions.

Students will find many different kinds of big challenges and questions in PBIS Units. Some ask them to think about why something is a certain way. Some ask them to think about what causes something to change. Some challenge them to design a solution to a problem. Most are about things that can and do happen in the real world.

Understand the Big Challenge or Question

As students get started with each Unit, they will do activities that help them understand the *Big Question* or challenge for that unit. They will think about what they already know that might help them, and they will identify some of the new things they will need to learn.

Project Board

The *Project Board* helps you and your students keep track of their learning. For each challenge or question, they will use a *Project Board* to keep track of what they know, what they need to learn, and what they are learning. As they learn and gather evidence, they will record that on the *Project Board*. After they have answered each small question or challenge, they will return to the *Project Board* to record how what they have learned helps them answer the *Big Question* or *Challenge*.

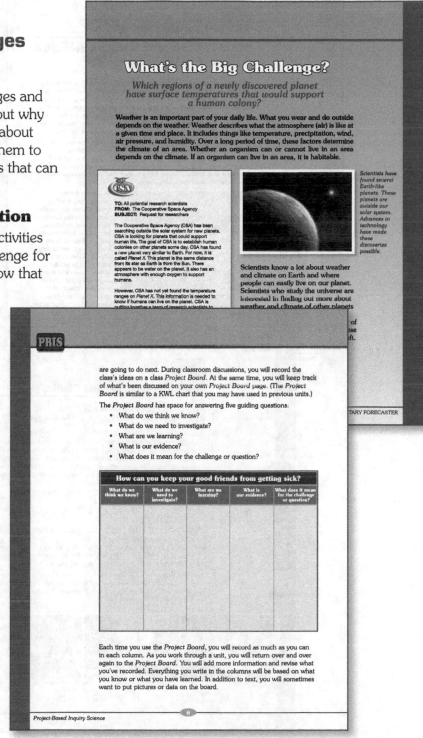

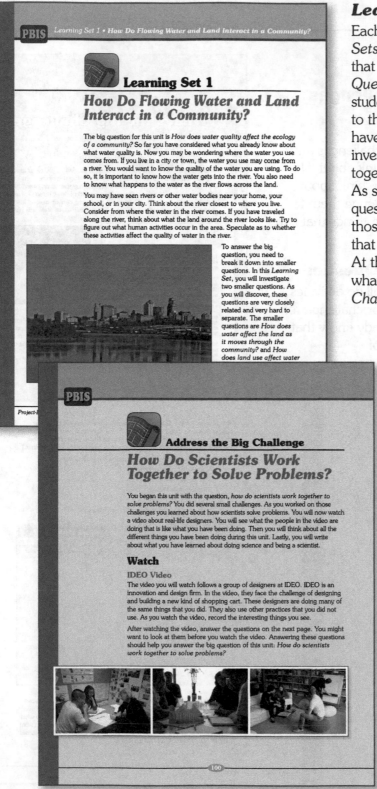

Learning Sets

Each Unit is composed of a group of *Learning Sets*, one for each of the smaller questions that needs to be answered to address the *Big Question* or *Challenge*. In each *Learning Set*, students will investigate and read to find answers to the *Learning Set's* question. They will also have a chance to share the results of their investigations with thier classmates and work together to make sense of what they are learning. As students come to understand answers to the questions on the *Project Board*, you will record those answers and the evidence they collected that convinces them of what they have learned. At the end of each *Learning Set*, they will apply what they have learned to the *Big Question* or *Challenge*.

Address the Big Challenge/ Answer the Big Question

At the end of each Unit, students will put everything they have learned together to tackle the *Big Challenge* or *Question*.

2) Scientists...address smaller questions and challenges.

What Students Do in a *Learning Set*

Understanding the Question or Challenge

At the start of each *Learning Set*, students will usually do activities that will help them understand the *Learning Set's* question or challenge and recognize what they already know that can help them answer the question or achieve the challenge. Usually, They will visit the *Project Board* after these activities and record on it the even smaller questions that they need to investigate to answer a *Learning Set's* question.

Investigate/Explore

There are many different kinds of nvestigations students might do to find answers to questions. In the *Learning Sets, they* you might

- design and run experiments
- design and run simulations
- design and build models
- examine large sets of data

Don't worry if your students haven't done these things before.
The text will provide them with lots of help in designing their investigations and in analyzing thier data.

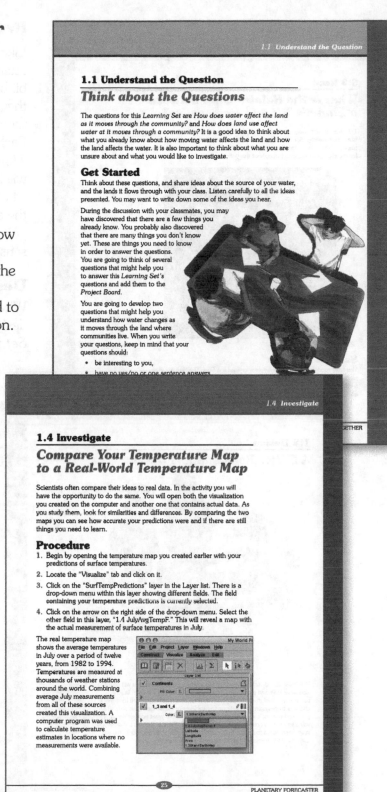

1.1 Understand the Question

1.1 Understand the Question

Think about the Questions

The questions for this *Learning Set* are *How does water affect the land as it moves through the community?* and *How does land use affect water at it moves through a community?* It is a good idea to think about what you already know about how moving water affects the land and how the land affects the water. It is also important to think about what you are unsure about and what you would like to investigate.

Get Started

Think about these questions, and share ideas about the source of your water, and the lands it flows through with your class. Listen carefully to all the ideas presented. You may want to write down some of the ideas you hear.

During the discussion with your classmates, you may have discovered that there are a few things you already know. You probably also discovered that there are many things you don't know yet. These are things you need to know in order to answer the questions. You are going to think of several questions that might help you to answer this *Learning Set's* questions and add them to the *Project Board*.

You are going to develop two questions that might help you understand how water changes as it moves through the land where communities live. When you write your questions, keep in mind that your questions should:

- be interesting to you,
- have no yes/no or one sentence answers

1.4 Investigate

1.4 Investigate

Compare Your Temperature Map to a Real-World Temperature Map

Scientists often compare their ideas to real data. In the activity you will have the opportunity to do the same. You will open both the visualization you created on the computer and another one that contains actual data. As you study them, look for similarities and differences. By comparing the two maps you can see how accurate your predictions were and if there are still things you need to learn.

Procedure

1. Begin by opening the temperature map you created earlier with your predictions of surface temperatures.
2. Locate the "Visualize" tab and click on it.
3. Click on the "SurfTempPredictions" layer in the Layer list. There is a drop-down menu within this layer showing different fields. The field containing your temperature predictions is currently selected.
4. Click on the arrow on the right side of the drop-down menu. Select the other field in this layer, "1.4 JulyAvgTempF." This will reveal a map with the actual measurement of surface temperatures in July.

The real temperature map shows the average temperatures in July over a period of twelve years, from 1982 to 1994. Temperatures are measured at thousands of weather stations around the world. Combining average July measurements from all of these sources created this visualization. A computer program was used to calculate temperature estimates in locations where no measurements were available.

25

PLANETARY FORECASTER

Read

Like scientists, students will also read about the science they are learning. They will read a little bit before you investigate, but most of the reading they do will be to help them understand what they have experienced or seen in an investigation. Each time they read, the text will include *Stop and Think* questions after the reading. These questions will help students gauge how well they understand what they have read. Usually, the class will discuss the answers to *Stop and Think* questions before going on so that everybody has a chance to make sense of the reading.

Design and Build

When the *Big Challenge* for a Unit asks you to design something, the challenge in a *Learning Set* might also ask them to design something and make it work. Often students will design a part of the thing they will design and build for the *Big Challenge*. When a *Learning Set* challenges you to design and build something, they will do several things:

- Identify what questions you need to answer to be successful;

- Investigate to find answers to those questions;

- Use those answers to plan a good design solution;

- Build and test your design.

Because designs don't always work the way one wants them to, students will usually do a design challenge more than once. Each time through, they will test your design. If thier design doesn't work as well as they would like, they will determine why it is not working and identify other things they need to learn to make it work better. Then they will learn those things and try again.

Explain and Recommend

A big part of what scientists do is explain, or try to make sense of why things happen the way they do. An explanation describes why something is the way it is or behaves the way it does. An explanation is a statement one makes built from claims (what you think you know), evidence (from an investigation) that supports the claim, and science knowledge. As they learn, scientists get better at explaining. You will see that students get better too as they work through the *Learning Sets*.

A recommendation is a special kind of claim—one where you advise somebody about what to do. Students will make recommendations and support them with evidence, science knowledge, and explanations.

3.5 Explain
Create an Explanation

After scientists get results from an investigation, they try to make a claim. They base their claim on what their evidence shows. They also use what they already know to make their claim. They explain why their claim is valid. The purpose of a science explanation is to help others understand the following:

- what was learned from a set of investigations
- why the scientists reached this conclusion

Later, other scientists will use these explanations to help them explain other phenomena. The explanations will also help them predict what will happen in other situations.

You will do the same thing now. Your claim will be the trend you found in your experiment. You will use data you collected and science knowledge you have read to create a good explanation. This will help you decide whether your claim is valid. You will be reporting the results of the investigation to your classmates. With a good explanation that matches your claim, you can convince them that your claim is valid.

Because your understanding of the science of forces is not complete, you may not be able to fully explain your results. But you will use what you have read to come up with your best explanation. Scientists finding out about new things do the same thing. When they only partly understand something, it is impossible for them to form a "perfect" explanation. They do the best they can based on what they understand. As they learn more, they make their explanations better. This is what you will do now and what you will be doing throughout PBIS. You will explain your results the best you can based

4.3 Explain and Recommend
Explanations and Recommendations about Parachutes

As you did after your whirligig experiments, you will spend some time now explaining your results. You will also try to come up with recommendations. Remember that explanations include your claims, the evidence for your claims, and the science you know that can help you understand the claim. A recommendation is a statement about what someone should do. The best recommendations also have evidence, science, and an explanation associated with them. In the *Whirligig Challenge*, you created explanations and recommendations separately from each other. This time you will work on both at the same time.

Create and Share Your Recommendation and Explanation

Work with your group. Use the hints on the *Create Your Explanation* pages to make your first attempt at explaining your results. You'll read about parachute science later. After that, you will probably want to revise your explanations. Right now, use the science you learned during the *Whirligig Challenge* for your first attempt.

Write your recommendation. It should be about designing a slow-falling parachute. Remember that it should be written so that it will help someone else. They should be able to apply what you have learned about the effects of your variable. If you are having trouble, review the example in *Learning Set 3*.

Create Your Explanation

Name: _____ Date: _____

Use this page to explain the lesson of your recent investigations.

Write a brief summary of the results from your investigation. You will use this summary to help you write your Explanation.

Claim – a statement of what you understand or a conclusion that you have reached from an investigation or a set of investigations.

Evidence – data collected during investigations and trends in that data.

Science knowledge – knowledge about how things work. You may have learned this through reading, talking to an expert, discussion, or other experiences.

Write your Explanation using the Claim, Evidence and Science knowledge.

81

DIVING IN TO SCIENCE

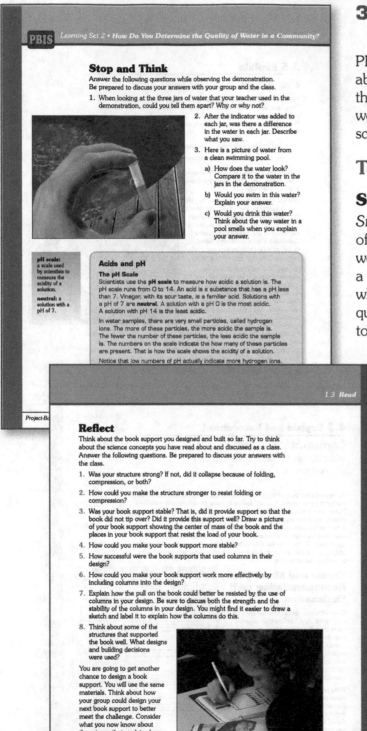

3) Scientists...reflect in many different ways.

PBIS provides guidance to help students think about what they are doing and to recognize what they are learning. Doing this often as they are working will help students be successful student scientists.

Tools for Making Sense

Stop and Think

Stop and Think sections help students make sense of what they been doing in the section they are working on. *Stop and Think* sections include a set of questions to help students understand what they have just read or done. Sometimes the questions will remind them of something they need to pay more attention to. Sometimes they will help students connect what they have just read to things they already know. When there is a *Stop and Think* in the text, students will work individually or with a partner to answer the questions, and then the whole class will discuss what they have learned.

Reflect

Reflect sections help students connect what they have just done with other things they have read or done earlier in the Unit (or in another Unit). When there is a *Reflect* in the text, students will work individually or with a partner or small group to answer the questions, and then the whole class will discuss what they have learned. You may want to ask students to answer *Reflect* questions for homework.

Analyze Your Data

Whenever students have to analyze data, the text will provide hints about how to do that and what to look for.

Mess About

"Messing about" is a term that comes from design. It means exploring the materials to be used for designing or building something or examining something that works like what it to be be designed. Messing about helps students discover new ideas — and it can be a lot of fun. The text will usually give them ideas about things to notice as they are messing about.

What's the Point?

At the end of each *Learning Set*, students will find a summary, called *What's the Point*, of the important things we hope they learned from the *Learning Set*. These summaries can help students member how what they did and learned is connected to the *Big Challenge* or *Question* they are working on.

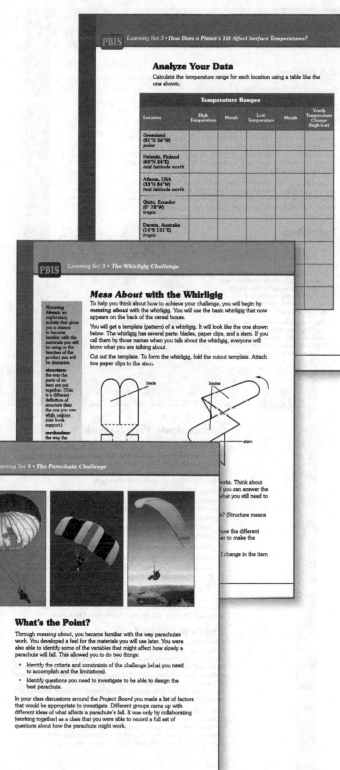

3.5 Explore

Connections to Other Living Things

You looked at how small organisms and plants in an aquatic ecosystem can be affected by changes in water quality. It might seem obvious that organisms that interact with the water would be affected. The question for this *Learning Set*, however, is how water quality affects living things in an ecosystem. So, the important question to consider now is *How might the effects of water quality on a few living things affect all of the living things in the ecosystem?*

To get a sense of how connected other living things are to one another, you can look at your own interaction with living things. Earlier, you learned about the needs of living things. You know that most living things require food or nutrients in order to survive. Consider exactly where you get your nutrients.

Procedure

1. Think about a simple breakfast of cereal and milk. You can buy cereal and milk at a grocery store. However, from where does it actually come? Use a diagram like the one shown. Trace the parts of this breakfast back to their source. Add to the diagram as you trace the sources of this food. You will do this step with your teacher and class.

2. Your breakfast, what you eat, relies on other living things. As a group, work together on another example. Examine a meal that students your age often enjoy, a cheeseburger and fries!

Communicate Your Results

Investigation Expo

Scientists always share their understandings with each other. Presenting their results to others is one of the most important things that scientists do. You will share what you have found in an *Investigation Expo*. To prepare for this, you will use an overhead transparency.

Trace the diagram that you drew of your model onto an overhead transparency. Be ready to describe your investigation and clearly detail all your results. The answers to the following questions will be very helpful in preparing your presentation.

• Describe how the water moved in the model. (What patterns did you see?)

• Describe why you think your prediction was accurate or inaccurate.

• How did the outcome compare to your prediction?

• Where did the water flow more quickly? How was the flow different from what you predicted?

• Where did the water pool?

As you look at the overheads presented by other students, make sure you can answer these questions. Ask questions that you need answered to understand the results and the explanations others have made.

What's the Point?

In this section, you built a model to simulate how water flows across a landscape when it rains. Placing different-sized objects under the paper created the higher and lower elevations. You also drew a sketch of the model, and predicted how water will run over the paper. When you ran the simulation you probably noticed that the water always moved from areas of high elevation to areas of lower elevation. Water cannot move uphill. You also noticed that water flowed and created puddles in several places as it flowed. These puddles represent lakes or ponds in the real world.

Water on land works that way too. If you watch where rain falls in one rainstorm, you will be able to predict the path water will take in the next rainstorm. This is the case as long as the land stays the same from the first rainstorm to the next. You will need to consider how new construction in Wamego might change the land and affect how water flows.

---

4) Scientists...collaborate.

Scientists never do all their work alone. They work with other scientists (collaborate) and share their knowledge. PBIS helps students by giving them lots of opportunities for sharing thier findings, ideas, and discoveries with others (the way scientists do). Students will work together in small groups to investigate, design, explain, and do other science activities. Sometimes they will work in pairs to figure things out together. They will also have lots of opportunities to share thier findings with the rest of thier classmates and make sense together of what they are learning.

Investigation Expo

In an *Investigation Expo*, small groups report to the class about an investigation they've done. For each *Investigation Expo*, students will make a poster detailing what they were trying to learn from thier investigation, what they did, their data, and their interpretation of the data. The text gives them hints about what to present and what to look for in other groups' presentations. *Investigation Expos* are always followed by discussions about what students learned and about how to do science well. You may want to ask students to write a lab report following an investigation.

Plan Briefing/Solution Briefing/ Idea Briefing

Briefings are presentations of work in progress. They give students a chance to get advice from their classmates that can help them move forward. During a *Plan Briefing*, students present their plans to the class. They might be plans for an experiment for solving a problem or achieving a challenge. During a *Solution Briefing*, students present their solutions in progress and ask the class to help therm make their solutions better. During an *Idea Briefing*, students present their ideas, including their evidence in support of their plans, solutions, or ideas. Often, they will prepare posters to help them you make their presentation. Briefings are almost always followed by discussions of what students have learned and how they will move forward.

Solution Showcase

olution Showcases usually happen near ne end of a Unit. During a *Solution Showcase*, students show their classmates their finished products—either their answer to a question or solution to a challenge. Students will also tell the class why they think it is a good answers or solutions, what evidence and science they used to get to your solution, and what they tried along the way before getting to their answers or solutions. Sometimes a *Solution Showcase* is followed by a competition. It is almost always followed by a discussion comparing and contrasting the different answers and solutions groups have come up with. You may want to ask students to write a report or paper following a *Solution Showcase*.

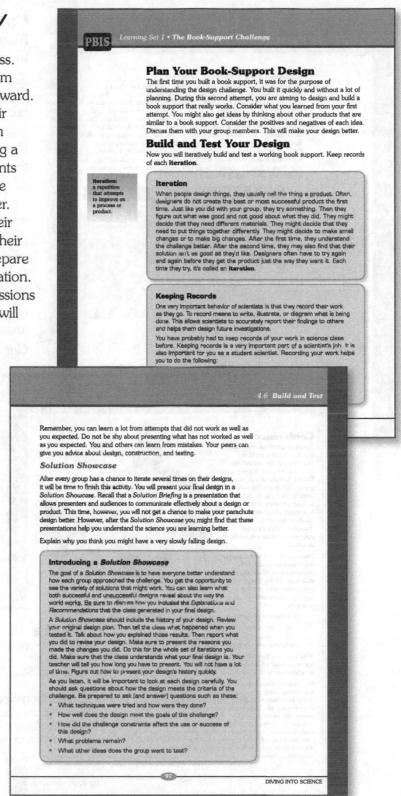

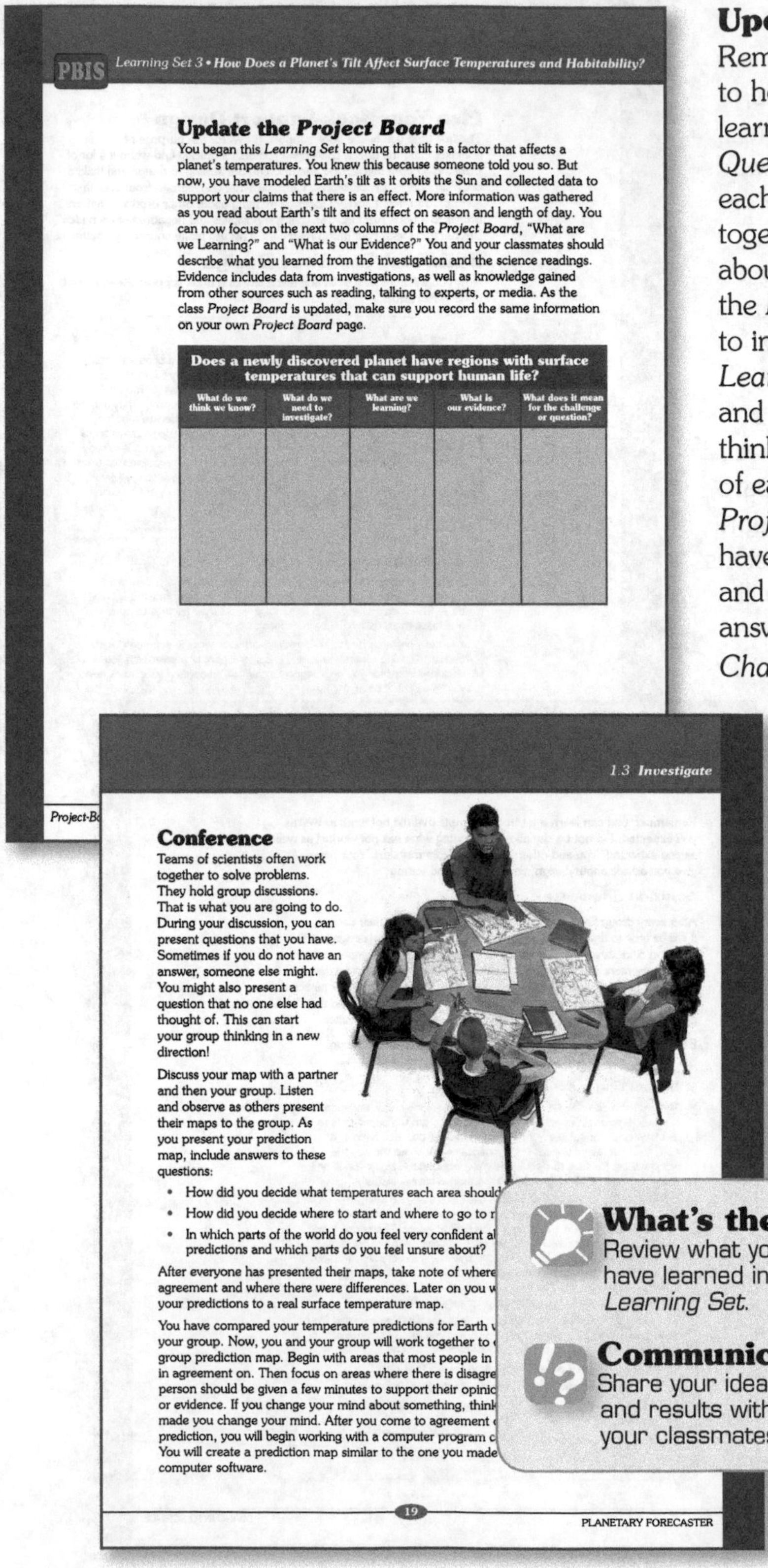

Update the *Project Board*

You began this *Learning Set* knowing that tilt is a factor that affects a planet's temperatures. You knew this because someone told you so. But now, you have modeled Earth's tilt as it orbits the Sun and collected data to support your claims that there is an effect. More information was gathered as you read about Earth's tilt and its effect on season and length of day. You can now focus on the next two columns of the *Project Board*, "What are we Learning?" and "What is our Evidence?" You and your classmates should describe what you learned from the investigation and the science readings. Evidence includes data from investigations, as well as knowledge gained from other sources such as reading, talking to experts, or media. As the class *Project Board* is updated, make sure you record the same information on your own *Project Board* page.

Does a newly discovered planet have regions with surface temperatures that can support human life?				
What do we think we know?	What do we need to investigate?	What are we learning?	What is our evidence?	What does it mean for the challenge or question?

Conference

Teams of scientists often work together to solve problems. They hold group discussions. That is what you are going to do. During your discussion, you can present questions that you have. Sometimes if you do not have an answer, someone else might. You might also present a question that no one else had thought of. This can start your group thinking in a new direction!

Discuss your map with a partner and then your group. Listen and observe as others present their maps to the group. As you present your prediction map, include answers to these questions:

- How did you decide what temperatures each area should
- How did you decide where to start and where to go to
- In which parts of the world do you feel very confident a predictions and which parts do you feel unsure about?

After everyone has presented their maps, take note of where agreement and where there were differences. Later on you your predictions to a real surface temperature map.

You have compared your temperature predictions for Earth your group. Now, you and your group will work together to group prediction map. Begin with areas that most people in in agreement on. Then focus on areas where there is disagre person should be given a few minutes to support their opinio or evidence. If you change your mind about something, think made you change your mind. After you come to agreement prediction, you will begin working with a computer program You will create a prediction map similar to the one you made computer software.

Update the *Project Board*

Remember that the *Project Board* is designed to help the class keep track of what they are learning and their progress towards a Unit's *Big Question* or *Big Challenge*. At the beginning of each Unit, the class creates a *Project Board*, and together records what students think they know about answering the *Big Question* or addressing the *Big Challenge* and what they think they need to investigate further. Near the beginning of each *Learning Set*, the class revisits the *Project Board* and adds new questions and information they think they know to the *Project Board*. At the end of each *Learning Set*, the class again revisits the *Project Board*. This time, they record what they have learned, the evidence they have collected, and recommendations they can make about answering the *Big Question* or achieving the *Big Challenge*.

Conference

A *Conference* is a short discussion among a small group of students before a more formal whole-class discussion. Students might discuss predictions and observations, they might try to explain together, they might consult on what they think they know, and so on. Usually a *Conference* is followed by a discussion around the *Project Board*. In these small group discussions, everybody gets a chance to participate.

What's the Point?
Review what you have learned in each *Learning Set*.

Stop and Think
Answer questions that help you understand what you've done in a section.

Communicate
Share your ideas and results with your classmates.

Record
Record your data as you gather it.

NOTES

NOTES

NOTES

NOTES

DIVING INTO SCIENCE

As a student scientist, you will...

Ask QUESTIONS

Pursue ANSWERS

APPLY MEANING

Make MEANING

Share ANSWERS

Diving Into Science

27 *class periods* *

What's the Big Challenge?

How Do Scientists Work Together to Solve Problems?

Launcher Units are designed to introduce students to the practices of science and social practices of the classroom. As students engage in the social practices of scientists, they learn what scientists do and how they do it, and begin to think of themselves as student scientists. The Launcher Unit provides anchoring experiences to refer to throughout the year. It is also where you, the teacher, set up expectations for rigor and ways of working together for the school year. During this Unit remember to emphasize collaboration, analyzing data, designing investigations, and constructing explanations.

Unit Overview

Content:

This Launcher Unit for Project-Based Inquiry Science (PBIS) builds experience with project-based inquiry science learning and serves to create a culture of collaboration and rigorous scientific discourse in the classroom. In this Unit, the *Big Question* students focus on is *How do scientists work together to solve problems?* Within the context of physical science, students explore variables, reliable procedures, fair tests, and using evidence to construct explanations and make recommendations. Throughout the Unit, students engage in the social practices of scientists as they address a set of small challenges. The goals of *Learning Set 1* and *Learning Set 2* are focused primarily on the social practices of scientists and the investigative process, including iteration, collaboration, how to measure, running an experiment, analyzing experimental data, and reliability of results. In *Learning Set 3*, students continue practicing as scientists while designing their first experiment, constructing scientific explanations, and applying the science they are learning to make recommendations. They do this as they learn about what affects how a whirligig falls. In *Learning Set 4*, students have an opportunity to refine their understanding and use of the practices and concepts they've learned in the context of designing a slow-falling parachute. To conclude the Unit, students watch a video of a design team using all the practices students have been learning, to design a new type of shopping cart. Students see the value of collaboration and scientific reasoning practices

Looking Ahead

Many of the practices of scientists and social practices of PBIS are introduced to students in this Unit. There is information on each in the *Teacher's Resource Guide*.

*A class period is considered to be one 40 to 50 minute class.

in a real-world situation. They use this as a context to pull together what they have learned to answer the *Big Question.*

The physical science topics in this Unit (forces and their effects on structures and on falling) are taken up again more completely in other Units. This content provides a context for addressing the major goals of this Unit. The main focus here is science inquiry, investigation, learning, and establishing a collaborative environment consistent with the work of doing science.

Investigations:

Student groups have experiences that lead them to answers to the Unit's *Big Question.* In *Learning Set 1*, students learn the collaborative nature of science as they plan, build, and test a book support with their group and hear about other groups' designs during class presentations. Students learn about the importance of criteria, constraints of design, and the value of the iterative process as they redesign and build their book supports. Through group investigations of how many drops of water can fit on a penny in *Learning Set 2*, students realize the need for a standard set of procedures and the requirement of reproducible results for an investigation to be considered valid. Students practice graphing, analyzing data and making claims based on the trends in their data. Students engage in scientific social practices as their groups present results to the class and discuss them. While building a whirligig in *Learning Set 3*, groups apply these skills as they design experiments to investigate variables that affect falling objects and explain the behavior of their whirligigs based on evidence they've collected and scientific knowledge. In *Learning Set 4*, groups continue practicing collaboration, designing experiments, constructing explanations, and making recommendations while designing and building a parachute.

Nature of Science:

Through repeated practice, students learn how scientists refine their ideas as new information becomes available, and how scientists work together to refine their understanding and use what they know to answer important questions. Through an iterative process of designing and building a book support several times, students learn how scientific understanding can help them develop good solutions to everyday challenges. Students learn that knowledge is shared and used by the rest of the science community, in this case their class, and the importance of giving credit to the originator of an idea or invention. While engaging in the social practices of scientists, students realize the value of sharing and building on each other's ideas. While conducting investigations in *Learning Set 2*, students realize that for results to be considered valid, procedures must be replicable with repeatable results. This requires that procedures are communicated clearly and specifically enough so someone else can follow them. To help students reflect on how their ideas change in the same ways scientists' ideas do, they are introduced to the *Project Board* in *Learning Set 3*. A *Project*

Board is a visual tool for keeping a running record of what they know, what they need to investigate, their claims with the evidence they have to back these up, as well as how all the information fits together to answer a bigger question.

Artifacts:

In *Learning Set 1*, student groups design and build a book support satisfying a number of criteria and constraints that the class decides upon. Students keep records of their design iterations and the designs of others. In *Learning Set 2*, students write procedures, record their data, and use a graph of the class's data. In *Learning Set 3* and *Learning Set 4*, students design and build a whirligig and a parachute. The class uses a *Project Board* to keep track of how things fall in general, and in particular how a whirligig and a parachute fall. Student groups design investigations, gather data, and interpret their results on Experiment pages. They make claims and recommendations and explain them using *Create Your Explanation* pages. They also write letters of recommendations to a cereal company about how to design the whirligig and parachute.

Targeted Concepts, Skills, and Nature of Science	Section
Scientists often work together and share their findings. Sharing findings makes new information available and helps scientists refine their ideas and build on others' ideas. When another person's or group's idea is used, credit needs to be given.	1.1, 1.2, 1.3, 1.4, 2.3, 2.4, 3.1, 3.2, 3.3, 3.4, 3.5, 3.6, 4.1, 4.3, 4.5, 4.6, Unit *Big Challenge*
Criteria and constraints are important in design.	1.1,1.2, 1.4, 2.1, 3.2, 3.3, 4.1
Scientists must keep clear, accurate, and descriptive records of what they do so they can share their work with others, consider what they did, why they did it, and what they want to do next.	1.2, 1.4, 2.2, 3.2, 3.3, 4.2, 4.6
Graphs are an effective way to communicate results of scientific investigation.	2.2
Identifying factors that lead to variation is an important part of scientific investigation.	2.3, 3.2, 3.3, 4.1
Scientific investigations and measurements are considered reliable if the results are repeatable by other scientists using the same procedures.	2.2, 2.3, 2.4, LS2 *Big Challenge*, 3.3, 4.2
No measurement is exact.	2.3, 2.4
In a fair test, only the manipulated (independent) variable, and the responding (dependent) variable change. All other variables are held constant.	3.3, 4.2

Targeted Concepts, Skills, and Nature of Science	Section
The way an object falls through air depends on its mass, surface area, and other factors.	3.1, 3.4, 3.6, 3.7, LS3 *Big Challenge*, 4.4 LS4 *Big Challenge*
Earth's gravity pulls things toward Earth.	3.4, 3.6, 3.7, LS3 *Big Challenge*, 4.4 LS4 *Big Challenge*
Air resistance is a force opposing the motion of an object moving through air.	3.4, 3.6, 3.7, LS3 *Big Challenge*, 4.4 LS4 *Big Challenge*
Scientists make claims (conclusions) based on evidence obtained (trends in data) from reliable investigations.	3.5, 3.7, 4.2, 4.3
Explanations are claims supported by evidence, accepted ideas and facts.	3.5, 3.6, 3.7, 4.3, LS3 *Big Challenge*, 4.4 LS4 *Big Challenge*

PBIS Kits

The *Unit Materials List* contains all materials necessary to implement *PBIS* successfully. The list includes the following categories:

Durable Group Items–materials that can be reused by student groups throughout your classes. The expected life of these products is 2-3 years.

Durable Classroom Items–materials used in classroom demonstrations or teacher-led demonstrations. These can be reused throughout your classes and the expected life of these products is 2-3 years.

Consumable Group Items–materials to be used up throughout the course of the year. There are enough consumable materials to service six groups of students for five classes. These materials must be reordered at the end of the year. If you organize your classes into fewer than six groups per classroom, you may reduce the quantity per item.

Consumable Classroom Items–materials to be used up throughout the course of the year. There are enough materials in this section to service eight groups of students for five classes. These materials must be reordered at the end of the year. If you teach fewer than five sections per year or have fewer then eight groups per classroom, you may reduce the quantity per item. Please contact your sales representative for additional information.

Chemicals Needed–chemicals needed to conduct the activities. There are enough chemicals to service eight groups of students for of five classes. The chemicals are delivered with MSDS sheets and other pertinent handling instructions.

Additional Items Needed Not Supplied–additional items needed but not supplied in any *It's About Time Kit*. They represent items commonly found in a school district. If an item number appears beside the item, then you can place an order with *It's About Time*.

There are three ways to order equipment for the *PBIS* program: the *Extended Kit*, the *Standard Kit*, and *Customized Kit* orders.

The *Extended Kit* includes all scientific and most common items necessary to conduct student-led activities for five classes of eight groups. The *Unit Materials List* on the following page illustrates the *Extended Kit*.

The *Standard Kit* includes all scientific and some common items necessary to conduct, five sections of eight groups each student led activities. Some additional common items will need to be purchased by your district. The *Unit Materials List* minus items with asterisk illustrate the *Standard Kit*.

Please contact your sales representative for information about *Customized Kits*.

Unit Materials List

Quantity needed per group of 4-6 students.		
Unit Durable Group Items	**Section**	**Quantity**
Metric ruler	1.1, 1.4, 4.1, 4.2, 4.6	1
Paper cup, 5 oz	2.2, 2.4	2
Stopwatch	3.2, 3.3, 4.1, 4.2, 4.6	1
Safety scissors	3.1, 3.2, 3.3, 4.1, 4.2, 4.6	1
Washers, 1" outer diameter, 3/8" inner diameter	4.1, 4.2, 4.6	4
Measuring tape, vinyl, 152 cm/60"	3.2, 3.3	1

Quantity needed per classroom.		
Unit Durable Classroom Items	**Section**	**Quantity**
Learning Cycle Action posters	All	1
Heavy duty sponge	1.3	1
IDEO *Deep Dive* DVD	BBC	1

Quantity needed per classroom.		
Unit Durable Classroom Items	**Section**	**Quantity**
Paper clips, pkg. of 100	1.1, 1.4, 3.1, 3.2, 3.3	4
Laminated *Project Board*	3.1, 3.2, 3.4, 3.6, 3.7, 4.1, 4.2, 4.4, 4.6, 4.7	1 per section taught
Transparency of *Project Board*	3.1, 3.2, 3.4, 3.6, 3.7, 4.1, 4.2, 4.4, 4.6, 4.7	1

Quantity needed per group of 4-6 students.		
Unit Consumable Group Items	**Section**	**Quantity**
Unlined index cards, 3" x 5", pkg. of 100	1.1, 1.2, 1.4	5
Coffee filters	3.1, 4.1, 4.2, 4.6	20
Transparent tape	4.1, 4.2, 4.4, 4.6	1
Cotton string	4.1, 4.2, 4.4, 4.6	1

Quantity needed per classroom.		
Unit Consumable Classroom Items	**Section**	**Quantity**
Rubber bands, #33, 1 lb	1.1, 1.2, 1.4	1
Beral pipettes, 3 mL bulb draw, pkg. of 10	2.2, 2.4	10
Graph paper	2.2, 2.4	1
Restickable easel pad, 25"x 30"	3.3, 4.2, 4.5, 4.6	2
Colored markers, set of 8 colors	3.3, 4.2, 4.5, 4.6	6

Additional Items Needed Not Supplied		
Book	1.1, 1.2, 1.4, 3.1	1 per group
Paper towels	2.2, 2.4	1 per classroom
Access to water	2.2, 2.4	1 per class
Pennies	2.2, 2.4	5 per group
Whirligig template	3.1, 3.2, 3.3	1 per group
Heavyweight paper	3.1, 3.2, 3.3, 3.6	per student

NOTES

UNIT IMPLEMENTATION

What's the Big Question?

How Do Scientists Work Together to Solve Problems?

Welcome to your new science Unit. This Unit and the others you complete this year will offer you exciting challenges and opportunities to learn science. Science involves learning very interesting facts, but that's not all science is. A large part of *learning science* is being able to analyze and make sense of the world around you in an organized and logical way. Scientists learn how to do this to be successful at what they do. But scientists are not the only ones who can benefit from this kind of reasoning; you might find it useful too.

In this Unit you will learn how to tackle problems and challenges as a scientist does. There is a lot that scientists do to make sure that they solve problems in an organized and logical way. You will experience and use many of these scientific practices. You are not expected to learn everything about being a scientist in just a few weeks, but you will learn a lot. The lessons you learn will help you be more successful in this year's science Units. They will also help you in future science classes and even in your life!

Your challenge is to understand how scientists solve problems. Because this is such a BIG challenge, you will work on four smaller challenges in this Unit. Each one will give you a chance to learn a few practices and behaviors. Then you will use what you've learned to answer the *Big Question: How do scientists work together to solve problems?*

Some of you may have already begun learning about what scientists do and how they work together. Therefore, much of this Unit will be review. That review will be useful to you. It will give the members of your class a chance to learn to work together. It will also allow you to share what you've learned in other years with your new classmates. You will also find new things to learn in this Unit. There is new science content and practices of scientists that you haven't discussed a lot before.

Have fun being student scientists!

DIV 3

DIVING INTO SCIENCE

◄ *1 class period**

What's the Big Challenge?

How Do Scientists Work Together to Solve Problems?

10 min.

Introduce students to PBIS and the Big Question they will be attempting to answer throughout this Unit.

○ Engage

Help students know that this year they will be doing science the way scientists do. They will need help knowing what this means but there is no need to overwhelm them with details; that will become clearer as they engage in PBIS activities. The introductory text for the Unit can help as can the letter to the students in the student edition.

TEACHER TALK

"Do you ever think about what scientists do? Let's talk about that and make a list. What do you think scientists are like? What kind of people become scientists? What do people do when they do science?"

*A class period is considered to be one 40 to 50 minute class.

Record students' initial ideas so the class can refer back to them at the end of the Unit.

△ Guide

Tell students the *Big Question* of the Unit and that they will be doing many things in the same way that scientists do. Scientists answer big questions. They need to answer some smaller questions to answer the bigger questions. Inform students that in this Unit they will be having experiences that will help them learn how scientists work together to solve problems. Let students know that by the end of this Unit they will be able to answer the question: *How do scientists work together to solve problems?*

TEACHER TALK

66Scientists answer big questions, and that is what you are going to be doing this year. The first *Big Question* you are going to answer is: *How do scientists work together to solve problems?* Because this is a *Big Question*, you are going to answer a lot of smaller questions along the way. You'll solve some problems the way scientists would solve them, and by the end of this Unit, you'll have an answer to the *Big Question.*99

NOTES

....

....

....

....

....

....

....

LEARNING SET 1 INTRODUCTION

Learning Set 1
The Book-Support Challenge

◀ *4 class periods* *

Thinking about criteria and constraints, student groups build a book support out of paper clips, rubber bands, and index cards.

Overview

Students are introduced to criteria and constraints, the iterative process in design, and the social practices of scientists while they design a book support. They begin by quickly specifying criteria and constraints, assembling a design solution, and then presenting their solutions to their peers. Different groups build their supports in different ways, often because they interpreted what was required differently. Based on this experience and ideas from other groups' designs, the class updates their list of criteria and constraints. Next, groups redesign and rebuild their book supports. Here, students refine their ideas about how to best build a book support. As they redesign and rebuild their book support, they are applying two common practices in science: the iterative process and building upon others' ideas. Groups present their new designs to the class as they participate in their first *Solution Briefing,* and may accuse other groups of copying their ideas. Students are introduced to the importance of crediting other people's work, and they apply this in their next design. After this *Solution Briefing,* students are sometimes curious about the science of supports. After being introduced to what makes something structurally sound and stable, students redesign and rebuild the book support with the additional constraint that the book supports be cost-effective. This connects science and engineering with the common experience of going to a store to purchase a well-designed and cost-effective product. They begin to realize that knowing science can help them achieve everyday goals. The *Learning Set* closes with an examination of the practices of scientists that they have been using.

Looking Ahead
LS 1 – Throughout this *Learning Set* students should wear closed-toe shoes.

*A class period is considered to be one 40 to 50 minute class.

Targeted Concepts, Skills, and Nature of Science	Section
Scientists often work together and share their findings. Sharing findings makes new information available and helps scientists refine their ideas and build on other's ideas. When another person's or group's idea is used, credit needs to be given.	1.1, 1.2
Criteria and constraints are important in design.	1.1, 1.4

Students' Initial Conceptions and Capabilities	• Students generally believe that scientific knowledge changes, but they may think it changes only in facts and technology without realizing that a change in knowledge may suggest a reinterpretation of observations or new predictions. (Aikenhead, 1987; Lederman & O'Malley, 1990; Waterman, 1983)

Understanding for Teachers

The goal of this Unit is to familiarize students with the nature of science, the PBIS curriculum, and some of the tools used in this curriculum. It is not intended for the students to gain a deep understanding of the scientific concepts of mass, gravity, or balanced forces, however, students need to apply these concepts to achieve their challenge. Although enough information is provided for the students in their materials to achieve the goal, some may have more questions. In order for you to address any questions that arise, we provide you here with more details of the science concepts.

All matter we are familiar with is made up of atoms. Atoms are composed of a nucleus containing protons and neutrons (these are made up of quarks), and there are electrons that reside outside of the nucleus. There are particles with matter that are not commonly discussed in our everyday world, such as mesons.

All mass attracts mass. This is the source of gravity. Two objects with mass will pull on each other – this is the gravitational interaction. The objects do not have to be touching to feel a pull from each other (e.g., the Sun and Earth pull on each other but do not touch, same with the Earth and Moon). If one of the objects has a lot of mass (e.g., Earth) then the pull between the two objects interacting is strong. This is why things fall to Earth. (And this is why the Moon orbits around Earth and Earth orbits around the Sun.)

An object will not fall to Earth if there is a force equal in size but opposite in direction to the gravitational pull on it. For example, a book sitting on a table will feel the gravitational pull down exerted on it by Earth, and it will feel an equal but opposite force from the table pushing up on it. The force from the table is often called the normal force and it arises because of the contact between the book and the table. The normal force on the macroscopic level is a compression force. Just as the sponge compresses when a book is placed on it, so does the table, but the table's compression is not as noticeable. On the molecular scale, it has to do with the electromagnetic interactions between the particles that make up the surfaces in contact with each other.

Notice in the image that all the forces acting on the book are drawn at a special point on the book. This point represents the book's center of mass. One can think of all the forces acting on an object as acting on the center of mass of the object. This is because the center of mass is the point where the object's mass is distributed around. If we were to replace the object with a point object of equal mass, this is where we would put it.

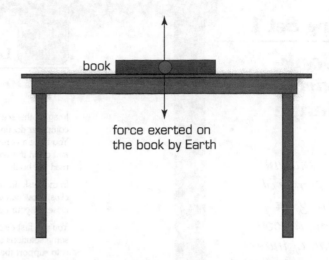

book

force exerted on
the book by Earth

The center of mass is very important for discussions of stability, but sometimes it can be confusing. For example, a hoola hoop's (or a ring's) center of mass is at the center of the circle it makes. There is no matter there, and certainly if you were to put a support structure right under the center of mass and not under other parts of the ring, it would just fall.

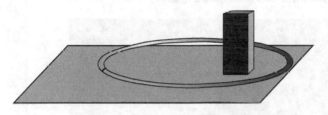

The idea of support is that it has to span the center of mass in order for the object to be stable (not tippy). If you were to support a ring or hoop on one of its sides, the Earth would pull the other side toward it.

You need to provide support to both sides for it to balance the hoop against the pull of gravity. Remember that although we can think of Earth's gravitational pull acting at the center of mass, it is actually pulling on each atom that makes up the ring, and these are distributed in the shape of a hoop, so we need to support the actual mass and make sure that it has balanced support around the center of mass of the object. See the image below.

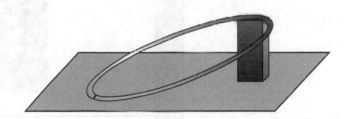

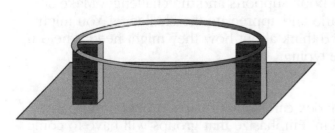

Columns are wonderful support devices because they distribute the normal force they supply over their entire surface area, hence they share the load or force on them. This is why a simple piece of paper can hold up a book when it is shaped into a cylinder.

Learning Set 1

The Book-Support Challenge

5 min.

Introduce students to the challenge of the Learning Set — building a book support out of index cards, paper clips, and rubber bands.

Learning Set 1

The Book-Support Challenge

Imagine this scene. You need to copy sections from a textbook into a computer document for a presentation. The job has to be done immediately. You have a computer and the textbook on a low desk. When you sit down and open the book, a problem arises. You forgot your glasses, and you can't read the book.

In the desk drawer you find some index cards, rubber bands, and paper clips. How can you quickly make a book support that will raise the book closer to your eyes?

You will first discuss this problem with your group. Then you will try out some solutions using the materials your teacher has provided. The goal is to support the book at least 7.5 cm (about 3 in.) above the desk. You must be able to read and turn the pages while the book stays on the support.

Your group will have ten minutes to complete a structure.

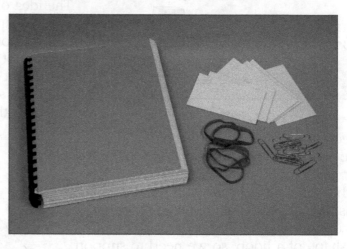

○ Engage

Begin students thinking about book supports and the challenge. Make sure students can picture the scenario and appreciate the challenge. You might have students open a book and think about how they might need it held up in order to read it easily while typing.

△ Guide

Show students the materials (index cards, paper clips, rubber bands, and a ruler) but do not distribute them. Emphasize that groups will have to come up with a design for a book support that is at least 7.5 cm (about 3") above the desk and must support the book so that it stays open and allows you to turn pages.

TEACHER TALK

"Imagine that you need glasses to read, but you forgot them. You have to copy some text from a book into the computer but you cannot read the text when it is on the desk. The challenge is to design a book support. It must be a certain height above the desk so that you can read the text. It must hold the book open, and it must allow you to turn the book's pages. All you have available at your desk are index cards, paper clips, rubber bands, and a ruler. What will you do?"

NOTES

SECTION 1.1 INTRODUCTION

1.1 Understand the Challenge

1 class period* ▶

Identify Criteria and Constraints
Overview

Students are introduced to the *Book-Support Challenge* and begin by listing the criteria and constraints of this design challenge. Groups then build a book support and present their designs to the class. Students describe ideas they tried and explain why they chose their current construction. Finally, the class updates their list of criteria and constraints.

Targeted Concepts, Skills, and Nature of Science	Performance Expectations
Scientists often work together and then share their findings. In sharing their findings, new information becomes available and scientists can refine their ideas and build on others' ideas. When another person's or group's idea is used, credit needs to be given.	Students should be able to describe how their ideas evolved as they were exposed to new information (ideas from other groups or things they read). Students should be able to work effectively together to build a book support. They should listen to each other, try out a variety of ideas, and prepare presentations in which they share their ideas.
Criteria and constraints are important in design.	Students should be able to describe what criteria and constraints are and create a list of criteria and constraints for the *Book–Support Challenge*.

*A class period is considered to be one 40 to 50 minute class.

Students should wear closed-toe shoes in case a book falls.

Materials

100	**per group**	3" × 5" index cards
50	**per group**	paper clips (jumbo size)
50	**per group**	rubber bands (3 ½" x ⅛")
1	**per group**	metric ruler
1	**per student**	*Book-Support Records* page
1	**per class**	poster paper or overhead for creating a class list of criteria and constraints

Activity Setup and Preparation

- Select student groups of three to four students. These groups should stay together for at least this *Learning Set*. There should be at least five groups and no more than eight.

- Remind students, prior to the lesson, to wear closed-toe shoes.

- You might want to think about how to best distribute them. Some teachers prepare small bags or trays of materials for each group; they find that for this beginning-of-the-year activity, this is better than a materials station.

Homework Options

Homework options provide students with some short, relevant work options. Each of these assignments encourages reflection on the current section or prepares students to make the connections between one section and the next. A variety of homework option tasks are included in different parts of the Unit.

Reflection

- **Science Process:** Why are criteria and constraints important in design? *(Criteria and constraints are important in design because they describe what needs to be accomplished and the limitations on doing that.)*

- **Science Process:** Sketch your most successful book support and describe the aspects that make it successful. *(Meeting one or more of the criteria should be mentioned in what makes it successful.)*

- **Science Process:** Imagine it is 3:00 p.m. and you just got home from school. You have a pet dog that needs to go out for a walk and be fed before it gets dark at 6:00 p.m. You also have estimated that you have three hours of homework to do and it must be done by 7:00 p.m. Your challenge is to get it all done. List the criteria and constraints of this challenge and your plan for meeting this challenge. *(Criteria = walk dog, feed dog, get three hours of homework done. Constraints = time –you only have four hours to complete everything, until 6:00 p.m. to walk and feed the dog, and homework must be done by 7:00 p.m.)*

Preparation for 1.2

- **Science Process:** Create a new design to discuss with your group, based on what you now know. Don't forget to draw a diagram and list the ways your design fulfills the new criteria and constraints! *(Check for accuracy of criteria and constraints.)*

NOTES

1.1

SECTION 1.1 IMPLEMENTATION

1.1 Understand the Challenge

Identify Criteria and Constraints

Before you start, it's a good idea to make sure you understand what your challenge is. Design challenges have two parts: criteria and constraints.

Criteria are things that must be satisfied to achieve the challenge. For the book support, this will include the job the book support must do. It will also involve how the book support must do that job. One criterion (singular of criteria) is that you must build the book support.

Constraints are factors that limit how you can solve a problem. For this challenge, one of the constraints is that you can only use the materials your teacher gave you. Think about the constraints that have been placed on you for this challenge.

criteria: goals that must be satisfied to be able to successfully achieve a challenge.

constraints: factors that limit how you can solve a problem.

Build and Test Your First Book Support

To help you to begin to think about how to achieve your challenge, you will begin by getting familiar with the materials you will be using. You will also take some time to figure out how the product that you are designing is supposed to function (work). You will get 100 note cards, 50 paper clips, 50 rubber bands, and a ruler. You will have about ten minutes to build and test a book support. As you build your first book support, try out different ideas. Think about which ones seem to work better.

Materials
• **100 note cards**
• **50 paper clips**
• **50 rubber bands**
• **ruler**

Communicate Your Work

Share Your Designs

Your group has built a book support. It is time to share your design with your classmates. Groups should take turns presenting their book-support solutions to the rest of the class. After each presentation, the teacher will test your design to see if it meets the criteria. Then there will be time for classmates to ask questions of the presenting group.

As you present your book support, try to give answers to these questions:
• How is your design constructed?
• Why did you design it the way you did?
• How did the challenge constraints affect the design?
• What things did you think about and try before getting to this design?

DIV 5

DIVING INTO SCIENCE

1.1 Understand the Challenge

Identify Criteria and Constraints
10 min.

Guide the class in describing the criteria and constraints for the Book-Support Challenge, *and then, using these as examples, introduce them to the terms "criteria" and "constraints."*

△ Guide

Lead students in thinking more about the challenge.

• What must be accomplished (i.e., criteria)?

• What are the limitations in how we can do this (i.e., constraints)?

As students identify criteria and constraints, record them on a class list. When there are several items for each, introduce the terms *criteria* and *constraints*. Criteria are goals that must be satisfied and constraints are limitations.

META NOTES

When groups present their book support to the class, they will check if the designs meet the class's criteria and constraints. After the presentations, the class will update their criteria and constraints.

◇ Evaluate

Make sure the following criteria and constraints are listed: at least 7.5 cm (about 3") above the desk, you must be able to read and turn the pages while the book stays on the support, the materials available are paper clips, index cards, and rubber bands; they have 10 minutes. Make sure these are on the list before moving on. If students are having difficulties, refer back to page 4, where the criteria and constraints are described.

Build and Test Your First Book Support

15 min.

Have student groups create their first book-support design.

---

for this

Build and Test Your First Book Support

To help you to begin to think about how to achieve your challenge, you will begin by getting familiar with the materials you will be using. You will also take some time to figure out how the product that you are designing is supposed to function (work). You will get 100 note cards, 50 paper clips, 50 rubber bands, and a ruler. You will have about ten minutes to build and test a book support. As you build your first book support, try out different ideas. Think about which ones seem to work better.

Materials
- 100 note cards
- 50 paper clips
- 50 rubber bands
- ruler

△ Guide

Tell students they are now going to design a book support to meet the criteria and constraints on the class list. They will first come up with a quick design and then they will present it to the class.

Emphasize that the class will use the criteria and constraints listed to assess their designs and that they will have an opportunity to redesign their book support later.

⬡ Get Going

Remind the class that each student has probably started thinking about how to build a book support since they were introduced to it, and that each student should contribute their thoughts to the group. They should test all the ideas out. Then the group should decide on their best design and build it.

Assign students to groups, distribute the materials and tell students they have about 10 minutes to design and build their book support.

△ Guide

While groups are working, visit the groups and remind students that each should contribute their ideas. You may have to model for students polite ways to discuss their ideas, "I disagree with this part of your design because I think ...., let's try it out and then let's try..." Emphasize contributing their thoughts openly and in a polite and considerate way.

META NOTES

It is O.K. for students to struggle with the design; they will be refining their ideas and building a book support two more times.

META NOTES

Remember you are setting the stage for the rest of the year. If only a couple of groups are not done, you may want to move forward to set the pace of the class and the need to be on task. One way some teachers manage time is to remind students halfway through and shortly before the end of the time period how much time they have left.

☐ Assess

While visiting groups, take note of what issues students have with both design and collaborative skills. Focus on these points later while guiding the class discussion and future group work.

Near the end of the 10 minutes, see how groups are doing. If most groups are not done in 10 minutes, give the class additional time.

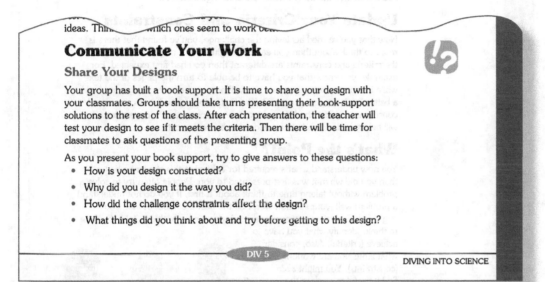

ideas. Thin~ ~~hich ones seem to work be~

Communicate Your Work

Share Your Designs

Your group has built a book support. It is time to share your design with your classmates. Groups should take turns presenting their book-support solutions to the rest of the class. After each presentation, the teacher will test your design to see if it meets the criteria. Then there will be time for classmates to ask questions of the presenting group.

As you present your book support, try to give answers to these questions:
* How is your design constructed?
* Why did you design it the way you did?
* How did the challenge constraints affect the design?
* What things did you think about and try before getting to this design?

DIV 5

DIVING INTO SCIENCE

△ Guide

Now that students have tried out a design with their group, it is time for groups to share their ideas with the class. This is the first time students are presenting to each other. Emphasize that they are presenting to each other, not to the teacher, and that others in the class may be interested in what they have to say and may want to ask questions. Students should speak loudly and clearly and think about what they want to say before they say it.

⬡ Get Going

Emphasize that presenting groups should organize their presentations so that they answer the questions from their text during their presentations and that other students will want to know the answers to these questions. Then give groups about two minutes to prepare their presentations.

Remind students that if they don't understand a design and how it works, then they should ask the presenting group to clarify.

Next, begin the presentations. Give each group two minutes to share and then two minutes for questions.

Communicate Your Work

Share Your Designs
15 min.

Have students share their designs and how they meet the class list of criteria and constraints.

> **META NOTES**
>
> The common PBIS practice at this point would be a *Solution Briefing*. This is not a *Solution Briefing*; it is a far less detailed presentation. Students will be introduced to *Solution Briefings* in the next section.

> **META NOTES**
>
> Like most design teams and scientists, students first work in small groups and then present their ideas to a larger group (the class). Hearing other groups' ideas will help students refine their own ideas.

PBIS *Learning Set 1 • The Book-Support Challenge*

META NOTES

Students may not have experience presenting to each other. You may need to give a lot of support to help them get used to presenting to each other and not simply to you, the teacher. It is therefore important during this first presentation to model discussion techniques and assist students in rewording and redirecting their questions as necessary. Read the tips on discussion techniques in the *Teacher's Resource Guide*.

META NOTES

Some groups will design strong complicated structures that can hold any book; others will design flexible structures that are easy to build but need to be moved around and adapted to individual books. These differences will be important to focus on later when revising the criteria and constraints.

Notice how students are communicating with each other. What are they having trouble communicating? Keep these in mind to help them in later presentation sessions.

As you listen to everybody's reports, make sure you understand the answers to these questions for each. If you don't think you have heard answers to each question, ask questions (like those on the previous page). Be careful to ask your questions nicely.

After each book support is tested, the class should quickly discuss and agree about how well the design fulfills the challenge's criteria.

Update Your Criteria and Constraints

Now that you've tried achieving the challenge, you've found that there is more to think about than you earlier imagined. You may now realize that the criteria and constraints are different than you had first expected. For example, you know that you have to be able to turn the pages of the text while it is on the book support. You will have a chance to design and build a better book support shortly. Before that, review your list of criteria and constraints. Update the list, making it more accurate. A more accurate list will help you design a better-performing book support.

What's the Point?

You now understand what's required for achieving this challenge better than you did when it was first presented to you. People often try to solve a problem without taking time to think about it first. If you do not understand a problem well, your solution won't be the best it can be. In fact, you might fail. Each time you are presented with a new problem, take the time to think. Identify what you have to achieve (criteria). Also, consider what limits you are working under (constraints). You might also find it useful to explore the materials you will be using. You can make a first simple try at a solution. With better understanding of a problem and what is required to solve it, you are more likely to be successful.

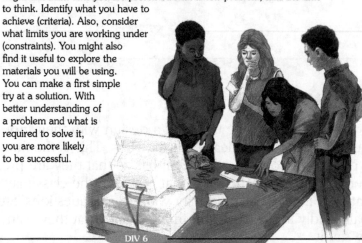

DIV 6

△ Guide Presentations and Discussions

This is an excellent time to begin modeling for students how to ask a question. You might want to discuss this before students start presenting. During the discussion, assist students in their questioning and comments by modeling respectful language such as:

TEACHER TALK

"I agree with... because...

I disagree with ... because...

Could you clarify...

How does that meet the criterion...

What did you see (observe) that made you think the design worked/did not work?"

Also, model appropriate volume and eye contact for the students.

While presenting, groups should address the four questions in the student text. Give students in the audience a chance to ask questions first, then guide presenters if needed:

- Help students point out and describe their design features.

- Remind them to provide the reasoning behind their design. What made them think to do that? Or what did they try out that led them to that idea? Listen for comments about the durability or stability of the design.

- Challenge them if you think that constraints have been violated.

- Ask what they decided against and their reasons why. This helps students recognize that there is valuable information even in ideas that do not work.

At the end of each presentation, pause to discuss how the criteria and constraints were met (or not). Assure students that ideas that work and those that don't work are both important. One gives you ideas to use, and the other gives you ideas that need to be refined or should not be used.

NOTES

....

....

....

Update Your Criteria and Constraints

5 min.

Hold a class discussion to refine the class's criteria and constraints based on what they learned from the presentations and discussions of groups' designs.

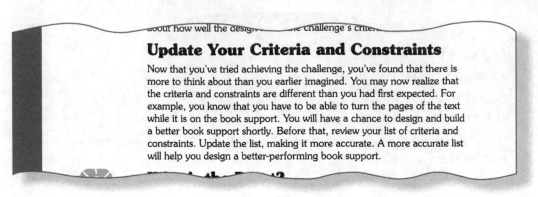

about how well the design ... the challenge's criter...

Update Your Criteria and Constraints

Now that you've tried achieving the challenge, you've found that there is more to think about than you earlier imagined. You may now realize that the criteria and constraints are different than you had first expected. For example, you know that you have to be able to turn the pages of the text while it is on the book support. You will have a chance to design and build a better book support shortly. Before that, review your list of criteria and constraints. Update the list, making it more accurate. A more accurate list will help you design a better-performing book support.

△ **Guide**

Transition the class by pointing out that now that they have seen lots of designs and considered how each have met or not met the criteria and constraints, that they should reconsider what the criteria and constraints are.

You may want to point out things everyone did that was not a criterion and make it one. Or the class might really have liked one person's design and picked out a particular feature of it to add to the list.

Edit the list as students make their suggestions.

Ask students to quickly note any ideas they have for their next design.

NOTES

....

....

....

....

....

....

....

....

Assessment Options

Targeted Concepts, Skills, and Nature of Science	How do I know if students got it?
Scientists often work together and then share their findings. Sharing findings makes new information available and helps scientists refine their ideas and build on others' ideas. When another person's or group's idea is used, credit needs to be given.	**ASK:** students if they can give an example from what they did today of how scientific ideas and methods change. **LISTEN:** to students describe how their ideas evolved as they were exposed to new information (ideas from other groups or things they read). **ASK:** students when another iteration is useful. **LISTEN:** to students describe how each iteration is done either to make use of new information and understanding, or to gain more information and understanding. **ASK:** students how working in a group and presenting their group's work to the class affected their design plans. **LISTEN:** to students discuss how they decided upon and built the final group idea based on all the ideas shared in the group, and how they updated the criteria and constraints based on the class presentations and discussions. Some may say they have new ideas for the book support based on what they saw and heard during the class presentations.
Criteria and constraints are important in design.	**ASK:** why it is important to know the criteria and constraints in a design. **LISTEN:** to students define *criteria* (requirements that must be met) and *constraints* (limitations), and how they should be able to describe why it is important to understand these when designing.

Teacher Reflection Questions

- What concepts, skills, and nature of science did you see students applying today? Which ones did they have difficulties with? How might you assist them in the next section?

- One of the goals in this section is to let students make mistakes without correcting them. What difficulties did you have with letting students make mistakes without correcting them? How would you handle it next time you teach this section?

- During the presentations, what did you do to assist in making the discussion student-centered? How could you better model the appropriate language during a class discussion, e.g., "I agree with the constraint John picked because ..." or "I disagree... because..."?

NOTES

1.2 Design

A Better Book-Support Design

◀ $1\frac{1}{2}$ *class periods* *

Overview

Groups redesign and build a new book support using the list of criteria and constraints they updated after hearing each other's initial designs. During the process of redesigning and building their book support based on what they now know, students learn about the importance of iteration and keeping good records. Groups present their designs to the class, engaging in a common social practice among scientists — sharing and refining ideas within their community. Like scientists, students may have used ideas from others in order to reach their goals. Students learn that scientists build their ideas on the ideas of others, and they learn about the importance of crediting the work of others.

*A class period is considered to be one 40 to 50 minute class.

Targeted Concepts, Skills, and Nature of Science	Performance Expectations
Science and engineering are dynamic processes, changing as new information becomes available.	Students should be able to describe how their ideas evolved as they were exposed to information involving the science behind their book support. Students should be able to describe how each iteration is done, either to make use of new information and understanding or to gain more information and understanding.
Scientists often work together and then share their findings. Sharing findings makes new information available and helps scientists refine their ideas and build on others' ideas. When another person's or group's idea is used, credit needs to be given.	Students should be able to describe how their ideas evolved as they were exposed to new information (ideas from other groups or things they read). Students should be able to work effectively together to build a book support. They should listen to each other, try out a variety of ideas, and prepare presentations in which they share their ideas.
Criteria and constraints are important in design.	Students should be able to describe what criteria and constraints are and create a list of criteria and constraints for the *Book-Support Challenge*.
Scientists must keep clear, accurate, and descriptive records of what they do so they can share their work with others, consider what they did, why they did it, and what they want to do next.	Students should be able to keep descriptive and accurate records of designing and building their book support.

Materials

100	per group	3" × 5" index cards
50	per group	paper clips (jumbo size)
50	per group	rubber bands (3 ½" x ⅛")
1	per group	metric ruler
1	per student	*Book-Support Records* page
1	per student	*Solution-Briefing Notes* page
1	per class	class list of criteria and constraints

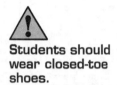

Students should wear closed-toe shoes.

Activity Setup and Preparation

- Remind students prior to lesson to wear closed-toe shoes.
- Think about how you want to distribute the materials. Some teachers prepare small bags or trays of materials for each group; they find that for this beginning-of-the-year activity, it is better than a materials station. You may want to include the two handouts for each student with the materials.

Homework Options

Reflection

- **Nature of Science:** What is the difference between copying and building on someone's idea? Describe an example of copying versus building on other's ideas. *(Copying does not credit another's work; building on someone's idea does. Also, "build" includes adding or modifying – not just using.)*

- **Science Process:** If you could redesign your book support, what ideas from the *Solution Briefing* would you like to build upon? Why? *(Check that students support their ideas with reasons related to criteria or constraints.)*

- **Science Content:** Based on the ideas from the *Solution Briefing*, sketch a design for a book support. Describe or explain. *(Check that the criteria and constraints are met in the sketch.)*

Preparation for 1.3

- **Science Content:** What makes a structure strong? What makes a structure stable? How could you make your book support stronger and less likely to topple? Support all your answers with reasons. *(This is an elicitation of what students think and it gets them thinking about what will be presented during the next section.*

Look for what ideas students have about strength and stability. Check that students support their ideas with reasons.)

- **Science Content:** Sketch a new design for your book support that you think is strong and stable. Describe what features in the design make it strong and stable. *(This is an elicitation of what students think and gets students thinking about what will be presented during the next section. Look for what ideas students have about strength and stability. Check that students support their ideas with reasons.)*

NOTES

....

....

....

....

....

....

....

....

....

....

....

....

1 class period* ▶

1.2 Design

A Better Book-Support Design

5 min.

Now guide students in revising their designs based on the new criteria, constraints and ideas from the presentations.

1.2 Design

A Better Book-Support Design

You have already taken some time to explore the materials you will be using. You have built and tested your first book support. You will soon build a better version of the book support. In this science class, you will have many chances to re-engineer solutions to problems or challenges. This time when you build the book support, you will need to record what you are doing. You will also need to communicate your results to others in the class. Before you start, read about the importance of recording your scientific work. You will then have ten minutes to build a working book support.

Materials
• 100 note cards
• 50 paper clips
• 50 rubber bands
• ruler

DIV 7

DIVING INTO SCIENCE

○ **Engage**

Remind students of the designs and new ideas they might want to try out based on what they saw and heard from other groups. Emphasize that they will get to rework solutions to problems or challenges a number of times in this course. This time while they are redesigning building their book support, they will be keeping records of what they are doing.

*A class period is considered to be one 40 to 50 minute class.

TEACHER TALK

"After you saw everyone's initial designs for the *Book-Support Challenge*, you probably thought of many new ideas for your book support. Today you will have a chance to design and create a new book support. In this class you will get to rework solutions to problems or challenges a number of times. In order to remember what worked and what didn't work, it is important to keep good records. Today you will be keeping records of your new design."

NOTES

....

....

....

....

....

....

....

....

....

....

....

....

Plan Your Book-Support Design

5 min.

Have groups record their plans for their revised book-support design.

Plan Your Book-Support Design

The first time you built a book support, it was for the purpose of understanding the design challenge. You built it quickly and without a lot of planning. During this second attempt, you are aiming to design and build a book support that really works. Consider what you learned from your first attempt. You might also get ideas by thinking about other products that are similar to a book support. Consider the positives and negatives of each idea. Discuss them with your group members. This will make your design better.

Build and Test Your Design

Now you will iteratively build and test a working book support. Keep records of each iteration.

iteration: a repetition that attempts to improve on a process or product.

Be a Scientist

Iteration

When people design things, they usually call the thing a product. Often, designers do not create the best or most successful product the first time. Just like you did with your group, they try something. Then they figure out what was good and not good about what they did. They might decide that they need different materials. They might decide that they need to put things together differently. They might decide to make small changes or to make big changes. After the first time, they understand the challenge better. After the second time, they may also find that their solution isn't as good as they'd like. Designers often have to try again and again before they get the product just the way they want it. Each time they try, it's called an iteration.

Be a Scientist

Keeping Records

One very important behavior of scientists is that they record their work as they go. To record means to write, illustrate, or diagram what is being done. This allows scientists to accurately report their findings to others and helps them design future investigations.

You have probably had to keep records of your work in science class before. Keeping records is a very important part of a scientist's job. It is also important for you as a student scientist. Recording your work helps you to do the following:

- Share your work better with others.
- Remember what you did and decided along the way.
- Remember why you decided to do those things.
- Make decisions about what type of investigation to do next.

DIV 8

Project-Based Inquiry Science

△ Guide

Remind students that when they are planning their design they should aim to make a book support that satisfies all the criteria and constraints. Also tell them to think about everyday things that are similar to book supports to help them with ideas for their designs.

⬡ Get Going

Each member of their group should take turns presenting their ideas to the group. The group should discuss each idea and consider the positives and negatives of each idea.

Next, groups should plan a design and record their plans.

Tell groups they have five minutes to plan.

○ Engage

While students are sharing their ideas, stop by a few groups and ask them how their design meets the criteria and constraints, or how it is better than their last design.

△ Guide

Focus students on testing, revising, and retesting their designs. Point out the importance of reworking a solution to a problem or challenge and that multiple attempts or iterations will help them improve their designs. Point out that designers and scientists go through many iterations in their work. Emphasize that iteration is not just redoing the same thing. It is first modifying the plan and then trying the revised plan.

> ### TEACHER TALK
>
> **"**All of you have just redesigned your book support. You have tried to make it better based on all the ideas you heard about during the class presentations. Designers (and scientists) rework problems or challenges to improve them. Each reworking is called iteration. Iteration means modifying and retesting and in design it is used to make something better. Your current design plan is your second iteration.**"**

Then focus students on the importance of record keeping. Point out that multiple iterations of designing and testing will require them to keep records of each iteration result so they will be able to keep track of the design changes and remember how each version worked. Emphasize the four points in the text box.

> ### TEACHER TALK
>
> **"**Each iteration is an improvement of your previous design, however, you might forget what you have done if you don't keep good records. Keeping good records is important. It helps you share your work with others. It helps you to remember what you did, why you decided to do it, how you did it, and what you think you should do next. When scientists keep records they want them to be very descriptive and provide their reasoning. They not only write down what went right, but also what went wrong and what not to do next time.**"**

Build and Test Your Design

15 min.

Have groups record each iteration as they build and test their book support.

Recording Your Work

This time, keep track of the number of index cards, paper clips, and rubber bands you use. Record this information on the *Book-Support Records* page. Each of you should fill in your own page.

One of the columns of the *Book-Support Records* page has room for you to draw your design after you have finished building it. You may create additional designs and continue to fill out the page. You will have a record of all the designs you attempted. This will allow you to see how you made improvements along the way.

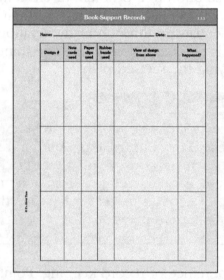

After completing your book support, your group will present it to the rest of the class. During your presentation, have your records page handy to report your quantities to the class.

Communicate Your Results

Solution Briefing

After you designed and built your first book support, you presented it to the class. You will present your new solution to the class too. This time you will

◯ Get Going

Have students use the *Book-Support Records* page to record their designs. Tell each student to write their reasoning for their design, as well as the design number, in the first column.

Inform groups they have 10 minutes to construct their designs, test each one, then select the best design. Distribute the materials or have students pick up the materials at a materials station.

△ Guide

While groups are building their designs, assist them in filling out the record page if they are having difficulty. They may need to be reminded to write down why they chose their particular design. To help them identify why they chose a design, you could ask what didn't work in their last design, what they could improve from their last design, and what they want to retest.

If you notice some groups are having trouble collaborating, assist them with their group skills by encouraging them each to take a minute to present their ideas to their group and then to decide which designs they want to try out first.

TEACHER TALK

"On the *Book-Support Records* page in the first column, you will be listing the design number and describing why you chose this design. In the next columns you will list how many note cards you used, how many paper clips you used, and how many rubber bands you used. You will draw what the finished design looks like, and in the last column you will describe what happened when you put a book on it. You might want to specify what worked well or what didn't work about the design. You can create additional designs while there is time. You should try out the group's favorite design ideas first."

△ Guide

Describe to students what a *Solution Briefing* is and how it works. Explain that they will be presenting their works in progress to share their ideas and gather advice. The goal is for the larger group (the class) to help each small group to make their solution better.

TEACHER TALK

"Now that you have all worked for a while on improving your designs, it is time for you to get some advice from outside of your group. Designers (and scientists) get together often to share their ideas and get advice from each other on ways to improve their designs (or explanations). PBIS calls this a *Solution Briefing*. We are going to have our first *Solution Briefing* so you can share your book-support designs and get advice from the class. Everyone is encouraged to ask questions so they understand your design and then offer suggestions on ways to improve it."

Communicate Your Results

Solution Briefing
20 min.

Prepare students for their first Solution Briefing. *Then conduct group presentations of each group's designs and results.*

DIVING INTO SCIENCE

PBIS *Learning Set 1 • The Book-Support Challenge*

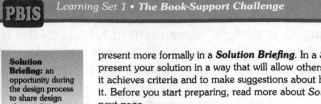

Solution Briefing: an opportunity during the design process to share design plans and get advice from others.

present more formally in a ***Solution Briefing***. In a *Solution Briefing*, you present your solution in a way that will allow others to evaluate how well it achieves criteria and to make suggestions about how you might improve it. Before you start preparing, read more about *Solution Briefings* on the next page.

As you prepare for the briefing, make sure you can answer questions like these:

- How is your design constructed?
- What materials did you use?
- Why did you design and build it the way you did?
- How does the design meet the criteria?
- How did the challenge constraints affect the design?
- What past experiences helped you make your design?
- What problems remain?
- What things did you try along the way?
- How well does your book support work? What else do you want to test?

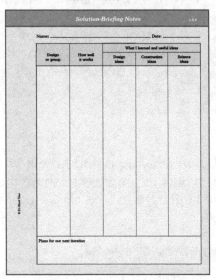

As you listen to your classmates' presentations, make sure you understand the answers to the questions above. If you don't understand something, or if they didn't present something important, ask questions. You can use the ones above as a guide. When you think something can be improved, make sure to contribute your ideas. Be careful to ask your questions and make your suggestions nicely. Record the interesting things you are hearing on your *Solution-Briefing Notes* page.

DIV 10

META NOTES

A *Solution Briefing* is a common pedagogical tool used in PBIS. In a *Solution Briefing* students present their ideas and hear other students' ideas so that students can build on each other's ideas. In this *Solution Briefing*, students are sharing and building on their ideas about how to design an effective book support. In this and many other class presentations students will learn how to communicate their ideas, ask questions, and sharpen their critical thinking skills. For more information please refer to the *Teacher's Resource Guide*.

○ Engage

Describe how to prepare for a *Solution Briefing*. Explain that student presentations should describe how they arrived at their current design solution. They can use questions on page 10 of the student text to help them think about what to present. Also explain that the audience should ask clarifying questions and offer suggestions. Everyone should voice their questions and ideas in a polite and considerate manner, using language such as "I agree with ... because..." or "I disagree with... because."

TEACHER TALK

"It is important that you all think about what you are going to say when you present your designs. On page 10 of the student text there is a list of questions that will help you think about what to talk about during your presentation. When you are in the audience or not presenting you will need to listen to make sure that you understand each design. You should also voice your opinions and ideas. Remember to always be polite and considerate whether you are presenting or are in the audience."

⬡ Get Going

First give students five minutes to prepare their presentation.

Then lead student groups in the *Solution Briefing*. Point out the *Solution-Briefing Notes* page for students to keep track of the presented designs and the ideas they found useful. Remind students that each group will be presenting their best design and that the audience will be asking questions and giving advice.

Remind the class to listen for how the designs work and to prepare their questions for the presenting group.

△ Guide

While groups are presenting, you and the class should be listening for descriptions of each design, how it is constructed, and how well it works to support a book.

If groups get off track or stuck, you can prompt them with one or two of the 10 questions listed in the student text. As the *Solution Briefing* progresses, encourage students in the audience to participate more in asking questions to help the presenters clarify their design descriptions.

Listen for the following types of responses to the student text questions.

- A detailed description of their design pointing out the design features. You could ask students what features of their design have changed or which part of their design they think is most important.

- The quantities of each material used.

- Reasons for design, and included in this should be the class's criteria and constraints. You could ask why they chose each part of the design and why they chose changes from their last design.

- How each criterion is being met. Students may have answered this in the previous point. Compare these against the class list.

- How each constraint affected their design. Students may have answered this in the previous point. Compare these against the class list.

> **META NOTES**
>
> Remember this is the first time students have seen a *Solution Briefing*, and it will take time for them to understand how to participate as presenters and as the audience.

Be a Scientist

Introducing a *Solution Briefing*

A *Solution Briefing* is useful when you have made one or more attempts to solve a problem or achieve a challenge and need some advice. It gives you a chance to share what you have tried and learned. It also provides an opportunity for you to learn from others. You can ask advice of others about difficulties you are having.

Real-life designers present their designs to each other and to others several times as they work on design projects. A team of designers sets up their design or design plans, and everybody gathers around. They make sure everyone can see. The design team presents their design plan to everyone. The other designers ask questions and give helpful advice about ways to improve the design.

You will do the same thing. In a *Solution Briefing*, each team presents their solution for others to see. Then teams take turns presenting to the class. Other classmates ask questions and offer helpful advice. You might walk around the class from design to design, or teams might take turns presenting in front of the class.

A *Solution Briefing* works best when everyone communicates well. Before you present your design to the rest of the class, think about what might be important to share. What aspects of your design should you present? What parts do you want to discuss with others? You need to be ready to justify to others what you decided to do and why.

When you are listening to a *Solution Briefing* it is important to pay close attention. Look at each design or plan. Think about questions you would like to ask about the design.

Each time you hold a briefing, you will take notes. You will fill out a *Solution-Briefing Notes* page as you listen to each group's presentation.

Collaboration is a group effort. A team of designers share sketches and ideas at the innovation and design firm IDEO.

DIV 11

DIVING INTO SCIENCE

META NOTES

If students say that another group copied their idea, tell them this is an important issue and will be addressed in a little bit and continue with the presentations. After the presentations the class will discuss building on each other's ideas versus copying.

- Past experiences (including the previous class) and how it affected the design. You could ask if there were any designs from the previous class that helped them decide on this design. At this point some students might say that a group copied from them. Let them know that the class will discuss this later and continue on with the presentations.

- Problems they feel remain and ideas they think might be good solutions to these problems. You could ask what they think they could improve. Some students might mention the work of others.

- All the ideas they tried today. You could ask what else they tried today or thought about trying. It is also important to bring out what ideas did not work and why these are helpful.

- What worked well and why, and ideas they still want to test.

After all groups have presented, wrap up the *Solution Briefing* by asking students if they heard any interesting ideas or thought of new ideas they would like to use to improve their own book-support design. Guide students to think about how sharing ideas will help them improve their own ideas.

Finally, compare this session with what scientists and designers do to improve their solutions. Reflect on the usefulness of iterations and keeping records. Tell students that scientists are always building on each other's ideas. Bring up the idea of giving credit to others when you build from their ideas. This is not copying. Emphasize that the difference between this and copying is that copying doesn't give credit to the people who thought of the ideas you used.

NOTES

....

....

....

....

....

....

....

....

Reflect

15 min.

Groups reflect on their designs and create plans for their next iteration based on what they now know.

Reflect

Following your *Solution Briefing*, answer the following questions. Discuss your answers and how they may help you achieve the *Book-Support Challenge*.

Draw your group's book support and label the parts. You may find looking at your drawing helpful as you answer the following questions:

1. Why did your group select the features you used in your book support?

2. Which criteria did your design fulfill?

3. What qualities make your book support a good design?

4. What are the problems with your current design?

5. Before the support was tested, what did you think would happen when the book was placed on it?

6. What worked the way you thought it would? What worked differently than what you expected?

Be a Scientist

Copying versus Crediting

When you build on someone else's idea, it is important to give them credit. Why isn't this "copying?" Copying means taking the work of someone else and claiming it as your own. If you simply build what some other group built, that is copying. But if you add to another group's idea and acknowledge from where you got your idea, you are doing what scientists and engineers do. When you explain how you used their ideas and made them better, you are adding your contribution to theirs.

This means that you will have to keep good records of where you got your ideas. When you use someone else's ideas, always record from whom you borrowed the idea. Record how you included it in your design, and why you did it that way. Then, make sure to give credit to the other person or group in your presentations.

Groups will build their next book support in *Section 1.4* and it will be based on an additional criterion.

⬡ Get Going

Transition the class by reminding them that they have just been introduced to many different ideas on how to build the book support. By this time they should have ideas about how to improve their book support. The six questions will assist students in achieving the book-support question. Groups should work together coming up with their best group answer to each question.

Tell groups they have five minutes to answer the questions.

△ Guide and Assess a Discussion

Hold a class discussion, briefly addressing questions 1 through 5 and focusing on question 6. You may want to ask just a group or two to answer

Reflect
(continued)

Be a Scientist

Build on and Benefit from Each Other's Ideas

You ask questions and offer suggestions during a *Solution Briefing*. When you do this, you are **collaborating** with each other. You are working together. You offer your ideas for others to think about. You provide suggestions that might help them improve their solutions. Sometimes you learn something that you want to try yourself.

collaborate: to work together.

Other teams may come up with solutions to design challenges that you want to borrow and make better. You may also find that other teams have used your suggestions. Is the other team copying from you? Are you copying from them?

Think about the other team's success as your success when they use something you suggested. Help them see that your success is theirs if you borrowed something from them.

When movie actors receive awards, they often thank many people. Even though they're getting the award, they know that it takes lots of people to put a movie together. It is the same with scientists and engineers.

They wouldn't be able to solve problems or learn new things without building on the work of others. Scientists and engineers write papers, or articles, in journals. They tell others what they have discovered. Others read those papers, talk about the ideas, and ask questions. When someone improves on an idea, they write a paper about it and publish it for others to read and improve. This is the way science is done.

questions 1 through 5. But you should get each group to discuss their response to question 6.

Listen for the following:

1. Answers based on the criteria, constraints, and what they previously heard and saw.

2. Criteria from the class list.

3. Qualities that make the book support good should include that it meets the criteria and constraints, and reasons should be provided that back up group responses.

Reflect
(continued)

4. Reasons, such as it does not meet the criteria and/or constraints, should back up group responses. Groups may also pick out a problem after deciding they liked a feature of another group's design better.

5. This is an elicitation of students' thoughts. You could ask students to provide their reasons as well.

6. This question will help prepare students for creating their next design iteration. Groups should describe what worked as they expected and what didn't. Ask students for their reasoning of why they didn't think something worked and why they expect their new idea to work.

○ Get Going

Now that students have thought about their design and what worked and what they would do differently, they will have new ideas about designing their book support. This is the time for them to complete the *Solution-Briefing Notes* page by filling out the next iteration of their design.

Ask groups to complete their *Solution-Briefing Notes* page based on what they now know. Let them know they may work together as a group but each student is responsible for completing the plans for the next iteration. Emphasize that they should give their reasoning behind their design. Let them know they have five minutes to complete this.

△ Guide

As groups are working, check their progress and guide them by asking them questions that help them articulate the reason behind their design. For example, "Why did you decide to put the note cards that way? Write it down. You need to give the reasons for your design too."

Then hold a class discussion emphasizing again the difference between copying and giving credit and that it is O.K. to build on others' ideas as long as credit is given. There are good examples given in the text boxes of the student text. You may want to go through these. Make sure you introduce the word "collaborate" and let students know that it means to work together, like they have been doing.

1.2

What's the Point?

The book supports you built the second time were probably more successful than the first ones. In general, the more designs you get a chance to build and test, the better your solution will turn out. Each attempt you make is an iteration. Each time you make another attempt, you can do better because you use knowledge gained from the previous attempt. This iterative approach to design and problem solving is what scientists do. Use this approach whenever you have a problem to solve.

You learned that there is a difference between copying and building on the ideas of others. As you took part in the first *Solution Briefing*, you may have seen some design ideas that worked well. You may have used some of those ideas to improve your book support. Others may have used some of your ideas. When you claim someone else's idea as your own, it is copying. If, however, you give credit to the group for their idea, you are building on the work of others. This is how scientists work and how science grows. Science builds on the ideas of others.

You probably have begun to realize the importance of keeping records as you work on a design challenge. You were able to use these records when you presented your ideas during the *Solution Briefing*. You also got a chance to see other solution ideas during the briefing. You saw what works and what does not work as well. This may help you develop better ideas as you continue to solve your challenge. You can learn a lot from attempts that "failed" as well as ones that succeeded. In either case, the goal is to understand the challenge better and create better solutions.

DIV 14

Project-Based Inquiry Science

What's the Point?

5 min.

It is important for students to understand that the more you work on the design, the better it gets. Also emphasize the benefit of *Solution Briefings* and building on each other's ideas – but being sure to give credit.

Assessment Options

Targeted Concepts, Skills, and Nature of Science	How do I know if students got it?
Science and engineering are dynamic processes, changing as new information becomes available.	**ASK:** Did your ideas for design change as you heard other ideas? Which ideas changed your design plans? **LISTEN:** Students' responses should contain information about how their ideas evolved as they were exposed to new information (ideas from other groups or things they read). **ASK:** Why is it important to do many iterations? **LISTEN:** Students' responses should contain information about how each iteration is done either to make use of new information and understanding or to gain more information and understanding. Iterations help create the best ideas/construction we can do within the criteria and constraints.
Scientists often work together and then share their findings. Sharing findings makes new information available and helps scientists refine their ideas and build on others' ideas. When another person's or group's idea is used, credit needs to be given.	**POLL** the class for the following: Did your group change their design plans based on ideas and input from more than one group member? Did your group get ideas from one or more of the other presenting groups? **ASK:** How many different people contributed to our knowledge base of building a good book support? What should we do when we build on someone's ideas? **LISTEN:** Students' response should refer to the need to give credit. This is an ethical issue and is important in the scientific community.

Targeted Concepts, Skills, and Nature of Science	How do I know if students got it?
(continued)	**ASK:** Do you think our knowledge may be considered a constraint? **LISTEN:** Students will have different answers. This is to prepare them for the next section, but most students should realize that our knowledge is limited, and as we learn more we can create better designs (e.g., for book supports). **TELL** the class that scientists, engineers, and designers all work together in small groups and then share their ideas with larger communities. By sharing their ideas, scientists can improve them and build on them. **ASK:** Do you think we did what scientists do? **LISTEN:** Students' responses should contain: Yes – Scientists first work in small groups and then share their ideas with a larger community to make sure their ideas are as good as they can be, and we do this to make sure our ideas are as good as they can be.
Scientists must keep clear, accurate, and descriptive records of what they do so they can share their work with others, consider what they did, why they did it, and what they want to do next.	**ASK:** Why is it important to keep good records? **LISTEN:** Students' answers should contain information about being able to accurately tell others of their work, what they did, and why they did it. **NOTE:** If students don't explicitly make the connection between the records and sharing of results with the *Book–Support Records* sheet and with the *Solution Briefing,* then explicitly make the connection for them.

Teacher Reflection Questions

- What difficulties did students have in understanding the importance of keeping records, sharing ideas, and building on other's ideas by giving credit? Where will your students need the most help with these ideas in the next lesson?

- What difficulties did students have in participating or understanding the social practices of working in small groups and holding presentations and discussions in larger communities? What might help students participate in the next small group or whole-class discussion?

- What questions or comments did students ask or say that might be rude or inappropriate? (For example, "S/He copied from us!" Or talking out of turn.) What will help your students to learn how to question or comment respectfully?

NOTES

SECTION 1.3 INTRODUCTION

1.3 Read

The Science of Structures

◀ *1 class period* *

Overview

Groups have completed two iterations of designing and building a book support. Now groups are introduced to the concepts of matter, gravity, center of mass, what makes a structure strong, and what makes a structure stable. Then students learn about the structure of columns. Students read about how columns distribute a load, making them very strong structures. After reflecting upon the reading, students consider how they could apply these concepts to their book-support design.

*A class period is considered to be one 40 to 50 minute class.

Targeted Concepts, Skills, and Nature of Science	Performance Expectations
Science and engineering are dynamic processes, changing as new information becomes available.	Students should be able to describe how their ideas evolved as they were exposed to information involving the science behind their book support. Students should be able to describe how each iteration is done, either to make use of new information and understanding or to gain more information and understanding.

Materials

1 per classroom	sponge 1" × 4" × 7", with a dot drawn along its central axis as shown in the image in the student text
1 per student	8½" × 11" sheet of paper

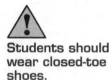

Students should wear closed-toe shoes.

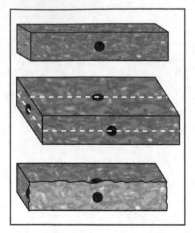

Activity Setup and Preparation

You will do two demonstrations using a square sponge. One illustrating folding and compression and one pointing out the center of mass. Prepare the sponge with a dark dot on the axis as shown.

The sponge's center of mass is actually located near the center of the sponge where you cannot see. To give students an idea of where the center of mass is, draw lines along the three axes of the sponge. If the matter is equally distributed, then the center of mass would be where all the lines (axes) cross each other in the middle of the sponge. The dot represents the location of one of the axes on which the center of mass lies, but it does not actually give the exact point.

Homework Options

Reflection

These questions not only have students reflect on what they have learned, but also prepare them for *Section 1.4*, which has students apply the ideas they have learned to a new situation.

- **Science Content:** In this section you learned about what makes a structure strong and stable. Use this information to design a strong and stable book support based on your previous list of criteria and constraints. Sketch your design and describe it. *(Students should meet all previous class criteria and constraints and discuss strength and stability.)*

- **Science Process:** How are the design structures you observed during the class presentations the same? How are they different? *(Students should describe how various designs are similar and different. Similarities should include satisfying the criteria and constraints. Students may point out the strength and the stability of the design.)*

Preparation for 1.4

- **Nature of Design:** Designers are often concerned with how well a design would sell. What additional criteria and constraints do you think would be important if you were going to sell your book support? *(Check that students support their ideas with reasons related to cost or other factors related to sales.)*

SECTION 1.3 IMPLEMENTATION

◀ *1 class period*

1.3 Read

The Science of Structures

You just finished your first two tries at building a book support. You also talked about the design ideas of other groups. You learned about some ideas that worked well and others that did not. Soon you will work on a revised challenge. Before you do, you probably want to know about the science of structures.

Matter

All objects are made of **matter**. Objects of any form (solid, liquid, or gas) are made of matter. All matter has mass and takes up space. The amount of space that something takes up is its **volume**. The book you are trying to support is made of matter. The matter we are most familiar with is made of extremely small particles called **atoms**. These atoms combine with other atoms to form very small particles called **molecules**. Molecules attach to each other to form the objects that you see, touch, hear, and even taste and smell.

Gravity

You have probably heard of **gravity**. You definitely have seen the effects of gravity. Gravity is a pull between objects. All objects experience this pull towards other objects. The pull between most objects is very small. You usually do not see the objects affected in any way.

However, when one (or both) of the objects is very massive (has a lot of matter) you can see the effects. Earth is very massive. There is a pull between Earth and a book. The job of the book support is to resist Earth's pull on the book. It must keep the book from falling toward Earth's surface. Your job is to use the materials you've been provided to construct something strong and stable enough to resist the pull of gravity on the book.

matter: anything that has mass and takes up space.

volume: the amount of space that something takes up.

atom: a small particle of matter.

molecule: the combination of two or more atoms.

gravity: a pull between two objects.

DIV 15

DIVING INTO SCIENCE

1.3 Read

The Science of Structures

5 min.

Guide students' reading about science ideas related to the strength and stability of structures.

META NOTES

The purpose of this section is to introduce students to the science of strength and stability of structures to make informed design decisions. These ideas are being introduced so students can see the value of science knowledge in building their design and of building on other's ideas as scientists do. The specific science ideas introduced here will be covered more completely in other PBIS Units.

○ Engage

Let students know that they will be doing a revised *Book-Support Challenge* and it will be helpful to learn some science ideas related to structures. By researching what is known — in this case what is known about the science of structures — they will be able to design a better book support.

You've already completed two iterations of your book-support design. You've learned from each other's designs and hearing each other's advice. When you are designing something it is also important to find out what research has already been done that pertains to your design. In building your book support, it is useful to know about the science of structures. That is what we will be doing today — learning about the science of structures. This will help you to build a better book support.

Matter

5 min.

Matter

All objects are made of **matter**. Objects of any form (solid, liquid, or gas) are made of matter. All matter has mass and takes up space. The amount of space that something takes up is its **volume**. The book you are trying to support is made of matter. The matter we are most familiar with is made of extremely small particles called **atoms**. These atoms combine with other atoms to form very small particles called **molecules**. Molecules attach to each other to form the objects that you see, touch, hear, and even taste and smell.

matter: anything that has mass and takes up space.

volume: the amount of space that something takes up.

atom: a small particle of matter.

△ Guide

Introduce the idea of matter (anything that has mass and takes up space). Then lead students in thinking about each of the ideas in the reading. Highlight that matter is anything that has mass and takes up space whether it is a solid, a liquid, or a gas. The book, the book support, the air, and Earth are all examples of matter. Many students mix up volume and mass. Assist students in understanding the difference between volume and mass. Volume measures how much space something takes up, and mass is how much matter (or material) it has.

TEACHER TALK

“Although both volume and mass measure how much "stuff" something has, they are very different. Volume measures how much space something takes up and mass measures how much matter it has. For example, consider I had two identical jars. I could fill one up with water and one with whipped cream. Both take up the same volume but the bottle of water has more mass than the bottle of whipped cream.”

Gravity

5 min.

hear, and even ... smell.

Gravity

You have probably heard of **gravity**. You definitely have seen the effects of gravity. Gravity is a pull between objects. All objects experience this pull towards other objects. The pull between most objects is very small. You usually do not see the objects affected in any way.

However, when one (or both) of the objects is *very* massive (has a lot of matter) you can see the effects. Earth is very massive. There is a pull between Earth and a book. The job of the book support is to resist Earth's pull on the book. It must keep the book from falling toward Earth's surface. Your job is to use the materials you've been provided to construct something strong and stable enough to resist the pull of gravity on the book.

molecule: the combination of two or more atoms.

gravity: a pull between two objects.

DIV 15

DIVING INTO SCIENCE

△ Guide

Introduce gravity as the pull between material objects. Let students know that scientists don't completely understand what gravity is, but they know that every object with matter attracts every other object with matter. They also know that this attraction between two objects is very small, so we don't notice it when we put two apples near each other on a table. But, when one of the objects has a lot of matter (when it is massive) then the pull between the objects is great enough to notice. Earth has a lot of matter, so we notice the pull between an object and Earth.

Then make the connection with how the pull of gravity affects their book support.

TEACHER TALK

"What causes the book to fall toward Earth if it is not supported properly? The book falls because there is a pull between the book and Earth that pulls the book toward Earth. But if the book is supported properly, it will not fall toward Earth."

NOTES

....

....

....

....

....

....

....

....

Strong Structures

5 min.

Now lead students in considering the strength and stability of structures – in particular, the strength and stability of columns – that will help students improve their book-support design. Begin by demonstrating strength.

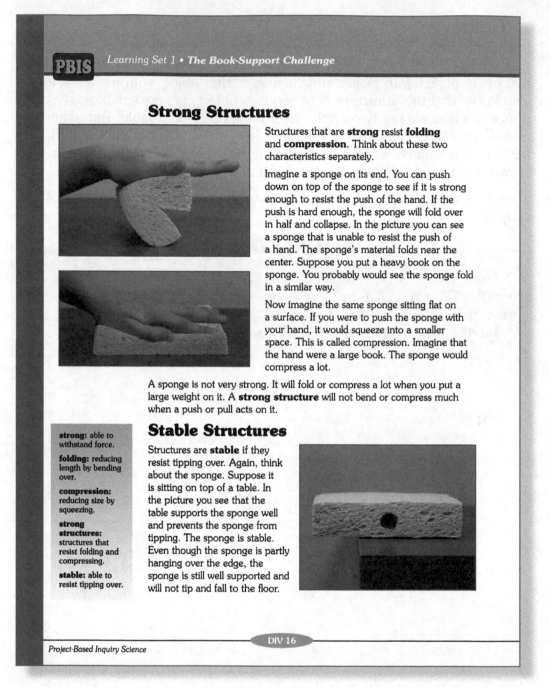

Strong Structures

Structures that are **strong** resist **folding** and **compression**. Think about these two characteristics separately.

Imagine a sponge on its end. You can push down on top of the sponge to see if it is strong enough to resist the push of the hand. If the push is hard enough, the sponge will fold over in half and collapse. In the picture you can see a sponge that is unable to resist the push of a hand. The sponge's material folds near the center. Suppose you put a heavy book on the sponge. You probably would see the sponge fold in a similar way.

Now imagine the same sponge sitting flat on a surface. If you were to push the sponge with your hand, it would squeeze into a smaller space. This is called compression. Imagine that the hand were a large book. The sponge would compress a lot.

A sponge is not very strong. It will fold or compress a lot when you put a large weight on it. A **strong structure** will not bend or compress much when a push or pull acts on it.

strong: able to withstand force.

folding: reducing length by bending over.

compression: reducing size by squeezing.

strong structures: structures that resist folding and compressing.

stable: able to resist tipping over.

Stable Structures

Structures are **stable** if they resist tipping over. Again, think about the sponge. Suppose it is sitting on top of a table. In the picture you see that the table supports the sponge well and prevents the sponge from tipping. The sponge is stable. Even though the sponge is partly hanging over the edge, the sponge is still well supported and will not tip and fall to the floor.

DIV 16

Project-Based Inquiry Science

○ Engage

Remind students of their book-support designs and ask them which design they thought was strongest. Then ask students why they thought it was strong. (Students should answer that it held up the book.) Then ask students what part of the design's structure they thought made it strong. If any groups used columns, ask if those were strong book supports. After hearing students' ideas, tell them that they are now going to think about what makes a structure strong.

△ Guide

Tell students that what makes a structure strong is that it resists folding and compression. Folding is reducing length by bending over. Compression is reducing size by squeezing.

Demonstrate and describe folding with the sponge. During the demonstration, describe again what folding is and how it is used to measure strength of the structure.

Demonstrate and describe compression with the sponge. During the demonstration, describe how compression is used to measure strength of the structure.

Emphasize that the strength of a structure is judged by how much it resists folding and compressing. Tell students that if their book supports crumple or break when the book was placed on it, then they are not strong enough.

○ Engage

First ask students which book support they think was most stable or least stable. If any groups used columns, ask if those were stable book supports. Then ask them why they think designs with columns are stable and what they think stable means.

Stable Structures

10 min.

Next demonstrate stability and center of mass to students. This will assist students in designing a structure that meets the criteria of the Book-Support Challenge.

NOTES

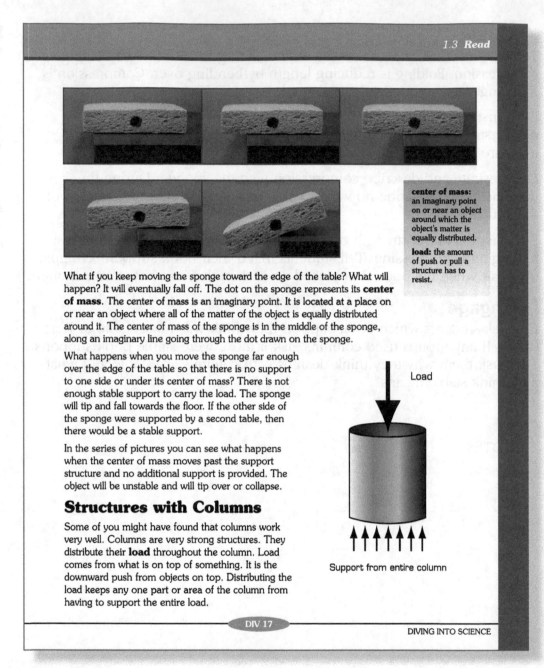

1.3 Read

center of mass: an imaginary point on or near an object around which the object's matter is equally distributed.

load: the amount of push or pull a structure has to resist.

What if you keep moving the sponge toward the edge of the table? What will happen? It will eventually fall off. The dot on the sponge represents its **center of mass**. The center of mass is an imaginary point. It is located at a place on or near an object where all of the matter of the object is equally distributed around it. The center of mass of the sponge is in the middle of the sponge, along an imaginary line going through the dot drawn on the sponge.

What happens when you move the sponge far enough over the edge of the table so that there is no support to one side or under its center of mass? There is not enough stable support to carry the load. The sponge will tip and fall towards the floor. If the other side of the sponge were supported by a second table, then there would be a stable support.

In the series of pictures you can see what happens when the center of mass moves past the support structure and no additional support is provided. The object will be unstable and will tip over or collapse.

Load

Support from entire column

Structures with Columns

Some of you might have found that columns work very well. Columns are very strong structures. They distribute their **load** throughout the column. Load comes from what is on top of something. It is the downward push from objects on top. Distributing the load keeps any one part or area of the column from having to support the entire load.

DIV 17

DIVING INTO SCIENCE

△ Guide

Tell students that stability is the ability to resist tipping over. Let students know that if their book support were to tip over when a book is placed on it, then it is not stable. Stability is different than strength.

First, tell students that the center of mass is actually in the center of the sponge, not at the dot. It is where all three lines (axes) cross each other — provided that the matter is equally distributed. Then, using the kitchen sponge, demonstrate that an object will tip over if its center of mass is not supported, by placing the sponge on top of a book on a table. Slowly push the sponge so that its center of mass is over the edge of the book and note that the sponge tips.

TEACHER TALK

❝I will be using a sponge, like the one shown in the book. I've drawn some lines on my sponge and dots in the center of the lines. These lines are drawn such that there is equal stuff (mass) above and below the line. It happens to be in the middle because we are assuming that mass is equally distributed throughout the sponge. Now, the center of mass is where these three lines intersect. It just so happens that this happens at the center of the sponge. You can't see where the center of mass is because it is inside the sponge, but we can see where it lies along these lines I've drawn.

Notice that as I slowly move the sponge over so that its edge is hanging over the book, it still remains on the book without tipping. But as soon as the sponge's center of mass is over the edge, the sponge tips over and falls off the book.❞

Next, demonstrate that the center of mass might not have a support directly under it, but it might have supports on each side. Place the kitchen sponge on top of two books that are side by side. Separate the books so that each book is under a small portion of the sponge's far edges. Emphasize that the center of mass does not have a support directly under it, but the support is still stable since the structure is able to carry the entire load without tipping. Ask students what would happen if either support were removed. (The sponge would tip over.) Demonstrate this by moving away one of the supports.

⭕ Engage

If you haven't already done so, ask the class who used columns for the book support. Ask if they think their columns were structurally strong and stable and why or why not. Tell them they are going to try out the strength and stability of a column.

Structures with Columns
10 min.

Demonstrate to students why columns are strong and stable structures.

META NOTES

Since a single column is being used, the center of mass of the book must be over the column so that the book does not tip over.

Structures with Columns (continued)

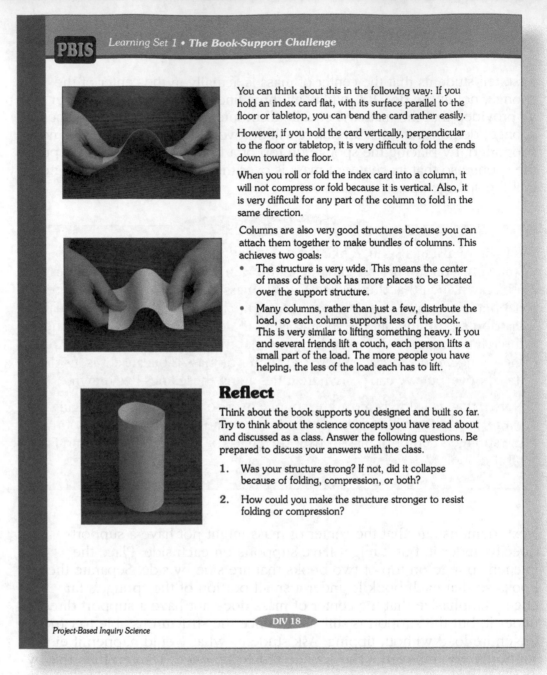

You can think about this in the following way: If you hold an index card flat, with its surface parallel to the floor or tabletop, you can bend the card rather easily.

However, if you hold the card vertically, perpendicular to the floor or tabletop, it is very difficult to fold the ends down toward the floor.

When you roll or fold the index card into a column, it will not compress or fold because it is vertical. Also, it is very difficult for any part of the column to fold in the same direction.

Columns are also very good structures because you can attach them together to make bundles of columns. This achieves two goals:

- The structure is very wide. This means the center of mass of the book has more places to be located over the support structure.

- Many columns, rather than just a few, distribute the load, so each column supports less of the book. This is very similar to lifting something heavy. If you and several friends lift a couch, each person lifts a small part of the load. The more people you have helping, the less of the load each has to lift.

Reflect

Think about the book supports you designed and built so far. Try to think about the science concepts you have read about and discussed as a class. Answer the following questions. Be prepared to discuss your answers with the class.

1. Was your structure strong? If not, did it collapse because of folding, compression, or both?

2. How could you make the structure stronger to resist folding or compression?

DIV 18

Project-Based Inquiry Science

⬡ Get Going

Give each student a regular sheet of paper (8 ½" × 11").

Then demonstrate for students how to make a column from the sheet of paper to hold a book. NOTE: When you do this, just roll the paper so the top and bottom of the page are overlapped (as shown in the image) and, while holding it in its column shape, place a book on it.

Emphasize that the simple sheet of paper can carry a book because it is a strong structure.

Ask students to try making a column from their paper and placing a book on it.

TEACHER TALK

"Here's a simple sheet of paper. I'm going to make a column out of it by just rolling it into a cylinder so that I can just hold it together. Now I'll place one end on the table and on the top I'll put a book. This paper can hold the book because the column is such a strong structure. Now you try it."

△ Guide

Then make a connection with the demonstration students have just done and the idea that the cylinder (column) is only strong if its surface is perpendicular to the desk. If you lay the rolled paper sideways (with its surface parallel to the desk) and place a book on it, the cylinder will flatten. Have students try it.

Then connect the idea of stability. Point out that if you make a book support with many columns, you can make the structure wide so they span the center of mass or you can place the column under the center of mass. The wider the structure the more stable it is because then you can move the book around more (the center of mass will be supported in more locations).

Connect the idea of strength. When you use many columns to make your book support, it can carry more mass, or support a heavier book. This is because each column shares the load. Use the analogy in the book of many friends carrying a couch to assist student understanding.

TEACHER TALK

"If eight friends carry a couch then ideally each would support ⅛ of the couch's weight; if two friends carry the couch each supports ½ of the couch's weight. Columns work in a similar way. Each part of the column supports some of the load. And the more columns you have the more "shared" the load is."

Reflect

10 min.

Lead a discussion of students' reflections on their designs, strength and stability, and how they could improve their book-support designs.

META NOTES

Groups will design and build another book support in the next section.

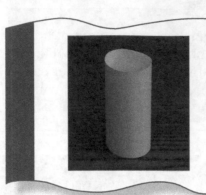

Reflect

Think about the book supports you designed and built so far. Try to think about the science concepts you have read about and discussed as a class. Answer the following questions. Be prepared to discuss your answers with the class.

1. Was your structure strong? If not, did it collapse because of folding, compression, or both?

2. How could you make the structure stronger to resist folding or compression?

◯ Get Going

First point out to the class that they have been introduced to a lot of science information that can be used to help them build a better book support. In order to help them think about how this information can help them, groups should discuss their answers to the *Reflect* questions.

Then let groups know that they will work the way scientists work, discussing their ideas for each question and coming up with their best group response for each. Emphasize that each student is responsible for contributing to the group discussion and writing down the group response on his or her own paper. Tell groups they have five minutes to answer the eight questions.

☐ Guide and Assess

Have a class discussion on the questions. During the discussion, listen for the following responses and guide students to these responses if they are having difficulty.

1. Students should say their structure was strong if it held a book. If their structure collapsed, they should describe whether it collapsed due to compression or folding. You could also ask students if they think the book support should be able to hold a certain weight.

2. Students should describe that columns or multiple columns could be more helpful if they did not already use columns in their design. If it does not come up during the discussion, you could ask how one might reduce compression in their design or how they might reduce folding. For example, folding and compression in a column made of paper can be reduced by using multiple sheets of paper to construct the cylinder.

3. Was your book support stable? That is, did it provide support so that the book did not tip over? Did it provide this support well? Draw a picture of your book support showing the center of mass of the book and the places in your book support that resist the load of your book.

4. How could you make your book support more stable?

5. How successful were the book supports that used columns in their design?

6. How could you make your book support work more effectively by including columns into the design?

7. Explain how the pull on the book could better be resisted by the use of columns in your design. Be sure to discuss both the strength and the stability of the columns in your design. You might find it easier to draw a sketch and label it to explain how the columns do this.

8. Think about some of the structures that supported the book well. What designs and building decisions were used?

You are going to get another chance to design a book support. You will use the same materials. Think about how your group could design your next book support to better meet the challenge. Consider what you now know about the science that explains how structures support objects.

3. You could start this discussion by asking students what it means to be stable. Students should be able to state that their book support was stable if the book did not tip and that it was not stable if their book did tip.

4. Some students might suggest a rigid structure and some might suggest moveable columns so that they can adjust the support structure for different book sizes to increase stability.

5. You should ask your class what they think "successful" means. All book supports meeting the criteria and constraints were successful. A more successful book support would be a stronger and more stable one.

6. Students should realize that columns make stronger and more stable designs.

7. Columns provide more support (resistance to the pull downward) because they share the load across the surface of the column. This makes the column strong because it does not fold or compress easily. Columns are stable because they provide a surface of support rather than a point so that the center of mass of the book can be located in more places. You can use multiple columns to span the center of mass of the book, providing more stability.

8. Designs that work well are ones that are strong, stable structures and meet the criteria and constraints. Students should discuss the use of columns and spanning the center of mass to provide more stability.

Wrap up the discussion by letting students know that they will be redesigning their book support in the next section.

Teacher Reflection Questions

- What difficulties did students have with the concepts of strong structures, stable structures, and columns? What ideas do you have to assist students next time in being able to apply the science knowledge in this section?

- One of the goals in this section is for students to realize that they are better able to reach their goals if they have more information. For example, scientists research their questions before they start designing an experiment. What difficulties did your students have in connecting the importance of science knowledge about structures to their ability to design a better book support?

- How well did students participate in the wrap-up class discussion? Did each group member feel responsible for the group responses? Did each student actively participate in listening to the other groups?

NOTES

....

....

....

1.4 Design

Another Book-Support Challenge
◀ *1 class period**

Overview

Students apply what they learned about the science of structures as they design and build another book support. This time there is an additional constraint of making the book support cost-effective. While designing, building, and presenting their new book supports, student practice the social practices of scientists.

Targeted Concepts, Skills, and Nature of Science	Performance Expectations
Science and engineering are dynamic processes, changing as new information becomes available.	Students should be able to apply what they now know to a new design and describe how their design and ideas evolved through each iteration.
Scientists often work together and then share their findings. Sharing findings makes new information available and helps scientists refine their ideas and build on others' ideas. When another person's or group's idea is used, credit needs to be given.	Students should be able to work effectively together to redesign and build their book support. Students should listen to each other, try out a variety of ideas, and prepare reasonable presentations in which they share their ideas.
Criteria and constraints are important in design.	Students should be able to identify, describe, and apply all criteria and constraints.
Scientists must keep clear, accurate, and descriptive records of what they do so they can share their work with others, consider what they did, why they did it, and what they want to do next.	Students should be able to refer to their records and describe in detail what they did and why.

Materials

100	per group	3" × 5" index cards
50	per group	paper clips (jumbo size)
50	per group	rubber bands (3 1/2" x 1/8")
1	per group	metric ruler
1	per student	*Book-Support Records* page
1	per student	*Solution-Briefing Notes* sheet
1	per class	class's list of criteria and constraints

*A class period is considered to be one 40 to 50 minute class.

61

Students should wear closed-toe shoes.

Activity Setup and Preparation

- Remind students prior to the lesson to wear closed-toe shoes.

- You might want to think about how to best distribute the materials. Some teachers prepare small bags or trays of materials for each group; they find that for the beginning-of-the-year activity, this method is better than a materials station.

Homework Options

Reflection

- **Science Content:** How did you use ideas about strength and stability in your new design? *[Students are expected to use the ideas of strength (folding and compressing) and stability (center of mass) of structures and columns in their new design and should discuss how they used these ideas.]*

- **Nature of Science:** Do you think your knowledge of structures could limit your ability to design a good book support? How did working in small groups and then sharing ideas with the class help to increase your knowledge? *(Knowledge is a constraint or limitation and that is why scientists share their ideas in groups and then with the larger scientific community — so they can build upon each other's ideas.)*

Preparation for the Big Challenge

- **Nature of Science:** How do you think scientists work together to solve problems? How do you think this is similar to how you worked on the *Book-Support Challenge?* *(Look for descriptions of scientists working in groups and presenting their ideas to the scientific community. Also check if students support their ideas with examples from how they worked on the* Book-Support Challenge.*)*

- **Nature of Science:** Write a story about a team of scientists working on a project, describing how they work together. *(Look for descriptions of scientists working in small groups and then in larger groups to build upon each other's ideas.)*

- **Nature of Science:** Draw a diagram representing your interactions with other members of your class while you were working on the *Book-Support Challenge.* Describe what you were doing during each interaction. Draw a diagram of how you think a scientist interacts with other scientists when working on a project. *(Students should draw a diagram showing interactions individually or in small groups connecting to larger groups, going back to the individual or smaller groups and connecting again with larger groups.)*

SECTION 1.4 IMPLEMENTATION

◀ *1 class period**

1.4 Design

Another Book-Support Challenge

Just when you thought you had it all figured out, the challenge has changed! You've realized how useful a book support might be for keyboarding, especially for someone who has forgotten their glasses. Imagine making money selling book supports. What would it take to make your first book support more appealing to buyers, but not be too expensive to produce?

Cost is one of the most important factors that product designers must keep in mind. The cost of your book support is directly related to how much material you use. Assume that each index card, rubber band, and paper clip costs 10 cents. You need to design a low-cost book support that can hold a book in an open position and still allow you to turn pages easily. Once again, keep track of the supplies you use in this final design.

Update Your Criteria and Constraints

Now that the challenge has changed, review your criteria and constraints. Update these lists. Then, consider these changes as you design and build your new book support.

Project-Based Inquiry Science

DIV 20

1.4 Design

Another Book-Support Challenge
5 min.

Introduce students to the new challenge — to design and build an improved book support with the additional constraint of making it cost-effective.

○ Engage

Remind students of the original challenge and introduce the new criterion. Emphasize that being cost-effective is important to designers and that they will need to build a cost-effective book support.

TEACHER TALK

❝You have been working on designing and building a book support. Now you know something more about how structures can be strong and stable. What if you also wanted to make a book support that other people might want to buy? Then it would be important to make sure it wasn't too expensive. This time your task is to design a book support that is cost-effective in addition to all the other criteria and constraints.❞

*A class period is considered to be one 40 to 50 minute class.

Update Your Criteria and Constraints

5 min.

Lead the class in updating their list of criteria and constraints based on what they have learned about strength and stability of structures and the new criteria of cost.

again, keep track of the supplies you use in this final design.

Update Your Criteria and Constraints

Now that the challenge has changed, review your criteria and constraints. Update these lists. Then, consider these changes as you design and build your new book support.

△ Guide

Now that a new criterion has been given, the class needs to update their list of criteria and constraints. Ask students what needs to be added or changed and update it accordingly. Students should add cost-effective to the list of criteria. They may want to add something about stability and strength also, or edit the criteria they already have listed.

◇ Evaluate

Make sure that the criteria include that the book support be cost-effective, meaning it costs as little as possible and still satisfies all the other criteria and constraints.

NOTES

....

....

....

....

....

....

Plan, Build, and Test Your Design

As you design your new book support, you are welcome to use ideas that other groups have developed, but you should make sure to give credit. Once again, keep track of the number of index cards, paper clips, and rubber bands you use in this second design. Record your quantities in the *Book-Support Records* page. Each of you should record this information on your own page.

After completing your book support, your group will present your new solution to the rest of the class. During your presentation, have the record page handy to report your quantities to the class. Good luck!

Communicate Your Solution

Solution Briefing

Now it is time to share your new book support with the class. Once again, you will participate in a *Solution Briefing*.

Like before, spend some time preparing for your presentation. Be prepared to answer questions like the following:

- How is your design constructed?
- What materials did you use, and how many of each?
- Why did you build it the way you did?
- What is the overall cost of the design?
- How well does it work?
- How does the design meet the criteria?
- How did the challenge constraints affect the design?
- What past experiences helped you make your design?
- What problems remain?
- Did you try anything different?
- What else do you want to test?

When you present your book support, your group will need to justify the design decisions you have made and show the results of any other designs you created. Once you have totaled all of the supplies, calculate the total cost of your book support and be prepared to discuss and justify your design and total cost during the *Solution Briefing*.

As before, keep notes on a *Solution-Briefing Notes* page. As you listen to the presentations, remember to ask questions if anything is unclear.

DIV 21

DIVING INTO SCIENCE

Plan, Build, and Test Your Design

10 min.

Have students design and build a book support applying the new criteria and constraints and what they now know about the science of structures.

◯ Get Going

Begin by reminding students of the importance of planning the design before building it, and the usefulness of building the design to see if it will work or what needs to be improved.

Distribute materials including the *Book-Support Records* page and let students know they have 10 minutes.

△ Guide

While groups are working, check to see how they are doing. Most groups should not have difficulty with creating a design since this is at least the third time they have designed and built a book support. However, they may still have trouble writing the reasoning behind their design choice. Ask guiding questions such as, "Why did you choose to place the columns where you did?"

Communicate Your Solution

Solution Briefing
20 min.

Have groups present their designs, discuss their results, and keep track of other groups' designs and results.

---

solutio... ...ass. During yo... ...ave the ...
page handy ... ...your quantities to the class. Good luck!

Communicate Your Solution

Solution Briefing

Now it is time to share your new book support with the class. Once again, you will participate in a *Solution Briefing*.

Like before, spend some time preparing for your presentation. Be prepared to answer questions like the following:

- How is your design constructed?
- What materials did you use, and how many of each?
- Why did you build it the way you did?
- What is the overall cost of the design?
- How well does it work?
- How does the design meet the criteria?
- How did the challenge constraints affect the design?
- What past experiences helped you make your design?
- What problems remain?
- Did you try anything different?
- What else do you want to test?

When you present your book support, your group will need to justify the design decisions you have made and show the results of any other designs you created. Once you have totaled all of the supplies, calculate the total cost of your book support and be prepared to discuss and justify your design and total cost during the *Solution Briefing*.

As before, keep notes on a *Solution-Briefing Notes* page. As you listen to the presentations, remember to ask questions if anything is unclear.

DIV 21

DIVING INTO SCIENCE

☐ Assess

Monitor groups' progress. If it looks like the majority of the class needs more time, then give groups extra time.

△ Guide

Transition students from building their design to preparing for sharing it by reminding them that during a *Solution Briefing*, ideas are shared and advice is given on how to improve the design.

TEACHER TALK

❝You've designed another book support. Now it is time to share ideas during a *Solution Briefing*. Remember that during a *Solution Briefing* we share our ideas to get advice and new ideas on how to improve our design.❞

Remind students that the questions will help them prepare for their presentation. They will also listen for design ideas from everyone's presentations and will keep track of how designs work using the *Solution-Briefing Notes* page.

Communicate Your Solution (continued)

> **TEACHER TALK**
>
> **"**It is important that you all think about what you are going to say when you present your designs. On page 21 of the student text, there is a list of questions that will help you think about what to say during your presentation.**"**

⬡ Get Going

Give groups about five minutes to prepare their presentations.

After groups have finished preparing, remind students that they will need to ask questions. If they don't understand a design and how it works, they should ask the presenting group to clarify. Remind students that they should also voice their opinions and ideas, but in a polite and considerate manner, using language such as "I didn't hear the answer to ...", "Could you clarify .... for me?", "I agree with ... because..." or "I disagree with... because..." Reasons should be given.

Next, begin the presentations. Give each group two minutes to share and then two minutes for questions.

Remind the class that they should fill out their *Solution-Briefing Notes* page.

△ Guide

During the discussion you want to highlight how students used the ideas about strength and stability to improve their designs and how iteration and collaboration have been important in the design process.

While groups are presenting, you and the class should be listening for answers to the questions listed in the student text. If any of these items are not answered during the discussion, give the class time to ask questions to obtain the answers. Otherwise, guide the presenting group to providing answers using the ideas below:

- Students should describe their design, pointing out its construction.

- Students should state how much of each material they used. You could ask the total number of parts they used. At this point students may also state the total cost, or they may state it later.

- Students should state the reasons for their overall design and for some of their specific design features. This may include how the criteria and constraints were met, but that question is also asked later so students may state it later.

Communicate Your Solution
(continued)

- What materials did you use, and ho~~w~~
- Why did you build it the way you did?
- What is the overall cost of the design?
- How well does it work?
- How does the design meet the criteria?
- How did the challenge constraints affect the design?
- What past experiences helped you make your design?
- What problems remain?
- Did you try anything different?
- What else do you want to test?

When you present your book support, your group will need to justify the design decisions you have made and show the results of any other designs you created. Once you have totaled all of the supplies, calculate the total cost of your book support and be prepared to discuss and justify your design and total cost during the *Solution Briefing*.

As before, keep notes on a *Solution-Briefing Notes* page. As you listen to the presentations, remember to ask questions if anything is unclear.

- Students should state the total cost of their design. (10 cents times each part.) You might ask students what the total number of parts they used first.

- Students should relate how well their book support works based on how it meets the criteria and constraints. They may also discuss what makes their book support strong (reducing folding and compression) and what makes it stable.

- Students should describe how their book support meets the criteria. They may have already answered this when answering how well it works.

- Students should describe how each constraint affected their design and in particular how the consideration of cost affected their design.

- Students should discuss their past book supports and how learning science knowledge affected the design. When students use examples of building on others' ideas, point this out if they did not give credit. Remind students to give credit.

- Students should describe any problems they feel still remain and ideas they think might be good solutions to these problems.

- Students should describe how their design is different from previous designs. In particular they should describe how they tried to increase the strength and stability of the design and they might mention how they tried to keep the use of materials down because of the cost constraint.

- Students should state what other ideas they have. You could ask them if they can think of any ways to reduce the cost of the book support or increase its strength or stability.

PBIS

Reflect

Answer the following questions. Be prepared to discuss your answers with your class. Answering the first four questions should help you answer the last one. Your answers to the fifth question are partial answers to the Unit's *Big Question: How do scientists work together to solve problems?*

1. Write the criteria and constraints for the first *Book-Support Challenge* and then for the second challenge.

2. Which criteria and constraints are different in the second challenge?

3. How did you change your original design to meet the new challenge?

4. What criteria and/or constraints were you unable to meet? Why?

5. Define or describe the following ideas that you have learned during the *Book-Support Challenge* and why they were important in tackling this challenge. You may use drawings to help explain your answers.

   a) iteration

   b) collaborating

   c) copying versus building on the work of others

   d) record keeping

   e) using science knowledge

What's the Point?

Now that you've redesigned your book support twice, you have seen again how useful iteration is. Each time you iterated on your design, you had a chance to use what you learned from the last time. Each time, as a result of using new knowledge, you made your book support better.

Sometimes the new ideas you had were based on new science you learned. Sometimes you learned from what other groups had done. Sometimes you remembered experiences that helped you have ideas. Ideas can come from all of these places. It is important, when ideas are borrowed from others, to give them credit. This is how science and engineering make progress. Also, people feel good when others use their ideas and give them credit.

DIV 22

Project-Based Inquiry Science

Reflect

10 min.

Lead a class discussion on how students improved their designs by applying ideas of strength and stability with a new criterion of affordability, building up to the importance of iterative design, collaboration, and building on the ideas of others. (Question 5.)

⬡ Get Going

Let groups know how much time they have (about 10 minutes) to answer the questions and be prepared for a class discussion.

☐ Assess

While groups are answering the questions, monitor their work and check their understanding of questions 1 through 4. Decide how you will focus the discussion based on students' responses. If students seem to understand questions 1 through 4, then briefly discuss the first four questions.

△ Guide

Begin with a discussion of how designs changed in response to science knowledge (strength and stability) and new criteria and constraints

META NOTES

This set of questions has 2 purposes. The first 4 questions are to guide a conversation or thinking. The last question (question 5) is the main point and reviews the key ideas of this *Learning Set*.

Reflect
(continued)

Reflect

Answer the following questions. Be prepared to discuss your answers with your class. Answering the first four questions should help you answer the last one. Your answers to the fifth question are partial answers to the Unit's *Big Question: How do scientists work together to solve problems?*

1. Write the criteria and constraints for the first *Book-Support Challenge* and then for the second challenge.

2. Which criteria and constraints are different in the second challenge?

3. How did you change your original design to meet the new challenge?

4. What criteria and/or constraints were you unable to meet? Why?

5. Define or describe the following ideas that you have learned during the *Book-Support Challenge* and why they were important in tackling this challenge. You may use drawings to help explain your answers.

   a) iteration

   b) collaborating

   c) copying versus building on the work of others

   d) record keeping

   e) using science knowledge

(affordability and cost of materials). Then transition the discussion to explore how the *Book-Support Challenge* is representative of challenges in general and what students have learned about iterations, collaboration, and building on ideas of others.

Note that students may have already brought up some of the answers to the questions in the *Solution Briefing*. If they have, you may want to very briefly discuss the first four questions and then discuss in detail question 5.

Listen for the following responses to the questions in the student text:

1. Students should list the criteria and constraints for the first challenge and this should match the original class list created during the first section. Students should also list the criteria and constraints for this challenge and it should contain the edits made during this section.

2. Students should list the criteria and constraints that were added or edited during this section. Point out that these may probably lead to design differences between their first iteration and their last.

3. Students should list the differences across their design iterations with the reasons for the changes in their design. Some students may say their reasons for changing their design were only the criteria and constraints. Others might point out gaining more knowledge or other reasons beyond the class list of criteria and constraints.

4. Students should list any criteria and constraints they could not meet and their reasons why. You could ask these groups what ideas they have to meet the criteria and constraints.

5. **a)** *An iteration* is a repetition — possibly with changes — of whatever you're trying to do. Alternatively, iteration is trying things over again. It is important in tackling the challenge because after each iteration we thought of new ideas that might make the design better. After many iterations we improved our design.

   b) *Collaborating* is working together and sharing ideas. This was important to the challenge because we got ideas and advice from the other groups and this helped us to improve our book-support design.

   c) *Copying* is when you use another's work without giving credit, and it is unethical. *Building on the work of others* helps everyone achieve their goals and increase understanding, and credit is given. This was important in our challenge because if we didn't give credit to the people's ideas we used then they may not share their ideas with us again and then we wouldn't be able to build a really good book support.

   d) *Record keeping* is keeping track of your planning and what you tried. It is important to keep clear and descriptive records so you can accurately report your findings to others and help them build on your ideas. This was important to our challenge because it helped us to remember the details of what we did and what we wanted to do, and that helped us to share our ideas.

   e) *Using science knowledge* is like building on others' ideas. Science knowledge helped us to achieve our goals.

NOTES

....

....

....

....

....

....

What's the Point?

5 min.

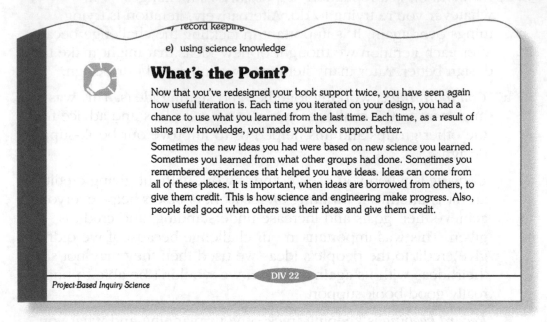

e) using science knowledge

What's the Point?

Now that you've redesigned your book support twice, you have seen again how useful iteration is. Each time you iterated on your design, you had a chance to use what you learned from the last time. Each time, as a result of using new knowledge, you made your book support better.

Sometimes the new ideas you had were based on new science you learned. Sometimes you learned from what other groups had done. Sometimes you remembered experiences that helped you have ideas. Ideas can come from all of these places. It is important, when ideas are borrowed from others, to give them credit. This is how science and engineering make progress. Also, people feel good when others use their ideas and give them credit.

DIV 22

Project-Based Inquiry Science

◇ Evaluate

Before concluding the discussion, it is important that students understand the importance of iteration, collaborating, giving credit, record keeping, and using science knowledge, when trying to solve a challenge or a problem (answers to question 5).

Teacher Reflection Questions

- What difficulties did students have with the ideas in question 5 of the *Reflect* section? What ideas do you have for the next time you teach this?

- Just as it takes iterations to improve the book support, it also takes iterations to improve the social practices used throughout PBIS. How did students' abilities to participate in the *Solution Briefings* improve in this section compared to *Section 1.2?* What do they still need to work on?

- What time-management issues occurred during this *Learning Set*? What ideas do you have for the next time you teach this section?

Learning Set 1

Back to the Big Question

How do scientists work together to solve problems?

Over the past few days, you and your classmates have been working to create a strong and stable book support. The last book support you built was probably a lot better than the first one. During this activity, you took part in several practices that scientists use when they solve problems. Think about some of the things you did in this *Learning Set*.

You identified the criteria and constraints of your challenge. Criteria are the requirements your solution must meet. Constraints are the factors that put limits on your solution. You also saw how criteria and constraints could change as you attempt to solve the problem.

You learned that there is a difference between copying and building on the ideas of others. You saw some designs of other groups that may have looked very good. In your next attempt, you may have used some of these ideas. Others might have used some of your ideas. This is how scientists work and how science grows as a field. Science builds on the ideas of others.

Scientists work together. They support each other. Working together to build ideas and understanding is called collaboration. In this class, you will collaborate to solve problems or meet challenges. As you collaborate, you will share ideas with others. Others will share ideas with you. One way you collaborated was to participate in a *Solution Briefing*. Scientists often present solutions or ideas while they are trying to solve problems.

DIV 23

DIVING INTO SCIENCE

△ Guide

Use the student text and the class's experiences with the book challenge to help students begin to link their ideas about criteria and constraints, collaboration, and building on other's ideas, and iteration to answering the Unit question: *How do scientists work together to solve problems?*

First discuss identifying criteria and constraints – when scientists solve problems they need to identify the criteria and constraints.

Then discuss collaboration and building on each others ideas versus copying. Scientists collaborate: they work together and share their ideas and then they build on each other's ideas. Scientists give credit when they build on someone's ideas.

Learning Set 1
(continued)

Iteration could help you achieve a challenge or solve a problem. You probably saw that it isn't always easy to achieve success the first time you try something. But, once you shared and saw the ideas of others and learned some scientific concepts, you were able to plan and build a better book support. Scientists also use iteration when solving problems.

In this *Learning Set* you probably approached problem solving differently than you have in the past. You now have a better idea of how scientists work together to solve problems.

Project-Based Inquiry Science

META NOTES

Remember, students won't need to have a complete answer to the question: *How do scientists work together to solve problems?* until the end of the Unit.

Last, discuss iteration — when scientists begin working on a problem they know that they may not be successful the first time and that they may improve the more they work on it.

Learning Set 2

The Sandwich-Cookie Challenge ◀ *4 class periods* *

Student pairs design and then redesign a procedure for determining how much water ("filling") can be put on a penny ("cookie") without overflowing. The importance of uniform procedures is highlighted when students' initial data are inconclusive.

Overview

Students are introduced to the importance of how procedures are designed and to tools to analyze their results. Students are challenged to gather and interpret evidence for how much filling will go in a sandwich cookie, using pennies and water drops as a model. First, student pairs create and run their own procedure for determining how many drops of water will fit on a penny. When the class compiles everyone's results on a line plot, the differences in their results become obvious, leading students to examine their procedures. Together, students identify the many ways their procedures were different and discuss just how specific a procedure needs to be to get repeatable results. When students design a more specific procedure for addressing this challenge, their results are much more consistent and informative. By revising and repeating their investigation, students will better understand the criteria and benefits of a well-designed procedure.

Looking Ahead

The introduction to this *Learning Set* and *Sections 2.1* and *2.2* are designed to be completed in one class period. There may not be time in one class period to complete analysis of data in *Section 2.2*, and that is O.K., but do your best to get at least that far.

*A class period is considered to be one 40 to 50 minute class.

Targeted Concepts, Skills, and Nature of Science	Section
Scientists often work together and then share their findings. Sharing findings makes new information becomes available and helps scientists refine their ideas and build on others' ideas. When another person's or group's idea is used, credit needs to be given.	2.3, 2.4
Scientists must keep clear, accurate, and descriptive records of what they do so they can share their work with others and consider what they did, why they did it, and what they want to do next.	2.2
Graphs are an effective way to communicate results of scientific investigations.	2.2

Targeted Concepts, Skills, and Nature of Science	Section
Identifying factors that lead to variation is an important part of scientific investigations.	2.3
Scientific investigations and measurements are considered reliable if the results are repeatable by other scientists using the same procedures.	2.2, 2.3, 2.4

Students' Initial Conceptions and Capabilities

- Most students will have a good idea of what a scientific investigation is and how it works, but they may not realize that investigations are usually carried out within a scientific group, and the results are shared among the scientific community. (Mead & Metraux, 1957.)

- Students may also initially be willing to accept conclusions based on very weak evidence. (Wollman, 1977a, 1977b; Wollman & Lawson, 1977.) Identifying all variables involved in an investigation may be especially difficult.

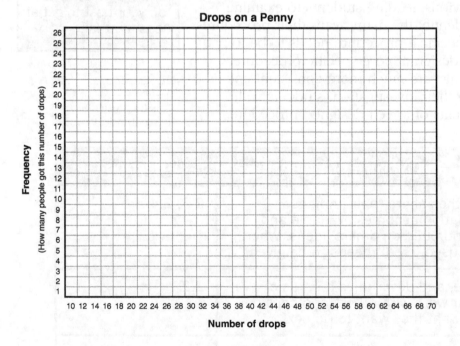

Drops on a Penny

Frequency (How many people got this number of drops)

Number of drops

Understanding for Teachers

The point of this *Learning Set* is for students to learn about how scientists design procedures that will give them reliable results, and how they figure out if results are reliable. In this *Learning Set*, students begin to understand that they can be more sure of reliability if their results are repeatable, that is, if results from doing the procedure many times are similar. Students will use line plots to communicate and interpret results, but they need not master line plots by the end of this *Learning Set*. However, since you will be guiding students, you will need to be comfortable with making and interpreting line plots.

Constructing a Line Plot

Begin with a blank grid. Label the columns with the numbers of drops that students might find will fit on a penny. These numbers will probably be between 10 and 70 drops, but consider finding out what the highest and lowest numbers are from the students' results before you label the columns. (Then you can label the leftmost column with the lowest number and the rightmost column with the highest number.) Label the rows with the numbers of groups that might report a given number. If there are 15 groups in your class, and each group runs 5 trials, it is unlikely that more than a third of the 75 trials will have the same result, so the largest number on the vertical axis can probably be around 25. See the example below.

Enter student data: Student groups will collect data on the number of drops that will fit on a penny in *Section 2.2*. To create a line plot for the class data, ask each group to report the result and mark this with an X on the grid. For example, if a student reports, "20," you will place an X above the number 20 on the *x*-axis. If another 20 is reported, you'll place another X directly above the previous X. As the number 20 is called out, the stack of X's grows. As you record these data on a graph transparency on the overhead, students will record the same data on their own line plots.

Interpreting Line Plots

In this investigation, line plots reveal how well students are controlling their procedure and repeatedly measuring the same event. Line plots of students' initial results will probably have a large range of numbers (with students reporting trials of anywhere from 10 drops to 100 drops), showing very few repeating data points (multiple X's in a column). An example is to the right.

Eventually, after the procedures are tightened up, you should see the columns of X's bunching together over a small range of numbers, say between 24-34. This bunching of data indicates that students have better standardized their procedure within each group and across all groups.

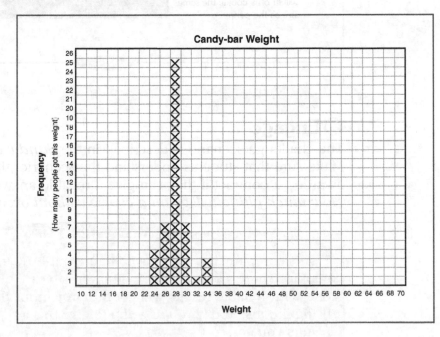

Learning Set 2

The Sandwich-Cookie Challenge

under 10 min.

Introduce students to the challenge of the Learning Set: *to determine how much filling will go on a sandwich cookie without overflowing.*

Learning Set 2

The Sandwich-Cookie Challenge

Have you ever wished that you could have a bite-size version of your favorite sandwich cookie? What would a company that makes these cookies need to know to be able to make a good product? Your next challenge will be to help a company develop a mini-sandwich cookie.

The company needs to know the amount of cream filling that should be placed on each cookie. The cookie must look like it has lots of filling. However, the filling cannot go over the sides.

The important question is this: *How much filling can be placed on the bottom cookie so it is completely covered but doesn't leak over the sides?*

The project is being sent to three labs. At your lab, you are assigned the job of finding how many drops of cream filling can be placed on the cookie without leaking. If your factory is chosen to produce the new product, it will bring in new jobs. It is important that you give this project your best effort!

You will work with a partner on this challenge. You will be given materials to imitate the dropping of cream filling onto the cookie. You will use a penny, a dropping pipette (similar to a dropper), and a cup of water. You will determine how much water fits onto the surface of the penny. Pretend that this is the same as how much cream filling will fit on a cookie the same size as the penny.

DIV 25

DIVING INTO SCIENCE

○ Engage

The challenge scenario is described in the *Sandwich-Cookie Challenge*. Make sure that students understand the scenario: their factory will be awarded a contract if they can give a reliable answer to the question: *How much filling will go on a cookie without overflowing?*

TEACHER TALK

"This company has asked us to figure out how much filling will go on a cookie. There's a catch: three different labs are doing tests, and only the one with reliable results will get the project for their factory, which will bring in jobs. Today you're going to give this a try and see what kind of results you get."

Next, connect the challenge to what students like about cookies and to what they think would make a popular cookie. Point out the advantages of a cookie with a lot of filling and the drawbacks of a cookie with too much filling, and lead students to the idea of just the right amount — as much filling as possible, without any overflow.

TEACHER TALK

"Do you like cookies? Do you like sandwich, or filled, cookies? (You might show a picture of some sandwich cookies since students might not call them that.) What do you like about cookies like this? Have you seen those cookies with the extra filling? What's good about those? What might be a problem with lots of filling? **"**

◇ **Evaluate**

Make sure students are ready to start this challenge by checking that they agree that a cookie with as much filling as possible with no overflow is just right, and that they understand that they are pretending a penny is a cookie and that the water they drop on it is filling.

NOTES

....

....

....

....

....

....

....

....

....

SECTION 2.1 INTRODUCTION

2.1 Understand the Challenge

Identify Criteria and Constraints

$\frac{1}{2}$ *class period* * ▶

Overview

Students have been challenged to help a company that makes sandwich cookies answer the question: *How much filling can be placed on a penny-sized cookie so it covers the cookie but doesn't overflow?* In *Understand the Challenge*, they identify the criteria and constraints of dropping water on a penny to answer this challenge, helping them to clarify the goal.

Homework Options

Reflection

- **Science Process:** Do you think it will be easy to meet the criteria working under the constraints? What might go wrong? *(Read students' answers to see what they are thinking about constraints. Some answers they may have are: the water could run off the penny, or our surface may not be level; the two sides of the penny are different; you can drop large drops or small drops; we won't be able to see when no more drops will go on the penny.)*

- **Science Process:** What lessons from *Learning Set 1* can you can apply to this challenge? *(Students might consider differences: the challenge in* Learning Set 1 *involved making something, but the challenge for* Learning Set 2 *is an investigation. Students might consider similarities: in both challenges we have to work with what we're given. Answers might include: collaborating with my classmates and keeping good records can improve my results.)*

> ### Looking Ahead
> Remember that this *Learning Set* was designed so that you can get through the introduction, *Section 2.1*, and at least reporting results in *Section 2.2* in one class period.

*A class period is considered to be one 40 to 50 minute class.

SECTION 2.1 IMPLEMENTATION

2.1 Understand the Challenge

Identify Criteria and Constraints

Before you get started, make sure that you understand what your challenge is. You must understand two features of the challenge: the criteria and the constraints.

Remember that criteria are things that must be satisfied in order to achieve a goal or answer a question. Constraints are factors that will limit how you can go about doing that. Think about and record the goals the company has asked your lab to meet. Think about the limits that have been placed upon you for this challenge (for example, the materials you have available).

What's the Point?

You have been given a new challenge. Remember, to be successful, you need to understand the parts of the challenge. You need to figure out what you need to achieve (criteria). You must also consider the limits you are working under (constraints). By identifying the criteria and constraints, you are more likely to be successful with your challenge.

DIV 26

Project-Based Inquiry Science

2.1 Understand the Challenge

Identify Criteria and Constraints
under 10 min.

To begin the Sandwich-Cookie Challenge, *lead students to identify the criteria and constraints of this challenge.*

△ Guide

Initiate a discussion of what students need to do to find the right amount of filling. Remind them that two important features of a challenge are criteria and constraints.

TEACHER TALK

❝Now we have a pretty good idea what the cookie company wants, and we know that we're going to pretend pennies are cookies and drops of water are filling to answer the question: *How many drops of water will fit on a penny without overflowing?* But we need to make sure that we have a clear picture of our goals and the limits we're working within. Another way of saying this is we need to know our criteria and constraints.❞

META NOTES

Analyzing the challenge in terms of criteria and constraints tests students' understanding of the challenge and provides direction for their investigation. In this case, once students identify the criterion of getting as much water as possible on the penny without any overflow, they will understand the goal of their investigation. Knowing the constraint of using water rather than filling, students will understand why they are counting drops.

With the class, identify the criteria and constraints of this challenge. If students are not able to identify criteria and constraints, remind them that criteria are goals that must be satisfied to achieve the challenge, and constraints are factors that limit how you can solve a problem. It might also help to have students think about what they need to accomplish (determine how many drops of water will stay on a penny) the criteria of the challenge. Then you can have students think about the materials they have available (pipettes, water, and pennies), which are constraints of the challenge.

As students identify criteria and constraints, write them on the board or on an overhead so that students can reference the list when they design their procedures.

Note: You will see references to students designing investigations. Since the students' investigations consist of running their procedures, this amounts to the same thing, and the phrases are used interchangeably in this section.

◇ Evaluate

Next, review the list to make sure the class is ready to begin planning their investigation. Make sure the list includes "the maximum amount of water that will fit on a penny without overflowing" as a criterion and "we have to use pennies, water drops, and pipettes in our procedures" as a constraint. If this constraint is missing, you might ask students whether they can do the investigation with real cookies.

What's the Point?

0 to 5 min.

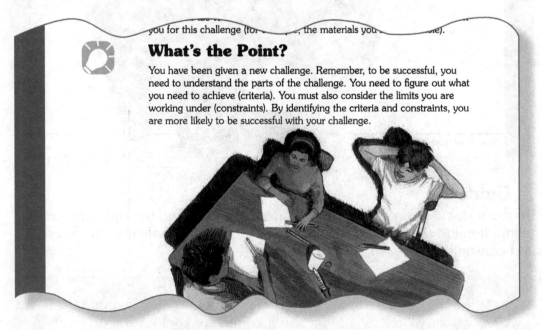

What's the Point?

you for this challenge (for _____ple, the materials you _____le).

You have been given a new challenge. Remember, to be successful, you need to understand the parts of the challenge. You need to figure out what you need to achieve (criteria). You must also consider the limits you are working under (constraints). By identifying the criteria and constraints, you are more likely to be successful with your challenge.

It is important for students to understand all parts of the challenge, particularly the criteria and constraints, before moving on.

Teacher Reflection Questions

- What criteria and constraints remain for students to identify later in their investigations? Which targeted skills, concepts, and dispositions of the *Learning Set* are connected to those criteria and constraints?

- What difficulties do you expect to encounter in helping students learn the targeted concepts, skills, and dispositions in this *Learning Set*? What can you do to plan for those difficulties?

- What problems came up when students were working in pairs? What can you do differently in future activities?

NOTES

SECTION 2.2 INTRODUCTION

2.2 Investigate

$\frac{1}{2}$ *class period* * ▶

How Many Drops of Water Fit on a Penny?

Overview

Looking Ahead
Do your best to get through collecting data and reporting them before the class period is over.

Students design and run an investigation to find out how many drops of water will fit on a penny, using the criteria and constraints identified in the previous section. They do not know, however, that half of the class is using different pipettes and, thus, different-sized water drops. When students graph the results of the class, they see that their results are not reliable, not only because of the different pipettes but also because of different procedures. From this experience, students see the need for uniform procedures and measurements and for collaboration and communication to confirm the reliability of results in scientific investigations.

Targeted Concepts, Skills, and Nature of Science	Performance Expectations
Graphs are an effective way to communicate results of scientific investigations.	Students draw and interpret line plots.
Scientists must keep clear, accurate, and descriptive records of what they do so that they can share their work with others and consider what they did, why they did it, and what they want to do next.	Students record their procedures and results in detail and describe why this is useful.
Scientific investigations and measurements are considered reliable if the results are repeatable by other scientists using the same procedures.	Students evaluate the spread of results and evaluate their procedure based on whether the results are likely to be repeatable.

*A class period is considered to be one 40 to 50 minute class.

Materials

1 per pair for half the class	pipettes (3 mL)
1 per pair for half the class	pipettes with bottom end cut (1 cm)
5 per pair	pennies
1 cup per pair	water
1 per pair	paper towels
1 per classroom	scissors and metric ruler for trimming the pipettes
1 per student	*Drops on a Penny* sheets
1 per class	*Projection of Drops on a Penny* sheet to make class graph
1 per student	graph paper

Activity Setup and Preparation

Watch for water spills.

- Decide how you want to arrange the classroom. Keep in mind that students will be working in pairs and with water.

- Have student materials ready to distribute. Hand materials out rather than creating a materials station, since you do not want students to notice differences in the pipettes.

- For half the student pairs, cut the tip of one of the pipettes 1 cm from the bottom end. This will introduce variation in student results. You should try out both types of pipettes to see that there is variation in the number of drops that will fit on a penny, due to the different pipettes.

Homework Options

Reflection

- **Science Process:** What do you think the line plot would have looked like if everyone had used the same procedure? What would the line plot have looked like if some groups had used nickels, some had used quarters, and some had used dimes? *(Check to see if the students correctly link the idea of uniform procedures to consistent results, and consistent results to clustered data. Also, check to see if, inversely, the students link differing materials to inconsistent results and a wide spread of data.)*

- **Science Process:** Based on the results of this investigation, could you say what results other researchers would get if they were given the same criteria and constraints and designed their own

META NOTES

Caution: Students should see this question only after they have done the activity, because it reveals information that students should discover during the activity.

DIVING INTO SCIENCE

procedure? Why or why not? *(Students may see that if they have not been able to get consistent results, they cannot say what results other researchers would get.)*

- **Science Content:** Consider the two line plots below. The line plots represent the weight of candy bars produced in a day by a manufacturing plant before and after they adopted new equipment. The manager of the plant wants the candy bars to have a standard weight. Which graph shows less variation in candy-bar weight? *(Check to make sure that students are using observations about how clustered each graph is to support their claims.)*

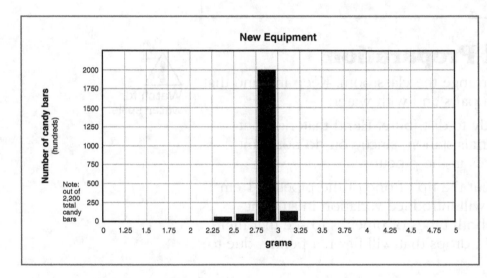

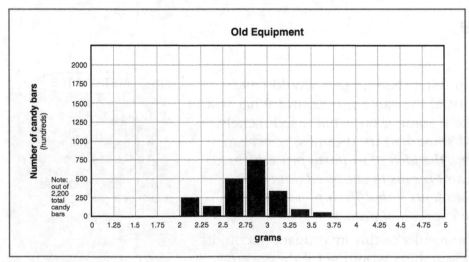

Preparation for 2.3

- **Science Content:** Graph what you think the class data would look like if the data were reliable. Do you think there would be any spread in the results? If so, what might contribute to different measurements between groups? *(Students should draw a graph with clustered data. Students might realize that it will be difficult to eliminate all variation. When the class graphs the results of the investigation in* Section 2.3, *you can compare the actual results with what students expected.)*

SECTION 2.2 IMPLEMENTATION

2.2 Investigate

How Many Drops of Water Fit on a Penny?

Design Your Investigation

Meet with your partner and discuss a procedure you could use to answer the question: *How much filling can be placed on the bottom cookie so it is completely covered but doesn't leak over the sides?* You will have about five minutes to develop a procedure. Use the materials shown in the list. Record your procedure on a sheet of paper. Each of you should have your own copy.

Materials
• dropping pipette
• 5 pennies
• cup of water
• paper towel

Run Your Investigation

You will have 10-15 minutes to carry out your procedure. You have five pennies. Your teacher will probably tell you to repeat your procedure five times.

You will need to record your data during this investigation. Remember, recording results allows scientists to accurately report their findings. Data help others understand a scientist's work. They also help other scientists do future investigations.

Record your results on the same sheet of paper you wrote your procedure on. Be prepared to share your results with your class.

Communicate Your Results

Share Your Data

Last time you communicated your work, each group presented in a *Solution Briefing*. This time you'll do it differently. Each group will report their results (number of drops that fit on each penny) to the class. You will record each group's results in a **line plot** on your *Drops and Penny Data* page.

The line plot will help you see if your class has accurately determined the correct amount of filling for the cookie. This is what the cookie company is looking for.

line plot: a display of data in which each data item is shown as an "x" above its value on a number line.

DIVING INTO SCIENCE

2.2 Investigate

How Many Drops of Water Fit on a Penny?

Design Your Investigation
5 min.

Have students spend up to five minutes designing a procedure to find out how many drops of water will go on a penny before they run off. There is no need to spend a lot of time introducing what they are doing.

⬡ Get Going

Once the list of criteria and constraints is complete, get students into groups of two and distribute the materials or have groups get them from a materials station.

When all groups have their materials, model the use of a pipette and get students started designing their procedures. Remind them that each student should record his or her group's procedure on a sheet of paper.

☐ Assess

As groups work on their procedures, check with each group to see how much progress they are making. You might ask what ideas they have discussed in order to encourage brainstorming. After five minutes, students should have written plans specifying how they will conduct each of the trials.

META NOTES

Remember that half of the class is using shortened pipettes, and they should not be made aware of this until after the results are discussed.

DIVING INTO SCIENCE

Each group will come up with a different procedure for this simple problem. That is the point. The variety of procedures they come up with will later show the need for uniform procedures.

Run Your Investigation

15 min.

> ### Run Your Investigation
>
> You will have 10-15 minutes to carry out your procedure. You have five pennies. Your teacher will probably tell you to repeat your procedure five times.
>
> You will need to record your data during this investigation. Remember, recording results allows scientists to accurately report their findings. Data help others understand a scientist's work. They also help other scientists do future investigations.
>
> Record your results on the same sheet of paper you wrote your procedure on. Be prepared to share your results with your class.

⬡ Get Going

Once students have written their procedures, give them a time frame (about 10 to 15 minutes) for their investigation. Emphasize that groups should record their results (one student can record the results while the other drops water on the penny).

Let the class know how many trials each pair of students should run. If your class is large, each pair should run five trials; if your class is small, up to 10 trials. This ensures that the class will generate enough data to see inconsistencies (you should shoot for at least 70 trials total). Then let students begin running their procedures.

△ Guide

META NOTES

Modeling the kind of evaluation of results that students should begin using is helpful here, since students have not done this kind of investigation or evaluated this kind of data before. This will help them begin to think about ways to improve their procedures.

As students run their investigations, walk around the class and notice how students are carrying out their procedures. Sometimes they will do things differently from what they have written (e.g., they will count drops differently, drop them from different heights on different trials, or drop more or less water at a time). Don't say anything at this time, but note anything that is inconsistent within groups and across groups, as you will be helping students identify what led to the large spread in the results later. Also, encourage and model the way students will begin evaluating their results, asking groups with wide results across trials, "Why do you think your results are so varied?" Finally, note the highest and lowest numbers of drops students are getting for their results. This will give you an idea how to label the columns in the line plot for communicating results.

Later, when students are trying to figure out why their results were inconsistent, you can point out specific procedures that were inconsistent or where groups didn't follow their procedures, to help students identify the causes of the varied results.

Some groups might notice that their results are different from the results of another group. Let them know they'll be sharing their results and comparing them with the rest of the class soon. There is no need to say more right now.

☐ Assess

Every five minutes or so, check to see how many trials each group has run. If any groups have barely begun after five minutes, see what you can do to get them moving.

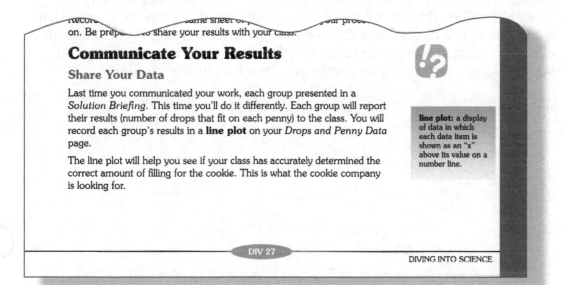

Recor̶d̶ ̶...same sheet o̶f̶... ̶your proc̶e̶...
on. Be prep̶a̶...to share your results with your class.

Communicate Your Results

Share Your Data

Last time you communicated your work, each group presented in a *Solution Briefing*. This time you'll do it differently. Each group will report their results (number of drops that fit on each penny) to the class. You will record each group's results in a **line plot** on your *Drops and Penny Data* page.

The line plot will help you see if your class has accurately determined the correct amount of filling for the cookie. This is what the cookie company is looking for.

line plot: a display of data in which each data item is shown as an "x" above its value on a number line.

DIV 27

DIVING INTO SCIENCE

Communicate Your Results

10 min.

Compile the results on a line plot with students. While graphing the class results, students will realize that the data are inconsistent across groups and consider why.

Expect the data to be between 10 and 70 drops. You might want to find out the highest and lowest students values before you begin recording so that you will know how to label the columns in your line plot. All groups' data are recorded together on one line plot.

△ Guide

When all groups have finished running their investigations, let students know that you will graph their results, and that they will use the graph to determine the correct amount of filling for the cookie. Explain that you will mark X's on the class graph for student groups' trials and that the height of the column of X's at any number along the horizontal axis shows how many times that number of drops was measured during the investigation. No need to introduce line plots right now; students will understand what the graph communicates after the data is collected.

TEACHER TALK

❝O.K., you've all collected your data. Let's plot it all on a graph. I've labeled each of the columns with the number of drops that might have fit on a penny. Then I'm going to put an X on the graph for each measurement. If one group got 24 drops, I'll put an X over 24 on the graph. This is called a line plot.❞

META NOTES

Students may pick the number with the highest frequency (the mode). This value is informative if a large percentage of the measurements are the same.

Students may pick the middle value (the median), in which half the data points are above the median and half the data points are below.

Students may suggest adding up the numbers and dividing by the number of trials (the mean or the average).

Students may average the highest and lowest numbers (the midrange point). You might point out that by using this method with some data sets, you could pick a number where there aren't even any data points.

All measurements have some error in them. The mean is the best value for multiple measurements of the same thing because it gives the value most likely to have the least amount of error.

Next, ask each group to report their data, and plot the data on the graph on the overhead. Make sure that students plot the data on their own graphs as well.

It's a good idea, before discussing the data, to make sure students know what the graph means. For example, make sure they know that if there are eight X's in a column, it means eight trials resulted in that measurement.

When all the data have been plotted, have students evaluate the results, asking, "How many drops will fit on a penny?" Since the data are wide-spread, it will be difficult to derive a conclusive answer from the graph. That is the point. You might ask if this seems right or reasonable. Would students expect a different number of drops to fill a penny each time? They should begin asking, "Why don't the results give us a conclusive answer?"

NOTES

2.2

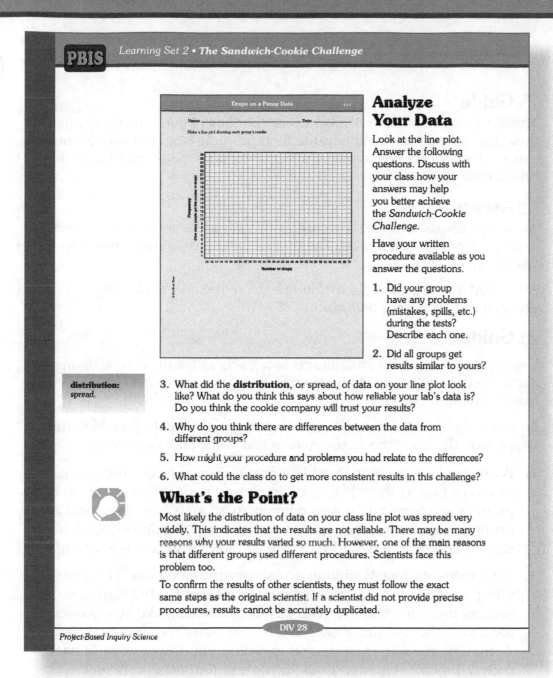

Analyze Your Data

Look at the line plot. Answer the following questions. Discuss with your class how your answers may help you better achieve the *Sandwich-Cookie Challenge.*

Have your written procedure available as you answer the questions.

1. Did your group have any problems (mistakes, spills, etc.) during the tests? Describe each one.

2. Did all groups get results similar to yours?

distribution: spread.

3. What did the **distribution**, or spread, of data on your line plot look like? What do you think this says about how reliable your lab's data is? Do you think the cookie company will trust your results?

4. Why do you think there are differences between the data from different groups?

5. How might your procedure and problems you had relate to the differences?

6. What could the class do to get more consistent results in this challenge?

What's the Point?

Most likely the distribution of data on your class line plot was spread very widely. This indicates that the results are not reliable. There may be many reasons why your results varied so much. However, one of the main reasons is that different groups used different procedures. Scientists face this problem too.

To confirm the results of other scientists, they must follow the exact same steps as the original scientist. If a scientist did not provide precise procedures, results cannot be accurately duplicated.

DIV 28

Project-Based Inquiry Science

Analyze Your Data
15 min.

Now that students see that their data are inconsistent and thus inconclusive, lead them in a discussion focused on finding out the reason their data are inconsistent.

△ Guide

Guide students in analyzing their graphed data. Focus students' attention on their procedures as they consider why their data are inconsistent.

○ Get Going

Tell students to use their copy of the class graph and their own procedures as they think about each of the questions in their text. Give groups about five minutes for this discussion.

If students are already asking each other these questions and making these suggestions, you can move ahead to the class discussion.

△ Guide

Monitor group discussion. If students are not beginning to recognize that their data were inconsistent because their procedures were inconsistent, you can ask them to tell you about how they measured the drops or how they set up their penny.

☐ Assess

As groups discuss the questions, listen for their ideas about their procedures and the effect on their results. These ideas will be developed further in the whole-class discussion.

Next, lead a whole-class discussion to explore the effects of using procedures that are not uniform.

△ Guide

Use the questions in the student text as a guide to get the class thinking about how important it is to have uniform procedures to get consistent and trustworthy results.

Let's talk about why our results are so spread out. Why do you think this happened? The questions in the student text will help us answer this.

META NOTES

Students will likely bring up accidents at this point, but listen for suggestions about having everybody know what to do better–using more precise and uniform procedures.

1. Focus students' thinking within a group's procedures. You can ask a group or two to share how they measured their drops or set up their pennies. Students will notice differences such as how they held the dropper, or whether the penny was heads up or tails up. Students should describe specifically what they did and what went wrong.

2. Now focus students' thinking across group procedures. Have two groups, whose procedures were similar except for the dropper, present their procedures, materials, and results. Make sure students are aware that the droppers are different. After the presentations, if students are still unaware that two different droppers were used, then tell them. Students should recognize that using different materials will lead to different results.

3. Guide students' attention on the data and how widespread the distribution is. Students' answers should show an understanding that the distribution of the data is widespread because different procedures and materials were used. They should also realize that a wide spread in data suggests that the results are untrustworthy.

4. Consider across-groups' data in particular. Students should note the different materials used and students should point out the difference in procedures and how this can lead to different results.

5. Consider within–group data. Students' answers should point to specific steps in their procedures that were problematic, or to differences from others' procedures.

6. Students should see that to have trustworthy results they will need to ensure that they are using the same procedures as everyone else. Listen for ideas about making sure that everyone is careful to run their procedures and count water drops the same way for each trial and making sure everyone knows what to do. You may guide this by asking what would indicate trustworthy results.

◇ Evaluate

Make sure that students understand that for their results to be considered trustworthy they have to have repeatable results, which requires that they follow a standard procedure.

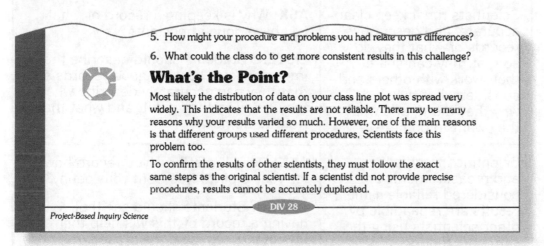

5. How might your procedure and problems you had relate to the differences?

6. What could the class do to get more consistent results in this challenge?

What's the Point?

Most likely the distribution of data on your class line plot was spread very widely. This indicates that the results are not reliable. There may be many reasons why your results varied so much. However, one of the main reasons is that different groups used different procedures. Scientists face this problem too.

To confirm the results of other scientists, they must follow the exact same steps as the original scientist. If a scientist did not provide precise procedures, results cannot be accurately duplicated.

DIV 28

Project-Based Inquiry Science

As you review the reasons for the wide spread of the data and discuss students' ideas for getting more trustworthy results, emphasize the importance of using precise procedures and following the steps in the procedures exactly.

Also, point out that scientists follow precise procedures so that their results can be repeated by others.

What's the Point?

0-5 min.

You can go directly to Section 2.3 — *where students design a class procedure* — *now, and discuss the* What's the Point? *for* Section 2.2 *along with the* What's the Point? *for* Section 2.3, *or discuss this* What's the Point? *first.*

Assessment Options

Targeted Concepts, Skills, and Nature of Science	How do I know if students got it?
Graphs are an effective way to communicate results of scientific investigations.	**ASK:** How did the graph help you to understand the data? **LISTEN:** Students should say something about observing variation in the results they graphed. From this, they can conclude that their results were not reliable.
Scientists must keep clear, accurate, and descriptive records of what they do so that they can share their work with others and consider what they did, why they did it, and what they want to do next.	**ASK:** Why is keeping a record of what you have done important? **LISTEN:** Students should describe the importance of keeping good records so that they can accurately describe what they did, why they did it, and what they want to do next.
Scientific investigations and measurements are considered reliable if the results are repeatable by other scientists using the same procedures.	**ASK:** Does it matter if you record how far your pipette was from your penny? **LISTEN:** Students should see that having a record of this will help them and others replicate the procedure.

Teacher Reflection Questions

- What difficulties did students have in making the connection between the wide variation in data and the need for standard procedures and materials? How did you assist them in making this connection? What else could you do?

- Standard procedures are not given to students right away so that students will recognize the need for them through experience. What discomforts did your students show with not being given a set of procedures right away? What discomforts did you have?

- What worked well and what could you do better during the collection and analysis of the class data?

2.3 Redesign Your Investigation

Getting to a Better Procedure

◀ *1 class period**

Overview

Students first identify factors in their investigation that lead to inconsistent results, and then design a new, more precise class procedure to control these factors. They design a class procedure that is specific and replicable, controlling each of the factors they identified. Finally, students reflect on their new procedure by comparing it to their original, varied procedures to see how their ability to plan an investigation has improved.

Targeted Concepts, Skills, and Nature of Science	Performance Expectations
Identifying factors that lead to variation is an important part of scientific investigations.	Students identify factors that can affect the results of an investigation.
Scientific investigations and measurements are considered reliable if the results are repeatable by other scientists using the same procedures.	Students describe how investigations and measurements are considered reliable if they can be repeated by following the same procedures. Supporting reasons should include observations from the previous section, such as when groups used different results, they all came up with different answers and they couldn't decide which answer was correct.
Scientists often work together and then share their findings. Sharing findings makes new information becomes available and helps scientists refine their ideas and build on others' ideas. When another person's or group's idea is used, credit needs to be given.	Students consult their peers in planning, and they share their results with their peers.

Materials

1 per class media for creating class procedures (e.g., butcher block paper, overhead)

1 per class list of criteria and constraints for the class

*A class period is considered to be one 40 to 50 minute class.

Homework Options

Reflection

- **Science Content:** Scientists in City A spent two hours one evening catching fish in a stream using an experimental new bait and caught five fish, while scientists in City B spent three hours one morning catching fish in a lake using the same bait and caught two fish. They could not reach any conclusion about how many fish a person can catch using the bait. What are the factors that led to the different results? What are some practical ways the scientists could reduce the variation? *(Check to see if the answer addresses the differences between the studies: in this case, a difference in settings — stream vs. lake — and a difference in time.)*

- **Science Process:** Think about the criteria and constraints you listed for your first investigation with the penny and water drops. Identify some additional criteria and constraints that will guide your next investigation with the penny and water drops. *(Answers may include: criteria — a set of procedures that everyone can follow; constraints — number of trials.)*

- **Nature of Science:** Describe the reasons for creating a clear, standard procedure. *(Answers should point out the need for other researchers to be able to run the same procedure and get similar results. Otherwise the results are not considered reliable.)*

Preparation for 2.4

- **Science Content:** If everyone in class follows the class procedure, what do you expect the line plot of the results will look like? Draw a picture to illustrate your answer. *(Answers should say something about the data being more clustered. The picture should depict a line plot with tightly clustered data.)*

SECTION 2.3 IMPLEMENTATION

2.3 Redesign Your Investigation

Getting to a Better Procedure

Your class probably did not agree on how much water can fit on a penny. Your line plot may have shown that your lab couldn't produce reliable results. You will now see if you can find a way to make the results more consistent across groups.

Think about what went wrong. You were all trying to answer the same question. You all dropped water onto pennies. You all counted how many drops of water fit on the penny. You also all had the same materials. But every group probably used a slightly different procedure. You all collected data in different ways. No wonder results were so varied.

repeatable: when someone follows the reported procedure, they get similar results.

replicate: to run a procedure again and get the same result.

Scientists only trust experimental results that are **repeatable** by other scientists. In order for other scientists to **replicate** the results of an experiment, the procedures must be reported very precisely. Then someone else can run the procedure again and get the same results.

For example, suppose you wanted to investigate the effect of a fertilizer on the growth of plants. You would need to keep many other factors the same. For example, you would need to control:

- soil type
- time spent in sunlight each day
- amount of water, and
- type of plant

DIV 29

DIVING INTO SCIENCE

2.3 Redesign Your Investigation

Getting to a Better Procedure
15 min.

Now that students have seen how unreliable their data are due to lack of uniform procedures, have them design a standard class procedure to get a smaller distribution of data.

○ Engage

Now that students have thought about why their results were inconsistent, ask them if they can design a procedure that would get them better results.

TEACHER TALK

❝So you've thought about what made your results different. Do you think you can design a procedure that will get all groups the same results?❞

△ Guide

Begin by reminding students of the differences in procedures and materials they identified and some of students' ideas for getting more trustworthy results.

Then lead the class in identifying all the things they will need to pay attention to when revising their procedure.

TEACHER TALK

❝Let's think about all the factors that need to be the same from trial to trial—things we need to think about in our new procedure.

❝Did anybody's procedures say what a drop is? How big is a drop? You could probably squeeze out a pretty small drop if you tried, and you could also squeeze out a pretty big drop. That's something to specify in the procedure.❞

As students identify factors in their investigations and ways their procedures were not uniform, list these factors on the board or an overhead so that students can reference this list when they revise their procedure in the next step.

Many of the factors will involve inconsistencies with measurement. Discuss how measurements can be precise — how they can address how students place the penny, how they measure a drop of water, and how they determine when there is as much water as possible without overflow. Emphasize that a standard procedure will need to describe how each of these factors will be measured and controlled.

NOTES

....

....

....

....

....

trial: one time through a procedure.

precision: how close together the measured values are.

range: the zone between the largest and smallest solution results.

Think about one factor, water. You would need to make sure that each group of plants got the same amount of water. They would need to be watered the same number of times. Also, they would need to be watered in the same way. You would need to follow these rules for watering every single time you watered each plant.

It is also important to make the same measurement each time. In this example, you could count the number of leaves on each plant. You could also measure the height of each plant.

The tools you use can often affect measurement. You have limits to what you can see when you make a measurement. Be sure to consider how accurate the tools you use are.

Here is a checklist that you can use to make sure your measurements are consistent:

• Measure from the same point.
• Measure with the same units.
• Repeat **trials** for more **precision**.
• Start fresh. Don't compare data from before you make a change to the data after you make a change.
• Measure under the same conditions.

Revise Your Procedure

With your class, work out a procedure for finding out how many water drops will fit on a penny. Try to describe each step in detail so it can be replicated. This way, maybe you'll collect more reliable results. Record your new class procedure.

Reflect

Review and answer the following questions:

1. What are three or four key differences between your previous procedure and the new class procedure?
2. What are you now controlling better in the new procedure?
3. What effect do you think this new procedure will have on the **range** of results across groups?

Revise Your Procedure
15 min.

Lead the class in deciding upon a standard procedure for the investigation.

⚠ Guide

Next, lead students in designing a new procedure, as a class, that will give them a more reliable answer. They will need to make sure that all factors are accounted for and that they describe how the factors will be kept the same. Remind students that every group should be able to do the procedure exactly the same and, thus, get very similar results.

One way to lead students in designing a new procedure is to model your thinking as you focus on one factor at a time. For instance, you might want to talk about the penny first.

META NOTES

Modeling thinking by verbalizing your thoughts helps students see how to think about designing a procedure. Modeling is helpful here since this is the first time students have designed a procedure. This will help them think through a procedure that controls variables the next time they do an investigation to answer a question.

META NOTES

Designing a procedure is a good opportunity to assess students' ideas about controlling factors. In this case, students should be thinking about how to measure all the things that might affect the number of water drops on a penny.

Reflect

10 min.

Now it is time to lead students in comparing the old and new procedures.

TEACHER TALK

"Let's start with the penny. What should we do with the penny? Each side is different; maybe one side holds more drops than the other. So, we would want to make sure the same side of the penny is always up. What if it were slanted? That might make the water run off sooner. Well, we don't want that to happen, so I am going to make sure the penny is sitting on a flat or level surface."

As you think through the procedure out loud with students, record the steps and decisions on the board or overhead so that students will be able to evaluate the procedure and use it to run their investigations.

Next, use the bulleted list to help the class assess their procedure for replicability.

☐ Assess

As you develop the procedure, listen to students' ideas about how to measure consistently and precisely and how to control factors in investigations.

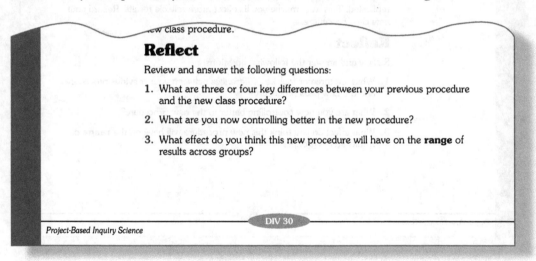

...ew class procedure.

Reflect

Review and answer the following questions:

1. What are three or four key differences between your previous procedure and the new class procedure?

2. What are you now controlling better in the new procedure?

3. What effect do you think this new procedure will have on the **range** of results across groups?

Project-Based Inquiry Science   DIV 30

△ Guide

When the procedure is complete, review it with your students. You can use the *Reflect* questions to assess students' understanding of what they have done and why. You might have students write their answers to the *Reflect* questions, and then lead a discussion of students' responses. Alternatively, you might want to lead a discussion of the questions without having students answer them first.

Help student answer the *Reflect* questions.

1. Student responses should reflect an understanding of what was important about their revisions. The key changes will probably be in the steps where there were differences between groups' procedures.

2. The factors in the student lists should generally correspond to the key revisions to the procedure. In this discussion, emphasize changes that were made in the steps where there were differences between groups' procedures and where factors were not specified.

3. The new procedure should reduce the range of the results.

NOTES

....

....

....

....

....

....

....

....

....

....

....

....

....

....

What's the Point?

5 min.

What's the Point?

The points you thought about in this section are important to the *Sandwich-Cookie Challenge*. Every group was using a similar procedure. However, your procedures were probably not identical. In fact, some of the groups may not have followed the same procedure each time they tested how many drops of water fit on a penny. You probably saw a wide spread of data in the line plot. This is called **variation**. It is important to use the same procedure every time you test. Your results will then be consistent, and they will probably be repeatable.

variation: a wide spread of data.

DIV 31

DIVING INTO SCIENCE

The reflection discussion you just had will sum up most of what is in this segment. The one remaining thing is to introduce the word "variation," which is the word that scientists use when they discuss how wide-ranging the data are.

As you finish the reflection discussion, listen for students recognizing the importance of using uniform procedures to get repeatable or consistent results. Uniform procedures should reduce variation.

Assessment Options

Targeted Concepts, Skills, and Nature of Science	How do I know if students got it?
Identifying factors that lead to variation is an important part of scientific investigations.	**ASK:** What are some of the reasons why you might get inconsistent results from an investigation? **LISTEN:** Students should recount some of the things that happened during their investigations that led to variation. **ASK:** What should the class graph look like when the investigation results are more consistent? **LISTEN:** The class graph should be more clustered.
Scientific investigations and measurements are considered reliable if the results are repeatable by other scientists using the same procedures.	**ASK:** How can you verify that another researcher's results are reliable? **LISTEN:** Students should know that if results are reliable, a researcher should be able to get similar results by following the same procedure. **ASK:** How can changing your procedure from trial to trial affect your results? Give an example. **LISTEN:** Students should link changing procedures to varied results and use examples from their investigation.
Scientists often work together and then share their findings. Sharing findings makes new information becomes available and helps scientists refine their ideas and build on others' ideas. When another person's or group's idea is used, credit needs to be given.	**ASK:** Why is it important for researchers to have carefully controlled procedures? **LISTEN:** Students should recognize that a researcher needs to have results verified by peers, and that a researcher needs to establish procedures that peers can replicate.

Teacher Reflection Questions

- What evidence do you have that students understand the need for a clear procedure that can be replicated and the need for repeatable results?

- Have you observed different attitudes toward success and mistakes among students? For example, did some students compete for the best results in either investigation? Have you observed any changes in these attitudes?

- What did you do to model appropriate language during discussions? What ideas do you have for next time?

NOTES

◀ *1 class period**

2.4 Investigate

How Many Drops of Water Fit on a Penny?

Overview

Students run their revised procedure and collect data, which they share on a class line plot. Using the spread of the data to evaluate their new procedure, the class identifies ways that the procedure is still not precise enough. Students once again revise their procedures and share their data. This time their results are much more consistent, providing evidence that a precise, standard procedure ensures consistent results.

Targeted Concepts, Skills, and Nature of Science	Performance Expectations
Scientists often work together and then share their findings. Sharing findings makes new information becomes available and helps scientists refine their ideas and build on others' ideas. When another person's or group's idea is used, credit needs to be given.	Students consult their peers in planning and they share their results with their peers.
Scientific investigations and measurements are considered reliable if the results are repeatable by other scientists using the same procedures.	Students follow the same procedure, analyze the data from the class, and describe, based on their experiences, why scientists consider results reliable if they are repeatable.

Materials

1 per pair	pipettes
5 per pair	pennies
1 cup per pair	water
1 per pair	paper towels
1 per class	class procedure
1 per class	class graph
1 per student	graph paper

*A class period is considered to be one 40 to 50 minute class.

Watch for water spills.

Activity Setup and Preparation

Decide how you want to arrange the classroom. Keep in mind that students will be working in pairs and with water.

Have supplies ready to distribute. Consider creating a materials station for investigations after the different pipettes have been identified, placing the pipettes for this investigation with the materials. You can put one of the other pipettes on display so that students can remember the last investigation and see one of the factors that caused a difference in their results.

Homework Options

Reflection

- **Science Content:** Based on the results of your last investigation, what could you say about the results that other researchers using your procedure would get? Why? *(Look for students to link the reliability or unreliability of the results with their usefulness for saying what results other researchers might get.)*

Trial	Time (s)
1	14.5
2	15.1
3	15.3
4	21.3
5	14.9

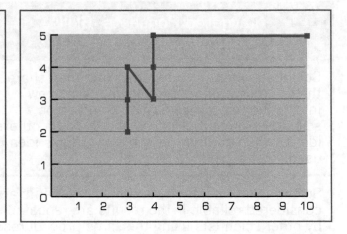

- **Science Content:** Look at the graph above. What are some possible reasons that one data point is far away from the rest? Can you use these data even though one data point is far away from the rest? *(Look for students to explain that outliers can often be excluded from analysis, since they are often due to accident.)*

- **Science Content:** Above is a set of measurements of the time it takes a pendulum to swing back and forth 10 times. Make a line plot for these results. Do you think all the trial values are reliable? Why or why not? Can you reliably say how long it takes the pendulum to swing back and forth 10 times? If so, how long? *(Check to see if students identify the outlier at trial 4, and if they exclude the trial from analysis.)*

SECTION 2.4 IMPLEMENTATION

◀ *1 class period* *

2.4 Investigate

How Many Drops of Water Fit on a Penny?

Materials
- dropping pipette
- penny
- cup of water
- paper towel

Run Your New Procedure

Now that you have a new procedure, can your lab produce more reliable results? Your class will soon collect another set of data and produce a new line plot. As a class, update the criteria and constraints of the challenge if you need to.

Follow your new procedure. Use the materials listed. Obtain results for 5 to 10 trials. (Your teacher will tell you exactly how many to complete.)

Record your results on the same sheet of paper where you wrote your procedure. Be prepared to share your results with your class and teacher. You will have 10-15 minutes to perform your procedure and collect your data.

Communicate Your Results

Share Your Data

Use another sheet of graph paper. Make another line plot from the new data.

As before, each group will read aloud their results. Everyone will plot them on the graph paper.

Analyze Your Data

After your class creates the second line plot, answer the following questions together:

1. How do the results from this investigation compare to the ones from your first set of trials?

2. Did you have any problems (mistakes, spills, etc.) during the tests? List them.

3. Did all groups get results similar to yours?

4. Do you trust these results more? Why or why not?

DIV 32

Project-Based Inquiry Science

2.4 Investigate

How Many Drops of Water Fit on a Penny?

Run Your New Procedure

10 min.

Guide students to run an investigation with the new procedure that the class designed in Section 2.3.

*A class period is considered to be one 40 to 50 minute class.

△ Guide

With the class, check to see if the list of criteria and constraints from *Section 2.1* needs to be updated for this investigation. The criteria and constraints should include specific requirements for reliable results, such as: groups need to follow the chosen procedure carefully and they need to ensure that they are all using the same materials.

○ Get Going

Next, distribute the materials or have students get them from a materials station. Make sure that only one size of pipettes is available; the others should be wrapped in a rubber band and set aside.

DIVING INTO SCIENCE

Then get students going with their investigation, emphasizing that pairs should record their results on the same sheet of paper where they wrote their procedure. One student can record results while the other drops water on the penny, as they did in their first investigation. Make sure students know how long they have (10 or 15 minutes) and how many times to repeat the procedure. Pairs should run five trials if your class is large and 10 if your class is small. This ensures that the class will generate enough data (you should shoot for at least 70 trials total).

☐ Assess

While students are running their investigations, you can observe how closely groups are following their procedure. If any group is doing anything differently from the rest of the class, note the difference as something to discuss later. Also, look at their data to get an idea of how consistent they are. Listen for students' ideas about carefully following a procedure or recording data.

Communicate Your Results

10 min.

When all groups have finished running their investigations, have student pairs share their results with the class to create a graph of everyone's data.

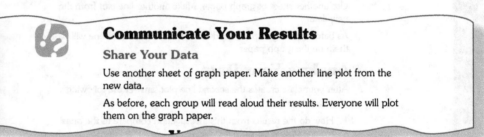

Communicate Your Results

Share Your Data

Use another sheet of graph paper. Make another line plot from the new data.

As before, each group will read aloud their results. Everyone will plot them on the graph paper.

△ Guide

First, make sure that all students have graph paper. Then, briefly review how to use graphs to share data and, with a fresh graph transparency on the projector, ask each pair how many drops they recorded for each trial. For each result, put an X on the graph. Remind students to record the results of the class on their own graphs.

TEACHER TALK

❝We're going to plot your data on a graph just like we did last time. Remember, each of the columns on the line plot represents a number of drops that might fit on a penny. If a group got 17, I'll put an X over the 17 on the graph. You should also do this on your graph. When we are finished, I will allow you some time to check your graph against the class graph.❞

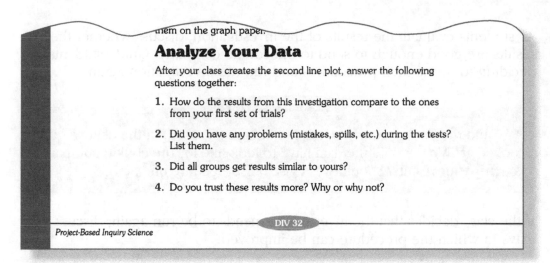

Analyze Your Data

After your class creates the second line plot, answer the following questions together:

1. How do the results from this investigation compare to the ones from your first set of trials?

2. Did you have any problems (mistakes, spills, etc.) during the tests? List them.

3. Did all groups get results similar to yours?

4. Do you trust these results more? Why or why not?

DIV 32

Project-Based Inquiry Science

△ Guide

Lead students to examine their graphed data and critique their new procedure. Begin by looking at the spread of data and then the precision of the procedures. The goal is to evaluate whether the procedure must be refined and repeated once again to get a result reliable enough to report to the cookie company. The answers to the first three questions in the student text will provide evidence for discussion about the trustworthiness of these new data (question 4). Use the questions to guide the discussion.

1. If students have effectively redesigned their procedure, they should find that the results of the second investigation are more consistent, with data points clustered together on the line plot.

2. This is a good place to discuss outliers. If a pair of students has one or two trials that are very different from their other trials, then perhaps that value is an outlier. Outliers are almost always caused by blunders, and show that trials should be redone if time permits. They should always be presented and discussed, but may be omitted from the analysis if you know they are blunders.

3. It is likely that the class will have a few outliers. You may be able to connect these with mistakes or accidents of some kind that happened during the investigation. You might also discuss the fact that no measurement is ever exact. There is always some range of values that the measurement may fall within.

4. Students may say that results that are more consistent can be repeated, and results that can be repeated are more reliable.

Analyze Your Data

15 min.

Using the class graph, lead students through an evaluation of their data for evidence that their procedure is refined enough to reduce the range of the results. If the data are still scattered, students will need to revise their procedure once again.

META NOTES

Groups may still be straying from the standard procedure, causing varied results. If you observed any groups straying, you can lead students to this source of variation. If groups are following the standard procedure and still finding different ways of doing things, then the procedure needs to be more precise, and you can lead them to this.

As students evaluate the results of the investigation, discuss whether the results are good enough to send to the cookie company. Guide students in deciding to revise their procedures and run the investigation again.

TEACHER TALK

"Would the cookie company trust your results, based on the data we just looked at? What would the data have to look like for the cookie company to trust your results? Should we revise our procedure once more?"

If the class decides that the investigation needs to be run again, discuss ways in which the procedure can be improved.

TEACHER TALK

"Were there any things other groups were doing differently? Could your procedures have been more precise? What else could you do to get more consistent results?"

NOTES

Revise Your Procedure

Think about and discuss how the new, more specific procedure provides a closer answer to the question: *How much filling can be placed on the bottom cookie so it is completely covered but doesn't leak over the sides?*

You might find that the range of results is still too large for you to trust. If so, come up with ideas to create an even better procedure.

Use this new procedure. Produce a third set of data that is more consistent. Be sure to run your procedure under the same conditions as you did before. You may need to do this part of the activity at home. As before, plot these new results on another line plot. Do you trust these results more? Why?

Reflect

After your class creates the second, or possibly third graph, answer the following questions:

1. What did the distribution, or spread, of data points on your latest line plot look like? What do you think this says about how precise your lab has been at determining the answer to the cookie company's question?

2. Do you think it would ever be possible, given the materials and conditions you have in the classroom, to find an exact answer? Why or why not?

3. What do you think it would take to find an exact answer?

Discuss your answers and how they may help you better achieve the *Sandwich-Cookie Challenge.*

What's the Point?

Revising your procedure was important for your *Sandwich-Cookie Challenge.* By developing a precise procedure for everyone in the class to use, your results became more consistent. The cookie company is relying on the "right" answer to their question of how much filling can be placed on the bottom of a cookie sandwich. The more consistent your class results are, the more the cookie company will trust your results.

Revise Your Procedure

up to 10 min.

If the class has decided that the results are still unreliable, lead the class in revising their procedure once more.

△ **Guide**

Guide students to think about the features and problematic differences they identified as you lead the class in designing a new procedure. Since this is possibly the third time students have worked on this procedure, focus on refining or adjusting the current procedure rather than starting from scratch.

META NOTES

If you observed any groups doing anything differently from the rest of the class, you can guide students to this source of inconsistent results here.

> **TEACHER TALK**
>
> ❝So there's still something that we can do better in this procedure. Are there any places where the procedure could be more specific? Were there any groups that got very different answers from other groups? What were they doing differently?❞

As students specify steps, record the new procedure on the board.

Once the class has revised their procedure, have students run their investigations. (If there is not enough time to do this in class, students can run their procedures at home and bring the results to class.) Graph the new data on a line plot with the class, and help them analyze the data and evaluate the results.

Reflect

15 min.

Now that students have two or three iterations of their investigation, lead a class discussion comparing the procedures and resulting graphs across the investigations.

Reflect

After your class creates the second, or possibly third graph, answer the following questions:

1. What did the distribution, or spread, of data points on your latest line plot look like? What do you think this says about how precise your lab has been at determining the answer to the cookie company's question?

2. Do you think it would ever be possible, given the materials and conditions you have in the classroom, to find an exact answer? Why or why not?

3. What do you think it would take to find an exact answer?

Discuss your answers and how they may help you better achieve the *Sandwich-Cookie Challenge*.

△ Guide

To get students thinking about the importance of precise and uniform procedures, have students look again at the graphed data from each iteration of their investigation.

If students have three graphs, first focus on comparing the graphs and procedures. If they did only two, then they've made the comparison already.

Focus students' attention on the spread of the data and remind them of the changes they made in their procedures that led to the improvements in the reliability of the data.

TEACHER TALK

"So how has the spread of the data changed? What changes in your procedures could have changed the spread of the data?"

Listen for the following students' answers and guide the class toward these responses if necessary. Try to always help students make a connection between their responses and how it will help them better achieve the challenge.

1. Students' responses should demonstrate an evaluation of the data, and an understanding of what the distribution of a data set indicates. For example, if students say the data are clustered tightly around a number, they should use this as evidence that the lab has used

precise procedures. If the students say the data are still scattered, they should use this as evidence that the lab's procedure still isn't precise enough. In order to achieve the challenge, they need to have results that are trustworthy. The results are more trustworthy when their data are more clustered.

> ## TEACHER TALK
>
> **"**How would you describe the data on the new graph? Are the data more or less clustered than the data in the last graph?
>
> What were the most important changes you made to your procedure? Is the new procedure more or less precise than the last procedure? Did all groups follow the procedure?
>
> How does this information help you to solve the challenge? **"**

2. Students' responses should be based on the evidence of the procedures that they have run. Students have probably made their procedures much more precise, and gotten their data much more clustered, but some variation probably remains. From this, they can conclude that it is unlikely that they could ever get an exact answer with the materials and conditions in the classroom.

3. Students might say that finer equipment, such as more precise tools to measure out water drops of more uniform size, and a level to ensure that the pennies are level, would get an exact answer. They should recognize, however, that all tools have limited precision, and thus no measurement is ever exact. Students should realize that there is no "exact" value, but that they can still have trustworthy results if, when following the same procedures under the same conditions, their results are repeatable.

> **META NOTES**
>
> An example of limited precision is a digital stopwatch. The stopwatch will give you measurements in increments of hundredths of seconds, but there is still some uncertainty in the thousandths of seconds range. At the very best, the stopwatch has an uncertainty of $\frac{1}{2}$ its smallest increment.

What's the Point?

5 min.

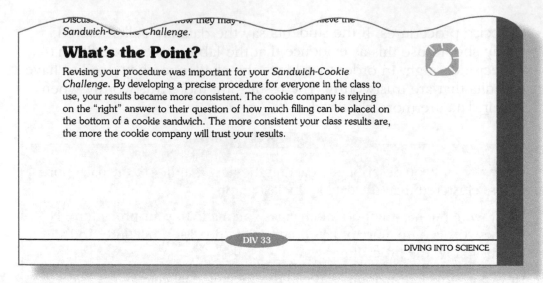

Discuss... ...ow they may ...eve the
Sandwich-Cookie Challenge.

What's the Point?

Revising your procedure was important for your *Sandwich-Cookie Challenge*. By developing a precise procedure for everyone in the class to use, your results became more consistent. The cookie company is relying on the "right" answer to their question of how much filling can be placed on the bottom of a cookie sandwich. The more consistent your class results are, the more the cookie company will trust your results.

DIV 33

DIVING INTO SCIENCE

META NOTES

Continue on to *Back to the Big Challenge.*

◇ Evaluate

As students reflect on their investigations, make sure they make the link between precise procedures and more reliable and trustworthy results.

TEACHER TALK

❝The first time we graphed our results, it turned out that everybody had a different answer. So you made your procedure more precise, and then the answers people came up with were closer together. It makes sense that making your procedure as precise as possible, and making sure everybody is using the same procedure, is going to help you get an answer that's pretty close to everyone else's.❞

NOTES

....

....

....

....

....

....

Assessment Options

Targeted Concepts, Skills, and Nature of Science	How do I know if students got it?
Scientists often work together and then share their findings. Sharing findings makes new information becomes available and helps scientists refine their ideas and build on others' ideas. When another person's or group's idea is used, credit needs to be given.	**ASK:** How would your conclusions be different if you had run all of the trials by yourself, without your classmates? **LISTEN:** Students may suspect that their trials would have been consistent, but they should recognize that they would not have been able to verify that other researchers would get similar results.
Scientific investigations and measurements are considered reliable if the results are repeatable by other scientists using the same procedures.	**ASK:** How do you know if measurements are reliable? **LISTEN:** If they can be repeated by using the same procedures of measurement, then they are reliable.

Teacher Reflection

- How did students make progress in graphing and analyzing data from the beginning of this *Learning Set* to this section? What evidence do you have that students understand the need for repeatable results?

- Did students stay focused on the goal of the investigations? What can you do to encourage this?

- What observations did you make during the class discussions that students were leading the discussions? What did you do to encourage this?

Learning Set 2

Back to the Big Question

10 min.

Now that the class has completed the Sandwich-Cookie Challenge, *have students reflect on what they have learned and how it connects to the* Big Challenge *of the* Launcher Unit: *How do scientists work together to solve problems?*

BACK TO THE BIG QUESTION IMPLEMENTATION

Learning Set 2

Back to the Big Question

How do scientists work together to solve problems?

You and your classmates have been trying to find the answer to a question. In the end, you've probably realized that it would be very difficult to find an exact answer. But as the different groups in the class used more similar procedures, their answers got closer to each other. You found that the way you collect data affects the answers you can find.

The first time everyone tried to determine the number of drops of water that would fit on a penny, each group had different results. That is because each group used a similar, but not an identical, method. The class then came up with a standard procedure. When everyone followed this procedure, the results were closer to each other. Your data became more consistent. You and others could trust your data.

There are three likely sources of inconsistent data:

- Different procedures are used for different trials.

- Factors that can affect the measured result are not carefully controlled.

- The constraints of the tools used.

It is important for scientists that the results of their experiments can be trusted. They must develop very precise methods to use that give similar results each time. Other scientists will want to repeat the experiments to see if they also get the same results. This is the only way that scientists can trust the work of others.

DIV 34

Project-Based Inquiry Science

△ Guide

Use the student text to help students connect their experiences in this *Learning Set* to the *Big Challenge* of the Unit, highlighting the three likely sources of inconsistent data. Pose questions to connect their experiences with the sandwich-cookie problem to the *Big Challenge*.

LEARNING SET 3 INTRODUCTION

Learning Set 3

The Whirligig Challenge

◀ $8\frac{1}{2}$ *class periods**

Groups design experiments and use their results to give advice about designing a slow-falling whirligig. They practice presenting to each other, actively listening to each others' presentations, and building on each others' ideas. During this challenge, students also investigate how things fall.

Overview

Student groups are challenged to create a whirligig pattern that fits on the back of a cereal box and that when constructed, falls as slowly as possible. To reach their goal, groups explore the materials, share design ideas, build on each other's ideas, and use the iterative process. By organizing their results, ideas, and experiences on a class *Project Board*, students can see how ideas in science evolve, and are better able to determine what they need to investigate to meet their goal. Student groups then design and run experiments to determine what affects the time it takes the whirligig to fall. They apply what they learned about measurements, and are introduced to the idea of a fair test. Students determine variables (independent, dependent, and controlled) for their experiments and obtain evidence to support scientific ideas about the forces of air resistance and gravity that act on the falling whirligig. Students construct explanations by backing up claims from their investigations with their observations and scientific knowledge. Students then make recommendations to the cereal company based on the evidence they obtained during their three iterations of constructing a whirligig, and the science knowledge. In *Learning Set 4*, students pull together skills from this *Learning Set* and the previous ones.

> **Looking Ahead**
>
> In *Section 3.1* a very important tool in the PBIS curriculum is introduced — the *Project Board*. How to set up and use *Project Boards* is described in detail in *Activity Setup and Preparation* and in the *Teacher's Resource Guide*.

*A class period is considered to be one 40 to 50 minute class.

Targeted Concepts, Skills, and Nature of Science	Section
Scientists often work together and then share their findings. Sharing findings makes new information available and helps scientists refine their ideas and build on others' ideas. When another person's or group's idea is used, credit needs to be given.	3.1, 3.2, 3.3, 3.4, 3.5, 3.6
Criteria and constraints are important in design.	3.2, 3.3
Scientists must keep clear, accurate, and descriptive records of what they do so they can share their work with others, consider what they did, why they did it, and what they want to do next.	3.2, 3.3
Identifying factors that lead to variation is an important part of scientific investigations.	3.2, 3.3
Scientific investigations and measurements are considered reliable if the results are repeatable by other scientists using the same procedures.	3.3
In a fair test, only the manipulated (independent) variable, and the responding (dependent) variable change. All other variables are held constant.	3.3
The way an object falls through air depends on its mass, surface area, and other factors.	3.1, 3.4, 3.6, 3.7
Earth's gravity pulls things toward Earth.	3.4, 3.6, 3.7
Air resistance is a force opposing the motion of an object moving through air.	3.4, 3.6, 3.7
Scientists make claims (conclusions) based on evidence (trends in data) from reliable investigations.	3.5, 3.7
Explanations are claims supported by evidence, accepted ideas and facts.	3.5, 3.6, 3.7

Students' Initial Conceptions and Capabilities	

- Students may not understand that scientists do investigations to test ideas, not to produce a desired outcome (Carey et al., 1989; Schauble et al., 1991; Solomon, 1992). In this *Learning Set* students will investigate what causes the whirligig to fall the way it does and then adjust the whirligig to produce their desired outcome (i.e., to make it go as slowly as possible).

- Students may not understand the need to vary only one manipulated (independent) variable during an experiment (Wollman, 1977a, 1977b; Wollman & Lawson, 1977).

- Students often have a difficult time interpreting experimental data and the relationship between the manipulated (independent) and responding (dependent) variables (Kuhn, Amsel, & O'Loughlin, 1988).

- Students may try to make conclusions to support their initial ideas, even if the evidence does not support those ideas (Schauble, 1990).

This is the first time some students are encountering the content concerning how things fall. This Unit does not go into it deeply and we do not expect students to understand it deeply at the end of this Unit. These concepts will come back in more detail in other Units. Nonetheless, it is good to be aware of some common initial ideas students may hold about how things fall.

- Students often associate force as a property of the object rather than the interaction between objects (Dykstra, et al., 1992; Jung et al., 1981; Osborne, 1985). For example, the air exerts a force on the whirligig and Earth exerts a force on the whirligig. The forces exerted on the whirligig are due to the interaction between the whirligig and the air and the whirligig and Earth, not to some inherent property of the whirligig.

- Many students believe that more massive or heavier objects always fall faster in air than lighter objects, not realizing that the surface area of the object and other factors play a role in how the object falls through the air.

Understanding for Teachers

It is important to realize that the intention of this Unit is to introduce students to the nature of science, the PBIS curriculum, and many of its tools. In this *Learning Set* and the next, students also study how things fall and are introduced to air resistance, but these concepts are not discussed in depth. It is not intended for students to learn about Newton's Laws, balancing forces, terminal velocity, or the details of air resistance. These ideas are taught in more depth in other Units. However, your students may still ask questions that you will need to address. Below, more detailed information about air resistance is provided.

Air Resistance

Gravity was discussed in *Learning Set 1*. Here we focus on air resistance or the drag force. The drag force is a resistive force, opposing the motion of an object and arising due to friction and collisions between the object and the fluid (gas or liquid) that it travels in. For objects moving in air, the size of the drag force depends directly on the area of the surface going through the air (affects how much air it collides with and how much it has to push away), the density of the air (affects how many air particles there are to collide with and how much it has to push away), and the speed of the object squared (affects how hard the particles hit and how much energy is needed to move the particles out of the way). As any of these variables (surface area, density, or speed) increases, the drag force increases.

As an example, hold your hand up in the air. You don't feel the air hitting it because you are not moving through it. Now place your hand so your palm is facing the floor and move your hand to the right and left. You should feel some air hitting your hand, particularly the side of your hand. Next, place your hand so your palm is facing to the right or left side of you and wave it through the air. You should feel more air against your hand now. This is because you have a larger surface area moving through the air so it collides with more air particles and has to move more air particles out of the way. Now try moving your hand (palm facing to the right or left) slowly and quickly through the air. You should feel more air hitting you the faster you go. When you get home, as a final test, try running or rollerblading with your hand in the air and feel the air go over it. Compare this to the air going over your hand when you are not in motion. The faster you go, the more you feel the air hitting your hand. The effect is slight in air. You may want to try this in water where the effect is more noticeable.

For any object being dropped, the instant it is released, the only force exerted on it is the gravitational pull exerted on it by Earth. As it begins to fall, it begins to experience the opposing drag force. The object will fall toward Earth, speeding up (accelerating), until the drag force is equal in size to the gravitational force. At this time the forces are balanced and there is no longer an overall push or pull on the object. Since there is no overall push or pull on the object, it cannot speed up or slow down or change direction, rather it moves with a constant speed and in a constant direction. This speed is called the terminal speed of the object. The sooner an object reaches its terminal speed, the less time it has to accelerate and the more time it has to fall at a constant speed.

When the whirligig falls, it experiences the force of gravity between it and Earth, and the drag force. When you add paper clips to the whirligig, the increase in mass increases the gravitational force exerted on the whirligig. This means that the whirligig will reach a greater terminal speed because it falls for a longer time before the size of the drag force equals the size of the gravitational force. Hence it reaches the ground in less time.

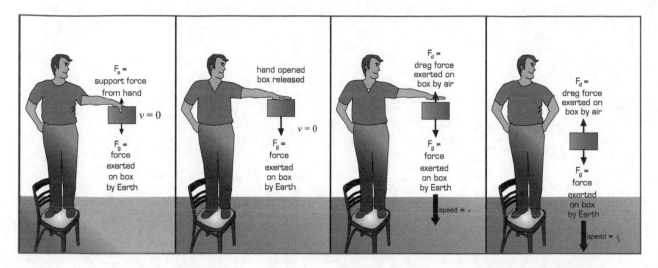

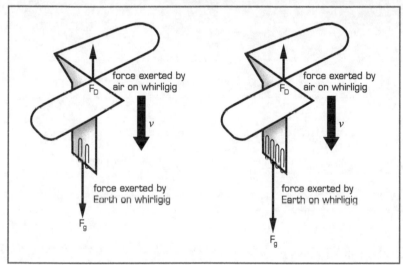

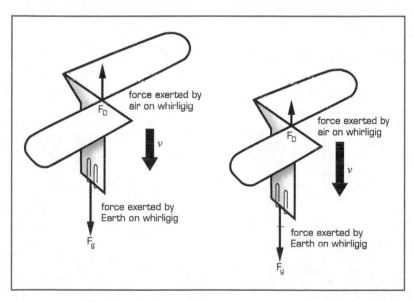

When you increase the blade size of the whirligig, you increase the surface area so more air particles collide with the whirligig and need to be pushed out of the way by the whirligig. This causes the drag force to reach its maximum value and the whirligig to reach its terminal speed in less time. And the terminal speed is smaller than when you had thin or short blades with smaller surface area. This means that the whirligig falls more slowly and for a longer period of time.

NOTES

_____

_____

_____

_____

_____

_____

_____

_____

_____

_____

_____

_____

_____

_____

_____

_____

_____

_____

_____

_____

LEARNING SET 3 IMPLEMENTATION

Learning Set 3

The Whirligig Challenge

Cereal companies like to attract attention to their products. One company prints a paper helicopter on the back of its cereal box for children to play with. They call their simple paper helicopter a whirligig. The whirligig is cut out from the box. Parts of it are folded and paper clips are attached. When a child drops the whirligig, it spins as it falls.

The cereal company wants to create a new whirligig that will fall more slowly than the one they have been using. They think that would be more fun.

Your challenge is to determine how to make a whirligig that will fall more slowly than the current one. The company gives you the criteria and constraints.

Criteria

- The whirligig should fall more slowly than the one now on the cereal box.

Constraints

- The whirligig **template** has to fit on the back of the box of cereal.

- The only materials available are the cereal box and paper clips. Assume that people have scissors to cut out the whirligig template from the cereal box.

You'll begin by identifying what you think you know about how things fall. You will then think about what you need to learn more about to be able to achieve the challenge. Then you'll design and carry out experiments to find out more about some of those things. You will also read some science about how things fall. After that, you'll use what you've learned to design a better whirligig. You will need to be able to explain what makes it fall more slowly than the old design.

template: a pattern.

DIV 35

DIVING INTO SCIENCE

◀ $1\frac{1}{2}$ *class periods*

Learning Set 3

The Whirligig Challenge

10 min.

Introduce students to the challenge – design a whirligig that falls as slowly as possible and will fit on the back of a cereal box.

○ **Engage**

Discuss why the cereal company would be interested in having a whirligig on their cereal box. Demonstrate the whirligig and ask what makes the whirligig fun.

TEACHER TALK

❝How many of you had cereal this morning? Do you ever have toys in your cereal box? Why do you think a cereal company would want to put a toy in their cereal box? This cereal company wants to put a whirligig like this one in their cereal box. What makes the whirligig fun? How could it be more fun?❞

META NOTES

Students may suggest adding color to the whirligig or making it bigger or smaller. These features may make the toy more interesting to look at on the box but are not related to how much fun it is to play with and may not make the whirligig fall more slowly. These ideas can be noted but will not be the focus of this challenge.

△ Guide

As students talk about their experiences with toys that fall, guide their attention to the fact that toys that fall slowly are more fun to watch and play with. Link this idea about fun toys to the challenge of designing a whirligig that falls as slowly as possible.

Next, lead students to think about criteria and constraints of this challenge. Link this task to students' previous experiences with the *Book-Support Challenge* and the *Sandwich-Cookie Challenge*.

TEACHER TALK

"We have already been challenged to design a book support and to determine how much filling will fit on a cookie. Like in those challenges, we need to think about the criteria and constraints before we begin. Let's talk about the criteria first."

META NOTES

Students might suggest that it will be more fun if the whirligig spins or glides. In order to design an investigation, students need to focus on one feature or variable at a time. In this section, students will focus on falling slowly. Those ideas would make the whirligig more fun. But for now we need to focus on one feature so we can begin our investigation.

Remind students that criteria are conditions that must be met. For the whirligig, the main criterion is to fall as slowly as possible.

Remind students that constraints are limitations in how the criteria can be met. For the whirligig, the main constraints are that the template must fit on a cereal box, and be made of a cereal box and paper clips.

NOTES

....

....

....

....

....

....

....

SECTION 3.1 INTRODUCTION

3.1 Understand the Challenge

Thinking about How Things Fall

◀ $1\frac{1}{2}$ *class periods**

Overview

Students are first introduced to the challenge of building a slow-falling whirligig. They then begin thinking about how things fall when they predict, observe, and compare three demonstrations of falling objects with the same and different weights and surface areas. The class is then introduced to the *Project Board* to organize their ideas about how things fall and what they need to investigate. Then students explore or *Mess About* with whirligig materials and how they fall. *Messing About* helps groups to identify what they need to know more about and encourages students to try out ideas freely. The section concludes with students updating the class's *Project Board*, which prepares them for designing an experiment in the next section.

Targeted Concepts, Skills, and Nature of Science	Performance Expectations
Scientists often work together and then share their findings. Sharing findings makes new information available and helps scientists refine their ideas and build on others' ideas. When another person's or group's idea is used, credit needs to be given.	Groups should be able to describe in a class discussion what they know and what they need to know and write these things on the *Project Board* before and after exploring the whirligig. Small groups and the class should be able to discuss and determine what they know and what they need to investigate.
The way an object falls through air depends on its mass, surface area, and other factors.	Students should be able to state that it is not just the mass that affects how much time it takes a dropped object to reach the ground. They should back this up with evidence obtained from the three demonstrations and their observations of the whirligig. This should also be reflected in the first two columns of the *Project Board*.

*A class period is considered to be one 40 to 50 minute class.

```
Materials

1  per classroom   completed whirligig for demonstration for Unit
                   introduction
1  per classroom   sheet of 8 ½" × 11" paper and book with a slightly
                   larger surface area (from ¼" to 1" larger on each
                   side) for a demonstration
8  per classroom   flat-bottomed coffee filters for a demonstration
1  per classroom   seven flat-bottomed coffee filters connected in a flower
                   pattern for a demonstration
1  per group       safety scissors
1  per student     whirligig template on heavyweight photocopy paper
2  per student     paper clips (jumbo size)
1  per class       class Project Board
1  per student     Demonstration Notes sheet
1  per student     Project Board sheet
1  per student     Messing-About Observations sheet
```

Activity Setup and Preparation

Consider whether you want to change student groups or keep the same groups as in *Learning Set 1*. Groups should be composed of 3 to 4 students.

Prepare the class *Project Board*. You will need one for each class. Students will keep their own personal copy of their *Project Board* sheets that they will update during the class discussion.

Project Board

How to set up the *Project Board* is outlined here. *Project Board*s are described more completely in the *Teacher's Resource Guide*, the teacher implementation notes on introducing the *Project Board*, and the student text. The *Project Board* is a tool used to organize information and ideas when working on a project. It consists of five columns labeled as follows: *What do we think we know?*; *What do we need to investigate?*; *What are we learning?*; *What is our evidence?*; *What does it mean for the challenge or question?*

- Each class is making their own *Project Board* and will be revisiting it and updating it through the end of the Unit. For every Unit you will need to create a *Project Board* for each class and update it throughout the Unit.

- To set up the *Project Board,* decide if you will use butcher block paper, a projected computer file, or some other medium. You will record the class's ideas and questions on the *Project Board* during *Project Board* discussions. Each student will also have their own record of the *Project Board* that they will keep with them. In the header of the *Project Board* leave room for *Big Questions.* In this Unit you should leave room for the question: *What affects how an object falls toward Earth?* You should also leave room for writing two more questions. One of which is: *How can we design a slow-falling whirligig?* The second question will be added in *Learning Set 4.*

Demonstrations

How to conduct the demonstrations is described in the *Implementation* section. Try the three demonstrations before you do them in class to make sure the objects fall as expected. You should make sure there are no drafts in the room by closing doors and windows and by performing the demonstrations away from blowing air vents. You should also make sure you drop the objects high enough from the ground so that there is a noticeable difference in how they fall that students can observe.

The **1st demonstration** consists of dropping a book and piece of paper from the same height at the same time. The paper and book should be parallel with the floor when you drop them. The paper should sway and fall more slowly than the book because it reaches its terminal speed more quickly than the book. (At the very end of this section you may want to show that the paper and book fall about the same rate when the paper is crumpled into a ball.)

The **2nd demonstration** consists of dropping a stack of seven coffee filters and a single coffee filter at the same time and from the same height. Both should be dropped with the bottom facing the floor and the "cup" part facing the ceiling as shown. The seven filters should hit the ground first.

For the **3rd demonstration** you should tape together the rims of seven coffee filters into a flower pattern as shown in the image on the next page. Make sure each filter is connected to the center filter and to its adjacent filter, placing the tape at the midpoints of the adjoining arcs that the rims form. Drop the single filter and floral-pattern filters at

DIVING INTO SCIENCE

the same time from the same height. Be careful to make sure they are at the same height — the floral pattern droops a little — line up the bottom of the middle filter with the bottom of the single filter. The single filter should reach the ground first. (You may also want to drop seven stacked filters against the floral pattern. The seven stacked filters should reach the ground first.)

Homework Options

Reflection

- **Science Content:** What do you think affects how slowly the whirligig falls toward Earth? Why? (This is to get students' ideas about what affects the whirligig. You may use this information to help you guide students during this *Learning Set*.)

- **Science Process:** Why do you think the *Project Board* might be a useful tool? *(Use the information to help guide the students in understanding the* Project Board.*)*

Preparation for 3.2

- **Science Process:** What do you think might be important considerations in designing an experiment? *(This is to get students thinking about experiment design. They will be designing an experiment in the next section.)*

- **Science Content:** What factors do you think affect how slowly the whirligig falls toward Earth? How would you test this? Write a clear set of procedures. *(This is to get students thinking about what causes the whirligig to fall the way it does – what it is interacting with.)*

3.1

SECTION 3.1 IMPLEMENTATION

3.1 Understand the Challenge

Thinking about How Things Fall

Demonstration

If you drop a book and a piece of paper at the same time, which will hit the ground first? You may have some ideas about the answer to this question. You also may have some ideas about what affects how things fall. To figure out how to make a whirligig fall slowly, it will be necessary to identify what you think you already know about how things fall. You will also need to identify what you might not understand yet. That way, you'll know what you need to learn to succeed in achieving the challenge.

Demonstration Notes 3.1.1

Name: _____ Date: _____

Demonstration	Predict	Observe	Compare
#1 Describe the event here			
#2 Describe the event here			
#3 Describe the event here			

You are going to observe three short demonstrations. They will help you to figure out what you know and what you need to learn about how things fall. For each demonstration, record your predictions and observations on a *Demonstration Notes* page. Afterwards, your class will share their predictions and observations. You will record the things you think you know and need to learn on a *Project Board*. (You will learn more about the *Project Board* later.)

Project-Based Inquiry Science DIV 36

3.1 Understand the Challenge

Thinking about How Things Fall

Demonstration
20 min.

Now that the challenge is clear, students need to begin thinking about how things fall. Lead students through the three demonstrations to illustrate that how things fall through air depends on surface areas as well as mass, an idea that may surprise students.

META NOTES

For some students, falling slowly may not mean the same as taking a long time to fall. One way to take a long to time to fall is to start from a higher place (e.g., jumping from an airplane versus jumping off a step). The parachute also slows the fall. Thus, it is important in the demonstrations, to drop all the objects from the same height.

◯ Engage

Begin by getting students thinking about how things fall. You can ask students about what things they have seen falling slowly or quickly and what they think affected the objects' fall.

Then introduce the demonstrations. Point out that they will see three demonstrations of objects falling to help them think about what affects how things fall.

TEACHER TALK

❝To help us think about what affects how things fall, I have three demonstrations to show you. For each demonstration you'll first predict what you think will happen and why, and then you'll watch the objects fall.❞

DIVING INTO SCIENCE

META NOTES

Students may use a variety of different words to express their thoughts on why things fall the way they do. They might use the words weight, mass, and heaviness without understanding the differences between them. They may also use surface area, shape, or size in their description. This is to be expected and there is no need to correct them at this time. There will be time later for those discussions.

Point out the importance of recording their ideas and introduce the *Demonstration Notes* page. Let students know that they will be sharing their ideas with their group members about how things fall after the three demonstrations.

TEACHER TALK

❝In science it is important to remember and think about our ideas. We do this when we think about what will happen and why. If we record our ideas then we can compare what we observed with what we thought would happen. In science, sometimes the observations support a scientist's ideas completely. Sometimes the observations cause a scientist to change his or her ideas a bit. Sometimes the observations require a scientist to toss out his or her ideas and start rethinking the problem. To help you remember and think about your ideas, you will record your predictions and observations on the *Demonstration Notes* page.❞

Demonstration 1

Book vs. Paper

Remember for all the demonstrations to make sure there are no drafts, that you drop all the objects from the same height, and that it is high enough so that students can notice a difference in when the objects reach the ground.

△ **Guide**

Show students the paper and book and point out that the book is heavier than the paper. Do not use the term *surface area* or *mass*. Ask students to predict what will happen when you drop a book and a piece of paper from the same height at the same time.

TEACHER TALK

❝I've got here a book and a piece of paper. They are about the same size, but the book is heavier than the paper. I am going to drop them from the same height at the same time. What do you think will happen? Don't tell me yet. Record on your paper what you think will happen and why you think it will happen.❞

Then drop the book and paper from the same height. The book should reach the floor first and the paper should sway and loop as it falls.

After dropping the book and paper, remind students to write down their observations and why they think it happened.

META NOTES

Most students will predict that the book will reach the floor first because it has more mass or weight. This is not the complete explanation. This common idea will be challenged by what students see during the three demonstrations.

☐ **Assess**

Briefly, have students share their ideas about why the paper and book reached the ground at different times. Listen for ideas about mass or other factors related to falling. You might ask one or two students to share their ideas and then ask if anyone had other ideas. (There is no need to judge any of the ideas right now.) Lead right into the next demonstration and save the full discussion until all three demonstrations are completed.

NOTES

....

....

....

....

....

....

....

....

....

....

....

....

META NOTES

Everyday experiences such as this first demonstration, lead many students (and adults) to think that more mass causes objects to fall faster. This is not always true. The next two demonstrations illustrate that falling speed is affected by surface area also.

META NOTES

It is also important to remember that mass only influences falling speed when the object is traveling through something that "pushes back", like air or water. In a vacuum, all masses fall at the same rate.

Demonstration 2

Stack of Seven Coffee Filters vs. Single Filter

This time you will drop a single coffee filter and a stack of seven coffee filters. Both have a similar shape but the stack of coffee filters has seven times the mass of the single filter. The seven filters will reach the ground first.

> **META NOTES**
>
> This demonstration is consistent with a common beleif that more massive things fall quicker. The seven filters in a floral pattern (with a greater surface area) will take more time to reach the ground.

> **META NOTES**
>
> Mass is a measure of matter. Weight is a measure of force pulling an object to Earth. Students often consider them the same. Decide whether or not your class will use these terms. These ideas and term are focused on in another PBIS Unit.

△ Guide

Tell students this time you are going to drop seven stacked coffee filters and a single filter from the same height at the same time. Point out that the stack of seven filters is seven times heavier (or seven times the mass) of the single filter since there are seven of them. Ask students to predict and record what will happen and why.

Then drop the seven stacked filters and the single filter from the same height as the book and paper in *Demonstration 1*. The stack of seven filters should reach the floor first.

After the demonstration, remind students to record their observations and why they think it happened.

☐ Assess

Again, briefly have students share their ideas about why the seven filters and the single filter reached the ground at different times. Listen for students commenting on how this shows that heavy things fall faster.

NOTES

....

....

....

....

....

....

....

....

△ Guide

Show students the seven filters arranged in the floral pattern and the single filter. Remind them that the seven filters have seven times the mass (or weight) of the single filter, as in the previous demonstration. Tell them again you are going to drop both from the same height at the same time. Ask students to predict and record what will happen and why.

> **TEACHER TALK**
>
> **"**Now I am going to drop seven filters and one filter again, but this time I'm going to arrange the seven filters so that they are in this flower pattern. The seven filters have seven times the mass of the single filter. I will drop them from the same height at the same time. Which one do you think will reach the ground first? Why? **"**

After students have recorded their ideas, ask a few students to share their predictions and reasons. This time the demonstration may surprise students. Listen for their ideas about the mass of the objects or if they are also thinking about the surface area. Students do not need to agree now because they will watch the demonstration to see if their predictions were accurate.

Drop the seven floral filters and the single filter from the same height as the previous demonstrations. The single filter should reach the ground first. Because this may surprise students, they may ask to see the demonstration again. Make sure everyone has a chance to see the result. Ask students to record their observations and why they think it happened.

☐ Assess

Let students briefly share their ideas or questions about why the seven filters and the single filter reached the ground at different times. Listen for students' ideas about mass, surface area, and falling objects. Not everyone will reconcile their ideas about falling objects but they should recognize that more than just mass affects how things fall.

Demonstration 3
Floral Pattern of seven Filters vs. Single Filter

In this third demonstration you will drop a single coffee filter and a set of seven coffee filters taped together in a floral pattern. The seven filters have seven times more surface area and mass as the single filter. Here, the heavier object will fall slower.

> **META NOTES**
>
> Students may wonder about the results of the past two demonstrations. They may want to see the seven stacked filters dropped against the floral-pattern filters. The mass is the same but the surface area is different. This is a good example of the effects of surface area.

> **META NOTES**
>
> Some students will have their initial ideas about mass challenged. They learn that mass is not the only factor in how things fall. They should be motivated to learn about why things fall the way they do.

Conference

5 min.

Based on all three demonstrations, have groups compare their predictions and observations, and identify what they think they know and what they still need to know about how objects fall.

META NOTES

During a conference, members of a group discuss their ideas together, in this case their ideas from the three demonstrations. This helps students refine and articulate their ideas to some degree. Later, during class discussions, groups' ideas are further refined, in this case, beginning to think about how things fall.

During each demonstration, you will be asked to do three things:

Predict – Your teacher will explain to you what he or she is going to do during the demonstration. You will predict what you think will happen. Record your prediction on your *Demonstration Notes* page.

Observe – You will observe the demonstration and record your observations.

Compare – After the demonstration, you will compare your predictions to what you observed. Note what you predicted well and what surprised you.

Conference

Share your predictions and observations with your group members. Make sure everybody has a chance to share. Your predictions and observations probably don't match exactly. As a group, see if you understand why the dropped objects behaved the way they did. Discuss what you think you know and what you thought you knew. Discuss what you think you still need to learn to fully understand your observations. Jot down notes so that you will remember what you discussed when you share again with the class. You will have about five minutes, so get started quickly.

Be a Scientist

Introducing the *Project Board*

When you work on a project, it is useful to keep track of your progress and what you still need to do. You will use a *Project Board* to do that. It gives you a place to keep track of your scientific understanding as you make your way through a Unit. It is designed to help your class organize its questions, investigations, results, and conclusions. The *Project Board* will also help you to decide what you are going to do next. During classroom discussions, you will record the class's ideas on a class *Project Board*. At the same time, you will keep track of what's been discussed on your own *Project Board* page.

The *Project Board* has space for answering five guiding questions:

- What do we think we know?
- What do we need to investigate?
- What are we learning?
- What is our evidence?
- What does it mean for the challenge or question?

Project Board: a space for the class to keep track of progress while working on a project.

DIV 37

DIVING INTO SCIENCE

⬡ Get Going

Introduce students to this conference by pointing out that now that they have recorded their predictions and observations, they need to work together to think about what they know about falling and what they need to explore further. Tell students they will use the ideas from their conference to create a class *Project Board* for everyone to use.

△ Guide

Describe to students the task for this conference. First, everyone in the group should compare their observations and predictions. How were they the same? How were they different? What was surprising? Second, each group should make a list of what they think they now know and what they still need to learn to understand what they observed.

Emphasize that scientific ideas must be supported by evidence from observations. Student groups' lists of what they now know should be supported by their observations. When observations don't completely support their ideas, scientists collect more evidence and revise their ideas. Student groups' lists of what they still need to learn will be ideas that their observations did not support.

Emphasize that everyone should participate by sharing ideas and listening to the other students' ideas.

Let students know they should be able to do this quickly so they only have about five minutes.

☐ Assess

Listen for questions the students are asking each other and for the places where tensions arise in their discussions. These are good indicators of where an investigative question might be extracted for the *Project Board*.

◇ Evaluate

Also, as groups are conferencing, check that each group has listed what they think they know and what they still need to find out to understand their observations.

○ Engage

Remind students that they were analyzing the demos to get them thinking about their challenge — to design a toy to fall slowly. Help them understand that as engineers and scientists work challenges, they need to keep a record of their ideas so they can monitor their progress. Tell them they will be doing this using a *Project Board*.

△ Guide

> **TEACHER TALK**
>
> **❝**Remember we are working on designing a toy for a cereal box. We are just getting started and we have lots of ideas and things to test before we get to a good design. We will need a way to keep track of our ideas and progress just as scientists and engineers do as they are addressing challenges. We'll do that using a *Project Board*.**❞**

Introduce the *Project Board* and how it is used to students, as this is their first experience using one to record their ideas.

Show students the class *Project Board*. Explain that the *Project Board* is a tool that will be used throughout the course. It is used by the class to organize ideas, questions, and answers when working on a challenge.

META NOTES

As students conference, they share and develop ideas as they listen to the other students' ideas. Conference conversations will include disagreements, which can help students rethink their ideas. This may also be uncomfortable for students who are not used to disagreements or having to justify their ideas. Until students learn how to discuss their different ideas fairly and productively, tensions may develop.

Introduce and Create the Project Board
15 min.

Students are now ready to share ideas about falling with the whole class (so they will be able to address the Whirligig Challenge). *At the same time, students need to learn to use a* Project Board *for monitoring progress on their challenge. Lead a class discussion using the* Project Board *to record students' ideas about how things fall.*

DIVING INTO SCIENCE

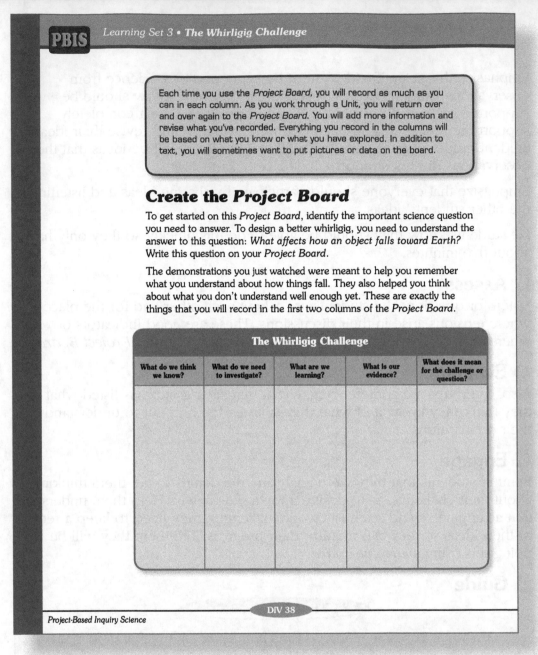

Each time you use the *Project Board*, you will record as much as you can in each column. As you work through a Unit, you will return over and over again to the *Project Board*. You will add more information and revise what you've recorded. Everything you record in the columns will be based on what you know or what you have explored. In addition to text, you will sometimes want to put pictures or data on the board.

Create the *Project Board*

To get started on this *Project Board*, identify the important science question you need to answer. To design a better whirligig, you need to understand the answer to this question: *What affects how an object falls toward Earth?* Write this question on your *Project Board*.

The demonstrations you just watched were meant to help you remember what you understand about how things fall. They also helped you think about what you don't understand well enough yet. These are exactly the things that you will record in the first two columns of the *Project Board*.

The Whirligig Challenge

What do we think we know?	What do we need to investigate?	What are we learning?	What is our evidence?	What does it mean for the challenge or question?

Project-Based Inquiry Science

Challenges are big questions that rely on many smaller questions and answers before they can be completed. The *Project Board* helps keep track of it all. Help students understand that the *Project Board* provides a way for the class to work together to plan and keep track of progress during a challenge.

Next, describe the five columns. Explain that the third and fourth columns go hand in hand (the thrid basically lists the claims and the fourth lists the evidence that backs up those claims based on observations and information from experts), and the fifth explains how it is connected with the challenge or a bigger question.

3.1

What do we think we know?

In this column of the *Project Board*, you will record what you think you know. As you just experienced, some things you think you know are not true. Some things are not completely accurate. It is important to record those things anyway for two reasons:

- When you look at the board later, you will be able to see how much you have learned.

- Discussion with the class about what you think you know will help you figure out what you need to investigate.

What do we need to investigate?

In this column, you will record the things you need to learn more about. During your group conference, you probably came up with questions about how to explain what happened in the demos. You might have figured out some things you are confused about too. And you might have found that you and others in your group disagreed about your predictions. This second column is designed to help you keep track of things that are confusing. Record what you don't understand well yet, and that you disagree about. These are the things you will need to investigate. They will be important for achieving your challenge (designing a better whirligig).

Sometimes you are unsure about something but don't know how to word it as a question. One of the things your class will do together around the *Project Board* is to turn the things you are curious about into questions that you can investigate.

Later in this Unit, you will return to the *Project Board*. For now, work as a class and begin filling in the first two columns.

> **Be a Scientist**
>
> **Messing About**
> *Messing About* is an exploratory activity. It gives you a chance to become familiar with the materials you will be using. It also lets you figure out how a product you will be designing should work. At this stage, you aren't ready to do a formal investigation or test. When you *mess about*, you explore in a way that will help you do that later.

DIV 39

DIVING INTO SCIENCE

Create the Project Board
10 min.

○ Engage

Emphasize that the class will be filling out the first two columns (*What do we think we know?* and *What do we need to investigate?*) today and that they will add to all the columns as they work on the challenge.

You may want to distribute the student *Project Board* pages at this time. Let students know that they should be keeping a personal copy of the class *Project Board* that they can refer to as needed and that you will be keeping the class *Project Board* and recording the class's ideas and questions on it until the end of the Unit.

⬡ Get Going

Begin students on the *Project Board* by starting with the question: *What affects how an object falls toward Earth?* Describe that they need to answer this question to design a slow-falling whirligig. Write this question across the top of the *Project Board* or have a student volunteer. Note that you will later want to write another question across the top: *How can we design a slow-falling whirligig?* Also, leave room for that and for a question that will arise in *Learning Set 4*.

TEACHER TALK

❝Over here I have set up our class *Project Board* for the *Whirligig Challenge*. We'll begin by recording what we think we know about how things fall and questions we have about how things fall. Our *Project Board* will help us organize our ideas and questions as we work on this challenge. It will allow us to remember what questions we have already addressed and which ones we still need to find answers to. It will also help us keep track of what we are learning.❞

△ Guide

Now it is time to help students post ideas and questions in the first two columns of the *Project Board*. This will require helping them share with each other what they've discussed in their conferences about the demos. To guide students in this discussion, ask questions such as:

- What did you list as things you think you know?
- What did you talk about in your group that everyone agreed on?
- What do you know about falling from the first demonstration with the book and paper?
- What do you know about falling from the second demonstration with the coffee filters? Did that demonstration agree with your ideas from the first demonstration?
- What did you list as things you need to investigate?
- What did you talk about that not everyone agreed on?
- Did the third demonstration with the flower-shaped coffee filters agree with your ideas about falling from the first or second demonstration?

As students share their ideas and questions with the class, record their ideas on the *Project Board*. Use the first column to record their current ideas. There is no need to figure out right now if these ideas are right or wrong.

Use the second column for their questions. This includes questions about ideas students don't agree on or have a hard time accepting. Students will disagree about some of the items in the first column. These are indications of questions that need to go in the second column. Things students are surprised by should go in the second column as well.

META NOTES

Linking items in different columns that are related to each other with arrows helps the students see how ideas and questions are connected.

◇ Evaluate

With students, look over the ideas and questions on the *Project Board*. Make sure everyone has had the opportunity to contribute and that their ideas are represented. Also make sure ideas or questions about mass (heaviness) and surface area (shape or spread) are included. Don't expect students to be experts at this point.

META NOTES

During the discussion, listen for students' ideas about how things fall and their reasoning.

The Whirligig Challenge				
What do we think we know?	What do we need to investigate?	What are we learning?	What is our evidence?	What does it mean for the challenge or question?

Mess About with the Whirligig

15 min.

Let students explore the whirligig materials to become familiar with the materials and think about how to make the whirligig fall more slowly.

Mess About with the Whirligig

> **Messing About:** an exploratory activity that gives you a chance to become familiar with the materials you will be using or the function of what you will be designing.
>
> **structure:** the way the parts of an item are put together. (This is a different definition of structure than the one you saw while making your book support.)
>
> **mechanism:** the way the parts of an item connect and move.

To help you think about how to achieve your challenge, you will begin by *messing about* with the whirligig. You will use the basic whirligig that now appears on the back of the cereal boxes.

You will get a template (pattern) of a whirligig. It will look like the one shown below. The whirligig has several parts: blades, paper clips, and a stem. If you call them by those names when you talk about the whirligig, everyone will know what you are talking about.

Cut out the template. To form the whirligig, fold the cutout template. Attach two paper clips to the stem.

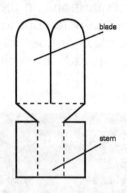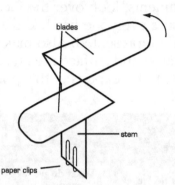

As you *Mess About* with the whirligig, explore how it works. Think about what it is capable of doing. While *Messing About*, see if you can answer the questions below. This will help you identify more about what you still need to learn and help you figure out what investigations to do.

- What is the **structure** of the item I'm working with? (Structure means the way the parts are put together.)

- What are its **mechanisms**? (Mechanism refers to how the different parts connect to each other or move with each other to make the object behave the way it does.)

- How is this item supposed to behave? What might I change in the item to affect that behavior?

○ Engage

Remind students that they have now thought about what affects how objects fall toward Earth. Now they can begin thinking specifically about why and how the whirligig falls toward Earth and how to make it fall more slowly. Show students the whirligig again and how it falls and remind them of the goal (to figure out a way to make a whirligig fall as slowly as possible to the ground). Remind them that the questions they need to investigate on their *Project Board* will help them find a way to solve the *Whirligig Challenge*.

3.1 Understand the Challenge

You will have about five minutes to construct and drop your whirligig several times. Watch it carefully. Try dropping it in different ways. Try changing some of the parts. Notice the effect these changes seem to have on the whirligig's fall. Discuss the observations you make with your group. Use *Messing-About Observations* pages to record your observations, ideas, and questions.

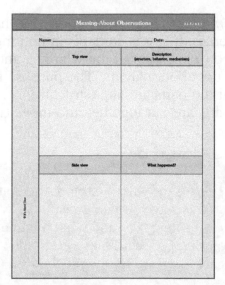

Update the *Project Board*

After you complete a small-group activity, your class will get together to review what you found out and what you were thinking about. This time, you will discuss the behavior of the whirligigs. Update the *What do we think we know?* and *What do we need to investigate?* columns based on your *Messing About* experience.

DIV 41

DIVING INTO SCIENCE

Mess About with the Whirligig
(continued)

Next, tell students they will explore these features as they *Mess About* with the whirligig materials. They will get to try out all their ideas about what can be changed on the whirligig that might make it fall slowly.

△ Guide

Explain to students that *Messing About* is an opportunity for them to become familiar with the materials. It assists students in figuring out what they know and what they need to learn about the whirligig and how it falls. Emphasize that this session is not about playing. The purpose is to explore how the whirligig works, what the parts are like (structure, i.e., size, shape, heaviness), and the way the parts are put together and move (mechanism, i.e., how the parts interact).

TEACHER TALK

❝The purpose of *Messing About* is for you to explore the materials you will use to make the whirligig. This way you will get familiar with the materials being used, how the whirligig falls, and what might affect the time it takes to fall. While exploring the whirligig, you should think about the structure (what the parts are like) and on the mechanism (how it is put together and moves).❞

⬡ Get Going

Let students know that they will be constructing their whirligig and then dropping it three or four times and in different ways to figure out what affects the whirligig and how it falls. Let students know that they may also change the parts of the whirligig.

NOTES

....

....

....

....

....

....

Describe what type of information is needed on the *Messing-About Observations* pages. Students should draw what the whirligig looks like in the top and side view boxes for each variation of the whirligig they use and label it as variation 1, 2, 3, or 4. In the description box they should describe the structure (what the parts are like), mechanism (how it is put together and moves), and its behavior when it falls (twirls, tumbles, etc.) for each variation and label it as variation 1, 2, 3, or 4. In the *What happened?* box, students should describe the time it took the whirligig to fall to the ground for each variation and compare them.

Tell students how much time they have to make their observations. Groups should take between five and ten minutes. Take no more than ten minutes for this and move on as soon as students seem to be off-task.

☐ Assess

As students are working, observe what they are trying and note their ideas. These can be discussed when the class returns to the *Project Board*. Students may try changing how the blades are angled, or how the paper clips are situated on the stem. If anyone has tried dropping the whirligig with no paper clips, they may note that the whirligig tips sideways and falls rapidly. This idea will be addressed later in the *Learning Set* and should not be a focus of this section.

◇ Evaluate

Make sure students have recorded at least three variations for dropping their whirligig and using that they are using the *Messing-About Observations* pages as described above.

NOTES

....

....

....

....

....

Update the Project Board

10 min.

Lead students in updating the Project Board *with information they obtained while exploring the whirligig.*

Update the *Project Board*

After you complete a small-group activity, your class will get together to review what you found out and what you were thinking about. This time, you will discuss the behavior of the whirligigs. Update the *What do we think we know?* and *What do we need to investigate?* columns based on your *Messing About* experience.

DIV 41

DIVING INTO SCIENCE

○ Engage

Remind students that the challenge is to figure out a way to make a whirligig that fits on a cereal box and falls slowly and that they have just explored the whirligig and materials. Remind them that when they started the *Project Board*, they were considering what they know about how things fall. Now they are going to fill out the first two columns —*What do we think we know?* and *What do we need to investigate?* — focusing on the whirligig which they have just explored.

> **TEACHER TALK**
>
> "Remember our challenge is to figure out a way to make a whirligig that fits on a cereal box and falls slowly. You've had a chance to explore the whirligig a bit and think about how it falls and what might affect how it falls. Now we are going to fill in the first two columns of the *Project Board* — *What do we think we know?* and *What do we need to investigate?* — based on your experience with the whirligig."

△ Guide a Class Discussion

Ask each group to contribute their ideas to the first two columns of the *Project Board*. Students may not be sure which items should go in the *What do we need to investigate?* column. You could ask what parts of the whirligig affect how it falls. You should guide students to discuss how the structure (what the parts are like) and mechanism (the way the parts connect or move) of the whirligig affects how it falls. During the discussion, record and edit the class's *Project Board* as needed.

Examples for the *Project Board*: These examples are provided to give you a sense of what students may say. It is O.K. if the class has a different set of ideas and questions listed.

- **Column 1:** *What do we think we know?* The whirligig flutters as it falls to the ground. Sometimes it turns sideways and falls rapidly;

"First column: What did you observe about how the whirligig falls? What do you think you know about how the whirligig falls based on what you observed? What parts of the whirligig did you change to affect how it falls? How did it affect the whirligig's fall, for example, did it take more time, less time, or the same time? Does the way the parts are connected or the way they move affect how the whirligig falls? In what way? What did you observe?

Second column: Were there any groups that had different observations when trying the same thing (like adding more paper clips)? If so, this is something we should investigate. How should we write it up on the *Project Board?* Are there other things we are not sure about or that groups disagree on? These are things we should write in the second column of our *Project Board?* How should we write these?**"**

when I put more paper clips on it, it takes less time to reach the ground (like the book and piece of paper — the heavier it is, the faster it falls).

- **Column 2:** *What do we need to investigate?* How does adding the paper clips (adding mass) affect the whirligig? Does it matter where we put the paper clips? How does the blade size/length/ width affect how the whirligig falls? How does the stem length affect how the whirligig falls?

◇ Evaluate

There should be many questions on the *Project Board.* Make sure that something like the following two questions are on the *Project Board.*

1. How does the length of the whirligig's blades affect the time it takes the whirligig to fall to the ground?

2. How does the number of paper clips on a whirligig's stem affect the time it takes the whirligig to fall to the ground?

If students have not suggested these two questions, continue eliciting their ideas, guiding them toward these two questions. Remember students' responses may be worded differently.

"Did anyone try using a different number of paper clips? If not, let's try it now. Did anyone try changing the length of the blade? If not, let's try it now.**"**

What's the Point?

10 min.

What's the Point?

In your previous challenge, you identified the criteria and constraints to help you understand the challenge. In this challenge, you were given the criteria and constraints. To help you understand this challenge, you tried to find out what you need to learn more about to be successful.

You made some predictions and observations about several demos. Then you compared your observations with your predictions. You may have found some surprises.

You started a *Project Board* to help track what you understand. You also added questions about how things fall. The *Project Board* is a space to help the class work together to understand and solve problems. Using it will help you have good science discussions as you work on a project.

You *Messed About* with a basic whirligig. You became familiar with how a whirligig moves and acts. This led to identifying more investigations you might do.

META NOTES

It is important for students to be able to figure out what they need to know when they are working on a challenge so that they can figure out what to investigate to solve the challenge.

Students should have a sense of the importance of understanding what it is they need to learn and how the demonstrations, *Project Board*, and *Messing About* were all helpful in forming their ideas and questions. Ask students why it is important to be able to identify what they need to know and how this connects to the challenge.

Assessment Options

Targeted Concepts, Skills, and Nature of Science	How do I know if students got it?
Scientists often work together and then share their findings. Sharing findings makes new information available and helps scientists refine their ideas and build on others' ideas. When another person's or group's idea is used, credit needs to be given.	**ASK:** students if they can give an example from what they did today of how scientific ideas and methods change. **LISTEN:** to students describe how the demonstrations, *Project Board*, and *Messing About* all added to their understanding of what they know and what they need to investigate. **ASK:** students how working in a group and presenting their group's work to the class helped them figure out what they know and what they need to know. **LISTEN:** to students describe how their group and class discussions helped them realize what they know and what they need to know. **ASK:** students if any other group or student influenced or changed their thinking. **LISTEN:** to students acknowledge that their thinking has been influenced by something they hear another student or group say during the discussions.

Teacher Reflection Questions

- What difficulties did students have in constructing the whirligig? What help will they need when it comes time to build the whirligig for the experiment?

- What was difficult or easy for students in coming up with experimental questions? What guidance will they need to improve their ability to describe experimental questions?

- What worked well in *Messing About*? What will you change the next time students *Mess About*?

1 class period* ▶

*A class period is considered to be one 40 to 50 minute class.

SECTION 3.2 INTRODUCTION

3.2 Plan

Whirligig Experiment
Overview

Students begin investigating what affects the time it takes the whirligig to fall. Half the groups in the class investigate how the length of the whirligig blade (surface area) affects the time it takes the whirligig to fall to the ground. The other half investigate how the number of paper clips on a whirligig's stem (mass) affects the time it takes the whirligig to fall. In this section, groups plan their experiment design and then present their design to the class. After studying everyone's designs, groups revise their own experiment designs. In the next section groups will run their experiments.

Targeted Concepts, Skills, and Nature of Science	Performance Expectations
Scientists often work together and then share their findings. Sharing findings makes new information available and helps scientists refine their ideas and build on others' ideas. When another person's or group's idea is used, credit needs to be given.	Groups should be able to work effectively together to design a plan and then share it with the class. Groups should be able to describe how the class discussion helped them to change their plan and helped others. Groups should revise their *Whirligig Experiment* plan based on what they hear and discuss during the class presentations of each groups' experiment plans.
Scientists must keep clear, accurate, and descriptive records of what they do so they can share their work with others, consider what they did, why they did it, and what they want to do next.	Students should be able to keep descriptive and accurate records of their experiment plan on their *Whirligig Experiment Planning Guide* page.
Identifying factors that lead to variation is an important part of scientific investigations.	Students should be able to describe variables as factors that influence a phenomenon being investigated.
Criteria and constraints are important in design.	Groups' experiment designs should take into account the criteria and constraints so far known to them (e.g., materials being used, explicit procedures, multiple trials, etc.).

Materials

1	per class	class *Project Board*
1	per $\frac{1}{2}$ the groups	KIT A – 3 whirligigs (long blade length, basic blade length, and short blade length); 2 paper clips (jumbo size); stopwatch; measuring tape.
1	per $\frac{1}{2}$ the groups	KIT B – whirligig (basic); 5 paper clips (jumbo size); stopwatch.
1	per student	*Whirligig Experiment Planning Guide*
1	per student	*Whirligig Experiment Planning Page*
1	per group	stopwatch

Activity Setup and Preparation

Decide where you want groups to display their experiment plans. They should be spread out enough that groups of four students can stand around the experiment plan and review it.

Homework Options

Reflection

- **Science Process:** How did you revise your investigation procedures based on what you heard in the class discussion? *(This gets students to think about what they did and what they will be doing in the next section.)*

- **Science Process:** Why is it important to make multiple trials of the same measurement? *(You cannot be sure if the results are reliable unless it is repeated many times.)*

Preparation for 3.3

- **Nature of Science:** Why do you think it is important to write down what you think will happen during the experiment? Do you think that your initial ideas (prediction) might influence how you carry out the experiment or analyze the results? How can you make sure it doesn't? *(Many students are biased toward their initial ideas and may bias the results or their analysis towards these beliefs. By being aware of what they think will happen, they can try to make sure they don't influence their results. For example, if they think it will fall faster, they may give the whirligig a push downward when they drop it and not even be aware of it.)*

1 class period ▶

3.2 Plan

Whirligig Experiment

5 min.

Introduce students to the two questions that will be the focus for their first whirligig experiment.

3.2 Plan

Whirligig Experiment

You've identified what you need to learn more about to be able to design a better whirligig. Some of the questions you came up with are about how different parts of the whirligig affect how fast it falls. It is time now to design and run experiments to answer some of those questions. You probably raised a lot of questions on the *Project Board*. Unfortunately, there is not time right now to investigate all of them. For now, you will focus on only two of them.

Materials
• whirligig template
• stopwatch
• paper clips

• How does the length of a whirligig's blades affect the time it takes the whirligig to fall to the ground?

• How does the number of paper clips on a whirligig's stem affect the time it takes the whirligig to fall to the ground?

To answer these questions, you will design and run experiments. Your group will investigate the effect of either the blade length or the number of paper clips on how long it takes the whirligig to fall to the ground. Then you will examine your results. You will try to draw some conclusions from these results to answer the questions. You can use a stopwatch for timing whirligig drops.

> **Be a Scientist**
>
> **Variables and Designing Experiments**
> When you investigate a **phenomenon**, you want to learn about the factors that influence it. In science, these factors are called **variables**. For the whirligig, the phenomenon you are studying is what affects the time it takes a whirligig to fall. The point of most experiments is to understand how one variable will affect the phenomenon you are investigating.

phenomenon: something that happens. The plural of phenomenon is phenomena. (The word comes from Latin.)

variable: a quantity whose value may change (vary) over the course of an experiment.

Design Your Experiment

Half of the class will study how the variable "blade length" affects the time it takes a whirligig to fall. The other half of the class will study how the variable "number of paper clips" affects the time it takes the whirligig to fall.

DIV 43

DIVING INTO SCIENCE

META NOTES

These two variables were chosen because they are easy to test and because it's easy to observe their effects on the time it takes a dropped whirligig to reach the ground. This introduces students to experiment design using a structured open-ended experience that won't present too many problems.

○ **Engage**

Tell students they are going to do an experiment to find the answer to two of their questions. With the class, review the *Project Board* and point out the questions in column 2 that most closely match the experiment questions – how blade length (surface area) and number of paper clips (mass) affect the time of fall. Explain that the wording may be different but these are their questions.

△ Guide

With students, compare the two questions to get students thinking about variables. Point out the similarities — how much time to fall — and the differences — blade length or number of paper clips.

META NOTES
Students might not know that a phenomenon means something that happens. Note that the singular is "phenomenon" and the plural is "phenomena."

TEACHER TALK

❝Look at the two questions as they are written in your book. Notice how they are both about how something affects the time it takes the whirligig to fall. But also see how they are different. One asks about the length of the blade and the other asks about the number of paper clips. These are things that we can change. Things that can change are called variables.❞

Then explain how variables are used in an experiment.

TEACHER TALK

❝When we drop the whirligig, it falls and we can measure how much time it takes to fall. If we vary or change something about the whirligig, such as its blade length or the number of paper clips on its stem, that might affect what happens – it might fall in less time, more time, or maybe it will take the same time. The time it takes to fall is the phenomenon we want to investigate when we vary or change the blade length or number of paper clips on the stem.❞

△ Guide

Point out that they will need to think about variables while designing their experiment to answer one of the two questions. Remind students of what they already know about procedures from the *Sandwich-Cookie Challenge*: careful planning for uniform procedures, measurements, and repeated trials.

Design Your Experiment
20 min.

Using the two questions as a focus, get student groups started on their first attempt to design an experiment.

TEACHER TALK

❝Look at the questions we are going to investigate: How does the length of the whirligig's blade affect the time it takes the whirligig to reach the ground? How does the number of paper clips on the whirligig's stem affect the time it takes the whirligig to fall to the ground? What do you think are the things we are going to intentionally change in the investigation (such as, blade length, number of paper clips)? What are we going to measure to see if it was affected by those changes we made? (The time it takes the whirligig to reach Earth.) Remember all we learned from the *Sandwich-Cookie Challenge*. We needed to make sure that we followed the same procedures each time we took a measurement and that we took more than one trial to ensure that our measurements were precise.❞

META NOTES

Designing an experiment can be challenging for students and they may struggle with this first attempt. This is why students will share and then revise their plans before running the experiment.

With your group, plan and design an experiment to answer the question that has been assigned to your group. Remember to discuss and record the following aspects of your experiment's design:

Question

What question are you investigating and answering with this experiment?

Prediction

What do you think the answer is, and why do you think that?

Variable Identification

- Which part of the whirligig will you be changing in your experiment?
- Which variable will you manipulate (change) in your experiment to test the effects of that whirligig part?
- What conditions and procedures will you keep the same (hold constant or control) in your experiment?
- What will you measure?
- How many trials will you do for each value of your manipulated variable?

Procedure and Data

Write detailed instructions for how to conduct the experiment. Include the following:

- how you will set up the whirligig
- how you drop it
- how you measure its performance
- how you record the data
- how many trials you will do

Make sure you can explain to the class why you think they will be able to trust your data.

Use a *Whirligig Experiment Planning Guide* page to plan your experiment. You will have about 15 minutes to plan. Use the hints on the planning page as a guide. Be sure to write enough in each section so that you will be able to present your experiment design to the class. The class will want to know that you've thought through all of the parts of your plan.

META NOTES

Notice the form of the experiment questions: "How does the value of the independent (manipulated) variable affect the value(s) of dependent (responding) variable(s)?" But note that you are not using this vocabulary yet. Students should experience the different kinds of variables before using the terms "dependent" and "independent."

Point out that the purpose of the *Whirligig Experiment Planning Guide* page is to help students organize their ideas so they can plan a good experiment and so they can share their experiment plan with the class for feedback. They will be able to revise their plan before they run their experiment.

Review the specifics of the planning guide with students as needed. Point out that the planning questions are there to help them think about variables and uniform procedures.

3.2

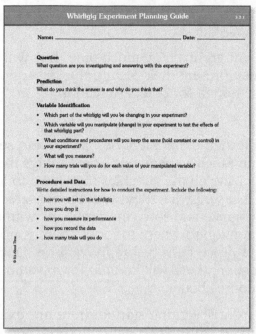

Whirligig Experiment Planning Guide   3.2.1

Name: _____   Date: _____

Question
What question are you investigating and answering with this experiment?

Prediction
What do you think the answer is and why do you think that?

Variable Identification
- Which part of the whirligig will you be changing in your experiment?
- Which variable will you manipulate (change) in your experiment to test the effects of that whirligig part?
- What conditions and procedures will you keep the same (hold constant or control) in your experiment?
- What will you measure?
- How many trials will you do for each value of your manipulated variable?

Procedure and Data
Write detailed instructions for how to conduct the experiment. Include the following:
- how you will set up the whirligig
- how you drop it
- how you measure its performance
- how you record the data
- how many trials will you do

Communicate

To help you as you learn to design experiments, you will share your experiment plan with the class. Others in the class have planned experiments to answer the same questions you are answering. You will probably see differences and similarities across these plans. In the class discussion, compare plans to each other. Notice similarities and differences. Identify the strengths of each plan. Think about what might need to be improved in each.

Revise Your Plan

With your group, revise your experiment plan based on the discussion you just had in class.

DIV 45

TEACHER TALK

"For the variable identification section, you need to think about the parts of the whirligig, which part you are changing, and how you are changing it. That is what the first three questions are about. Then you need to think about all the things you must keep the same. For example, you will want to drop the whirligig from the same place each time. What are some other things you should keep the same? How many trials will you do? Why?"

⬡ Get Going

Assign groups their investigative question.

Distribute materials and inform groups how much time they will have (10 to 15 minutes) before they present their plan to the class and that they must write their plan neatly enough for others to read it.

△ Guide

While groups are working on their experiment design, look to see if they are having difficulties planning their experiment. Some things they might have trouble with are recognizing all the variables they have to leave the same and knowing how to measure what they want to measure. The goal here is to get the kids to recognize and solve the problems with their procedures, to draw their attention to where to look. There is no need for all groups to have perfect procedures before moving on. During the upcoming *Communicate* section, there will be time for the students to help each other make their procedures better.

META NOTES

Listen for areas where they are having trouble to use in upcoming class discussions.

- If a group is having trouble getting started, here are examples of what to say: *Think about your experiment question. What are you changing? What are you going to measure? How are you going to do it?*

- If a group has not specified their procedure enough or thinks they are finished but they are not, ask questions like: *What is your procedure?* After one student answers, ask the next in the group: *Does that sound good? Is there anything else you want to add?* Then ask the next: *Is there anything changing besides the variable you're supposed to be changing?* Ask the next member: *What are you going to measure?*

☐ Assess

Note to yourself two groups for each question that you will select later to present their experiment plan to the class. Think about which groups' experiments will highlight the use of variables in their plan or a specific issue many groups are struggling with.

NOTES

....

....

....

Communicate

To help you as you learn to design experiments, you will share your experiment plan with the class. Others in the class have planned experiments to answer the same questions you are answering. You will probably see differences and similarities across these plans. In the class discussion, compare plans to each other. Notice similarities and differences. Identify the strengths of each plan. Think about what might need to be improved in each.

Communicate
15 min.

Now that students have an initial plan, lead groups in presenting their experiment plans to the class to discuss how plans can be improved.

△ Guide

Orient students to the goals of the task by telling them what they are going to do, how they are going to do it and what they are to look for. The goal of the task is to share initial plans to get feedback for improvements, come to some agreement on overall procedure (such as how to measure time or starting at the same height) and to think about what makes a good experiment plan (how variables guide planning). As students visit posters, they should consider the variables being measured, if they could carry out the procedures, and if the experiment answers the experiment question.

> **TEACHER TALK**
>
> **"**You are going to see everyone's plan and then we'll discuss it as a class. Look at how everyone's measuring their variables. Ask yourself if you could run their procedures without making mistakes, and if you think their experiment can answer the experiment question.**"**

○ Get Going

Ask groups to display their *Whirligig Experiment Planning Guide* page around the room. They should be placed so that each group can easily stand around the page and review it.

Let students know that they will have one minute to review each plan.

As students are visiting posters, review the plans and choose two groups from each question to present their plan to the class.

△ Guide

Transition students to a whole-class discussion. Remind students that the discussion is about improving our experiment plans and thinking about what makes a good plan.

> **TEACHER TALK**
>
> **"**What we'll be doing now is examining some of these plans, helping each other improve our plans, and thinking about what makes a good experiment plan. I've chosen four groups to present their experiment plans. They may have at least some small problems in them.**"**

> **META NOTES**
>
> Consider choosing four groups for presentation so that the students see two good plans (one for each question), so that they see common problems and have a chance to discuss those problems, and so that they can compare and contrast problematic portions of plans to good versions of the same thing.

Communicate
(continued)

Give students an example of what they should look for in the presented plans and what questions they should ask. List some questions to focus on the overall plans, such as, *Is this a good plan, and why?* and questions about uniform procedures and measurements, such as, *Do you think the experiment will answer the experiment question? Could you carry out the procedures? How does the plan measure the variable? Are there any other things changing besides the variable intentionally being changed?*

TEACHER TALK

"As you listen to the presentations, remember what to listen for. Could you run this procedure? If not, why not? How well does the procedure answer the question? What changes might you make? Why? How reliable do you think the results will be? How could you make them more reliable?"

Begin a discussion after each presentation. You may need to model asking a question or two for students. Then ask a student to ask a question, make sure the presenters respond to the student who asks the questions.

As students begin to take over asking questions, make sure the discussion focuses on the overall procedure and ask the questions or point out what they might forget. You could also ask more overarching questions such as, *Would you trust their answer?*

Encourage students to participate in the discussion with questions beyond those listed. Prompt them along if they hesitate and focus them if they get off track or run too long.

After the second group presents (same experiment question), begin adding in questions to compare and contrast the two experiment plans.

TEACHER TALK

"These two experiments are asking the same experiment question. Are the variables they are intentionally changing the same? What about the variables they are measuring? How are their procedures the same? How are they different?"

After all four presentations, compare the four experiment plans and guide the discussion to what makes a good procedure and think about variables. Begin with questions about how the plans are similar.

META NOTES

TEACHER TALK

"You've now heard all four experiment plans. Two experiment plans deal with the question of how the blade length affects how long it takes the whirligig to drop to Earth and two are about how the number of paper clips on the whirligig stem affect the time it takes the whirligig to fall to Earth. Although these experiments are different, there are things that are similar between the two. Let's look at the procedures. What is similar in all the procedures and how important is it? (For example, in more than one trial, some variables that are held constant like the height, the whirligig is dropped from should be the same each time.) What are some of the things that are kept the same in all the experiment plans? (For example, height and how time of fall is measured.)"

META NOTES

Expectations for a discussion – students will need support to ask questions and to not just ask the same question to every group. They need support to word questions as inquiries not accusations, and to use feedback as help.

Then move on to questions about how the plans are different and whether the differences are appropriate or should be modified to be uniform. Help students understand that the appropriate differences are directly related to the different questions, i.e., the independent variable of blade length or number of paper clips.

Wrap up the discussion by having students decide as a class what ideas groups should use to revise their plans.

META NOTES

Listen for ideas about procedures and variables. Listen for skills in sharing ideas, asking questions, and responding to peers.

NOTES

META NOTES

Remember it is important for students to lead the discussion and for you to guide the discussion so that it stays on the topic and moves toward the goal. At this point students probably do not have a lot of skills on how to participate in a discussion – you will have to model for them at times and guide them with helpful questions or suggestions at others.

Revise Your Plan

5 min.

Taking ideas from the whole-class discussion, have students return to their groups to revise their plans.

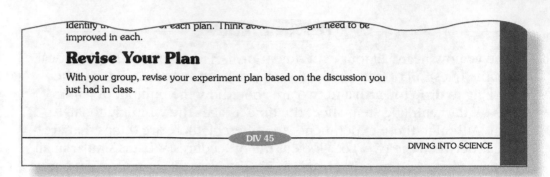

Identify t... ...of each plan. Think abo... ...ght need to be improved in each.

Revise Your Plan

With your group, revise your experiment plan based on the discussion you just had in class.

DIV 45

DIVING INTO SCIENCE

△ **Guide**

Ask groups to revise their plans based on everything they have heard during the discussion and tell them they will be running the experiment in the next section.

◇ **Evaluate**

Make sure each group has a plan that is safe and ready to run. See if groups are appropriately using feedback and ideas from the class discussion. For example, the class may have decided that everyone needs to do three trials for each value of their variable.

NOTES

....

....

....

....

....

....

....

....

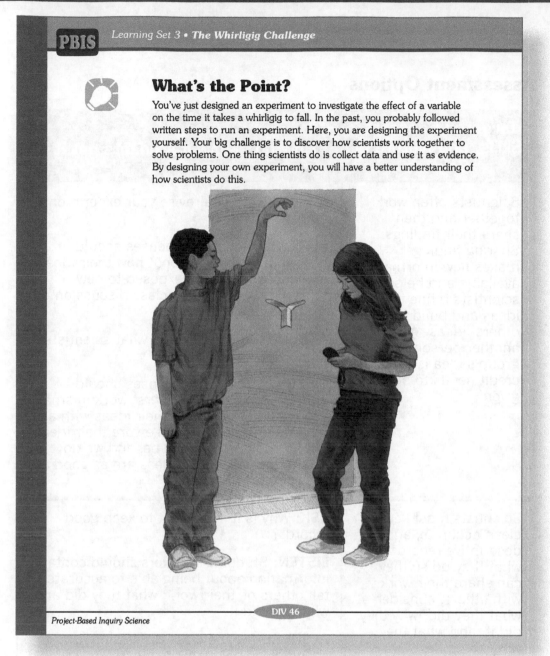

What's the Point?

You've just designed an experiment to investigate the effect of a variable on the time it takes a whirligig to fall. In the past, you probably followed written steps to run an experiment. Here, you are designing the experiment yourself. Your big challenge is to discover how scientists work together to solve problems. One thing scientists do is collect data and use it as evidence. By designing your own experiment, you will have a better understanding of how scientists do this.

What's the Point?

5 min.

It is important that students understand that scientists do experiments to collect data that will help them answer important questions. It can be challenging to design a good experiment.

META NOTES

You may be able to go to the next section without discussion here.

Assessment Options

Targeted Concepts, Skills, and Nature of Science	How do I know if students got it?
Scientists often work together and then share their findings. Sharing findings makes new information available and helps scientists refine their ideas and build on others' ideas. When another person's or group's idea is used, credit needs to be given.	**ASK:** Why did you revise your experiment plan? **LISTEN:** Students' responses should contain information about how their ideas evolved as they were exposed to new information during the class discussion of the experiment plans. **ASK:** Do you think we did what scientists do? **LISTEN:** Students' responses should contain: "Yes, scientists first work in small groups and then share their ideas with a larger community to make sure their ideas are as good as they can be, and we do this to make sure our ideas are as good as they can be."
Scientists must keep clear, accurate, and descriptive records of what they do so they can share their work with others, consider what they did, why they did it, and what they want to do next.	**ASK:** Why is it important to keep good records? **LISTEN:** Students' answers should contain information about being able to accurately tell others of their work: what they did and why they did it. **ALSO:** During the class discussion groups should have been able to clearly describe their initial procedure.
Identifying factors that lead to variation is an important part of scientific investigations.	**ASK:** Students why it is important to identify variables in scientific investigations. **LISTEN:** It is O.K. if students don't have a complete answer to this yet, they will learn more about this in the next section. However, some students may be able to describe how you deliberately change one variable, measure another variable's response to that change, and try to keep everything the same otherwise.

Teacher Reflection Questions

- What difficulties did students have in identifying what makes a good experiment question, prediction, or plan? What do you think will help students in these areas?

- What difficulties did students have working in small groups and holding presentations and discussions in larger communities? Have these improved since they started this Unit?

- In the next section students will run their experiments. What difficulties do you expect and how could you use these as tools for learning?

NOTES

SECTION 3.3 INTRODUCTION

3.3 Investigate

2 class periods * ▶

Experiment with a Whirligig

Overview

Students now run the experiment they designed in the previous section to determine how blade length (surface area) and number of paper clips (mass) affect the time of fall of the whirligig. Groups present their experimental results on posters during their first *Investigation Expo*. Students explore the idea of a fair test and the different types of variables (independent, dependent, and control), while preparing for their presentation and evaluating others' results. Like scientists, students share and learn from each other's observations and ideas about the whirligig.

*A class period is considered to be one 40 to 50 minute class.

Targeted Concepts, Skills, and Nature of Science	Performance Expectations
Scientists often work together and then share their findings. Sharing findings makes new information available and helps scientists refine their ideas and build on others' ideas. When another person's or group's idea is used, credit needs to be given.	Students should be able to describe their ideas about what affects the time it takes a whirligig to fall, and how they now think they could make the whirligig fall more slowly.
	Students should be able to describe how their ideas changed because of another group's ideas or critiques, and they should be able to give credit for ideas they are using or building on.
	Students should be able to describe the benefits of working with others during the experiment and then sharing the ideas with the class during the *Investigation Expo*.
	At this point students should realize that this style of discussing ideas with a few people first and then sharing ideas with a larger group, is a common social practice in science.
Scientists must keep clear, accurate, and descriptive records of what they do so they can share their work with others and consider what they did, why they did it, and what they want to do next.	Students should be able to describe their experiment procedure, results, and ideas during their class presentation by using their experiment page.

162

Targeted Concepts, Skills, and Nature of Science	Performance Expectations
Identifying factors that lead to variation is an important part of scientific investigations.	Students should be able to identify variables that may affect their experiment and describe ways to keep these variables constant.
Scientific investigations and measurements are considered reliable if the results are repeatable by other scientists using the same procedures.	Although students conducted different experiments, the groups testing the same question should have similar conclusions. Students should be able to recognize this as a way of affirming that their conclusions or claims are reliable.
In a fair test only the manipulated (independent) variable and the responding (dependent) variable change. All other variables are held constant.	Students should be able to describe what a fair test is, and what the manipulated, responding, and control variables are in their experiment.
Criteria and constraints are important in design.	Students' experiment design should account for the criteria and constraints of an experiment.

Materials

1	per student	*Whirligig Experiment Results* page
1	per $\frac{1}{2}$ the groups	KIT A – 3 whirligigs (long blade length, basic blade length, and short blade length); 2 paper clips (jumbo size); stopwatch; measuring tape.
1	per $\frac{1}{2}$ the groups	KIT B – whirligig (basic); 5 paper clips (jumbo size); stopwatch.
1	per group	poster paper and markers
1	per classroom	safety scissors
1	per group	stopwatch

Activity Setup and Preparation

- Read the *Teacher's Resource Guide* pages on the *Whirligig Experiment Results Guide* and *Investigation Expo*. Students are introduced to both of these during this activity. These will be used throughout the PBIS curriculum. Decide how you want to present these to the class.

- Prepare the whirligig kits. The whirligig templates are located in the Blackline Masters. To save class time, you should cut out the whirligigs.

- Decide how you want to arrange the *Investigation Expo*. You should have groups display their posters around the room, perhaps grouped by experiment question, and let the class circulate around the room. At least two groups present for each experiment question and all groups should participate in the discussion.

Homework Options

Reflection

- **Science Process:** What is a fair test? Describe how your experiment was or was not a fair test and why. *(Student responses should include that a fair test is one in which things that are being compared are tested under the same conditions, and that the test matches the question being asked.)*

- **Science Process:** Describe what independent (manipulated), dependent (responding), and control variables are and give examples of these using your experiment. *(Students should recognize that the independent variable is the variable the experimenter changes, the dependent variable is the variable the experimenter measures, and a control variable is a variable that the experimenter keeps from changing.)*

- **Science Process:** Why is it important to control certain variables in an experiment? How do you know which variables to control? *(It is important to control variables you are not interested in testing so that you can assure the results you observe are not due to those variables. The control variables are the ones not being tested.)*

Preparation for 3.4

- **Science Content:** If you dropped a whirligig and a book from the same height at the same time, the whirligig would take longer to reach the ground. Why do you think this happens? Think about surface area and the mass of both the book and the whirligig. What is the whirligig interacting with besides Earth? *(From this, the students should realize that the whirligig falls toward Earth because of the gravitational pull between Earth and the whirligig. Students may not realize that the whirligig takes longer to reach Earth than the book. It does because air resistance affects the falling whirligig more prominently than the book. Students will read about the science behind this in the next section. Eliciting their responses here will help you guide them during the next section.)*

SECTION 3.3 IMPLEMENTATION

3.3 Investigate

Experiment with a Whirligig

Materials
- cutout whirligigs
- stopwatch
- paper clips

Run Your Experiment

It is time to run your whirligig experiment. Use the materials given in the list. You will run the experiment, analyze your data, and then report your results to other groups.

Recording Your Work

As you do the experiment, record your results on your *Whirligig Experiment Results Guide* page. These pages have guidelines on them. They will help you with each task you need to do. Look at the guidelines for hints.

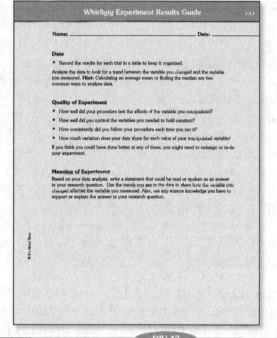

Whirligig Experiment Results Guide

Name: _____ Date: _____

Date
- Record the results for each trial in a table to keep it organized.

Analyze the data to look for a trend between the variable you changed and the variable you measured. **Hint:** Calculating an average mean or finding the median are two common ways to analyze data.

Quality of Experiment
- How well did your procedure test the effects of the variable you manipulated?
- How well did you control the variables you needed to hold constant?
- How consistently did you follow your procedure each time you ran it?
- How much variation does your data show for each value of your manipulated variable?

If you think you could have done better at any of these, you might need to redesign or re-do your experiment.

Meaning of Experiment
Based on your data analysis, write a statement that could be read or spoken as an answer to your research question. Use the trends you see in the data to show how the variable you changed affected the variable you measured. Also, use any science knowledge you have to support or explain the answer to your research question.

DIV 47

DIVING INTO SCIENCE

⚠ Be sure to have your teacher check your plan before you conduct any experiment.

3.3 Investigate

Experiment with a Whirligig

Run Your Experiment
15 min.

Have groups run their experiments to see how the number of paper clips on the stem or the blade length affect the time it takes the whirligig to fall.

*A class period is considered to be one 40 to 50 minute class.

◯ Engage

Remind students of the goal: to figure out for the cereal company how to build a whirligig that fits on the back of a cereal box and falls as slowly as possible.

⬡ Get Going

First, let students know how they are going to record each of their trials in a table to keep the data organized. After collecting their data, students will analyze it. Remind students that as part of their analysis they should calculate the average (mean) of each set of trials. They will then look for trends (patterns or a tendency) in their data. They will be looking for what happens to the falling time as they increase blade length or number of paper clips.

META NOTES

The average (mean) is the sum of all trials of the same measurement divided by the number of trials. If one trial is very, very different from the others, then there was probably a mistake in the measurement and this value should be recorded but not used in calculating the average. If time allows, students should redo that trial.

Run Your Experiment (continued)

META NOTES

Students may not understand the term *manipulated variable* at this time. Remind them that the *manipulated variable* is what they intentionally change.

Then tell students that they will also have to determine the quality of their experiment. There are a set of questions to guide them on the *Whirligig Experiment Results Guide* page. Distribute this page if you haven't yet. Go through the set of questions on the page and emphasize that they will need to have a clear set of procedures. Let groups know that after they check the quality of their experiment, they may feel they need to redesign their experiment. Before they run their new experiment you must check it, guiding students as needed and making sure it is safe. After you have approved their new experiment, they may run it.

TEACHER TALK

❝To determine the quality of your experiment, you will need to answer the four questions listed on the *Whirligig Experiment Results Guide* page. For example, for the second question you might have felt that you didn't make sure that the whirligig was dropped from the same height each time and you may want to add that to your experiment procedures. Perhaps your results had a lot of variation in it and didn't show any pattern or trend because of this. In this case, the quality of your experiment was not very good and you should rewrite your procedures to clearly specify that the whirligig is dropped from the same height each time you drop it. So, you would rewrite your procedures and call me over to make sure everything is O.K. Then, after I give the O.K., you should run your revised experiment and complete the *Whirligig Experiment Results Guide* page for your new experiment. Make sure you also leave your old results on the sheet.❞

Let the class know that after they record their data, analyze it, and check for the quality of their experiment. Then they will have a class discussion to help them with the meaning of the experiment. Tell students how much time they will have to work with their group (about 10 minutes). If they have extra time, they should discuss the meaning of their results, but they should not write anything down yet.

△ Guide

META NOTES

Not all variables can be held constant, like air currents. However, these variables can be minimized so that their effects are negligible.

While groups are running their experiments, circulate around the room looking at their data. If results have a lot of variation in them, it is an indicator that they are either not being consistent in their procedure or they are not keeping the other variable. Assist students in creating consistent procedures in which only the manipulated variable is intentionally changed and all other variables (besides the time of flight) are held constant.

Also, guide groups with analyzing their data as needed. Prompt them to average their trials for each blade length or number of paper clips. Ask students to look at what happens to the dependent variable (time of fall) as the manipulated variable (blade length or paper clips) is increased or decreased. Ask groups if they see a pattern or trend.

Experiment Results Guide page. These pages have guidelines on them. They will help you with each task you need to do. Look at the guidelines for hints.

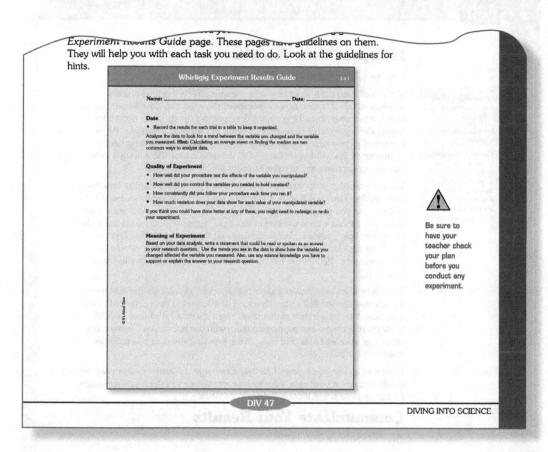

Whirligig Experiment Results Guide　3.3.1

Name: _____　Date: _____

Date

• Record the results for each trial in a table to keep it organized.

Analyze the data to look for a trend between the variable you changed and the variable you measured. **Hint:** Calculating an average mean or finding the median are two common ways to analyze data.

Quality of Experiment

• How well did your procedure test the effects of the variable you manipulated?

• How well did you control the variables you needed to hold constant?

• How consistently did you follow your procedure each time you ran it?

• How much variation does your data show for each value of your manipulated variable?

If you think you could have done better at any of these, you might need to redesign or re-do your experiment.

Meaning of Experiment

Based on your data analysis, write a statement that could be read or spoken as an answer to your research question. Use the trends you see in the data to show how the variable you changed affected the variable you measured. Also, use any science knowledge you have to support or explain the answer to your research question.

Be sure to have your teacher check your plan before you conduct any experiment.

DIV 47

DIVING INTO SCIENCE

If all the groups seem to have similar problems, then you should stop the class and discuss the problem as a class.

◇ Evaluate

When all groups have completed what they think to be a quality experiment, move on to the next section.

NOTES

....

....

....

....

....

Interpret Your Results

10 min.

Now that students have collected their data and checked the quality of their experiment, explain how to make a claim based on trends in their data.

Interpret Your Results

Finding Trends and Making Claims

interpret: to find the meaning of something.

trend: a pattern or a tendency.

claim: a statement of what you understand or a conclusion that you have reached from an investigation or set of investigations.

You've collected data about how your variable affects the time it takes a whirligig to fall. It is time now to **interpret** those results. To interpret means to figure out what something means. Interpreting results of an experiment means identifying what happens as a result of changing a variable. What happened as you added paper clips? What happened as you lengthened or shortened the whirligig's blades? Did the time it took the whirligig to fall increase or decrease as the value of your variable increased?

You'll do two things to interpret your results. First, you'll identify **trends** in your results. Then you'll state a **claim** based on those trends. A trend is a pattern that you can see over several examples. A claim is your statement about what those trends mean. For example, suppose you varied the width of the whirligig's blades. You would find that the whirligig takes less time to fall, as the blades get narrower. This is a trend. Your claim would be your statement: "When the blades are narrower, the whirligig takes less time to fall."

Every time a scientist makes a claim, other scientists look for the evidence the scientist has for that claim. One kind of evidence is data collected in an experiment and the trends in that data. You'll spend a lot of time in PBIS Units making claims and supporting them with evidence. You'll learn more about that in other Units. For now, make sure that the data you collected matches your claim.

Make sure to record on your *Whirligig Experiment Results Guide* page the trends you see in your data. Also include any claims you think you can make so that you can share them with your classmates.

Communicate Your Results

Investigation Expo

You will share what you've found with the class in an *Investigation Expo*.

Remember, no groups in the class investigated both variables. Therefore, others will need your results to complete the challenge. They will rely on your report to design a better whirligig.

○ Engage

Begin the class discussion by reminding students of the challenge — to build a slow-falling whirligig. Connect this with their experiment by letting them know that now is the time to figure out what their data means and how it might apply to the challenge. Let students know that it is important to support their ideas with reasons.

△ Guide

First, use an example like the one on the next page to make sure everyone was able to analyze their results. Students should have done multiple trials for each condition they are measuring and then calculate the average of those trials. Students should have considered all the averages of their data and looked for a trend.

META NOTES

If your class is familiar with graphing then you may want students to graph their data. Graphing helps students visualize the data and identify trends.

"Imagine my experiment is designed to answer the question: *When decreasing the blade width what happens to the time it takes the whirligig to fall from a fixed height above the ground?* In my experiment, I used three different blade widths. For each blade width (slim, medium, and wide) I dropped the whirligig from the same height and measured the time it took to reach the ground. For each blade width, I dropped it four or five times and then calculate the average of those trials. When I looked at my data I saw that as the blades got narrower, the time it took for the whirligig to reach the ground decreased. This is a trend."

If your students had trouble with averaging or looking for trends you might want to use sample data with your imaginary experiment. This will make your example more concrete and you can work through the mathematics together with your students.

Then explain how to make a claim based on a trend in their data. Model for students the steps and thought process involved by walking them through an example such as the one below.

"Recall my example of the experiment that asked how decreasing the blade width affects the time it takes the whirligig to fall from a fixed height above the ground. My claim is for this experiment is: When the blades are narrower, the whirligig takes less time to fall. This is supported by my data that shows that as the blade width goes from wide, to medium to slim, the time decreases from say 10 seconds to 8 seconds to 7 seconds. If someone asked me how I know my claim is reasonable, I could point to my data and show them the trend."

Students often confuse evidence and opinion when supporting their ideas. Scientific claims, however, are statements based on trends in a set of observations. These claims are based only on the data and do not contain opinions. If students bring in an opinion, guide them back to their data.

⚪ Get Going

Now that you have explained what a claim is, ask groups to discuss the meaning (or interpretation) of their data.

Tell students that the claim their group decides on should answer the experiment question and should be based on their data and their science knowledge.

You may want to ask students to also write what their claim might imply for the *Whirligig Challenge*.

Remind the students that they will be presenting their experiment and their claim to the class.

☐ Assess

While groups are working, listen for their ideas about trends and claims. Note any areas that should be discussed when groups communicate their results.

Communicate Your Results

Investigation Expo
40 min.

Lead student in their first Investigation Expo *to share their experimental results, interpretations, and claims on posters.*

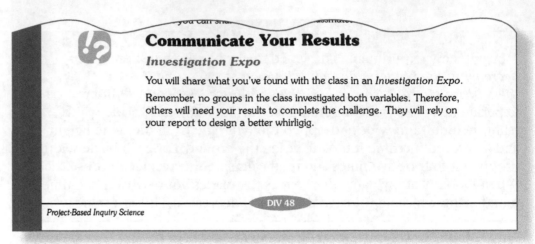

Communicate Your Results

Investigation Expo

You will share what you've found with the class in an *Investigation Expo*.

Remember, no groups in the class investigated both variables. Therefore, others will need your results to complete the challenge. They will rely on your report to design a better whirligig.

DIV 48

Project-Based Inquiry Science

△ Guide

First, describe an *Investigation Expo*. It is similar to other presentations but it is designed for sharing information about investigations. Explain that there are two parts: poster presentations and then discussions to share their procedure, results, and interpretations. Emphasize that the student text has all this information and that they should refer to the student text while they are preparing for the *Investigation Expo* (pages 49 and 50 in the student text.)

TEACHER TALK

❝Throughout this class you will be using *Investigation Expos* to share ideas. During an *Investigation Expo,* you behave like scientists sharing their results and their ideas. After we discuss everyone's ideas you will then have a chance to reflect on what you have heard and refine your ideas.❞

Point out the bulleted list and emphasize that students will need to be able to inform the class of their investigative question, their predictions, their procedure and what makes the procedure a fair test (to be discussed next), their results and how confident they are of them, and their interpretations and their confidence in their interpretations. Emphasize also that they should be able to inform the class of their claims. Remind students that a claim is a statement of what a trend means or a conclusion of an experiment.

Fair tests compare things under the same conditions. For an experiment to be a fair test, you want to be sure that the only variables significantly changing are those you intentionally change (blade length or number of paper clips) and the variable that you are measuring in response to that change (time of flight). Of course, you cannot take into account all potential variables, such as air currents, but you should minimize them as much as possible so that they are not a significant factor in your results. You need to make sure as many other variables as possible are kept the same. For example, the height at which you drop the whirligig, or how you are measuring the time of flight.

Be a Scientist

Introducing an *Investigation Expo*

An *Investigation Expo* is like other presentations you've done. However, it is specially designed to help you present results of an investigation. You will include your procedure, results, and interpretations of results.

Scientists present results of investigations to other scientists. This lets the other scientists build on what was learned. You will do the same thing.

There are several things scientists usually want to know about investigations. These include the following:

- questions you were trying to answer in your investigation
- your predictions
- the procedure and what makes it a **fair test**
- your results and how confident you are about them
- your interpretation of the results and how confident you are of it.

To prepare for an *Investigation Expo*, make a poster that includes all of the five items listed above. Present them in a way that will make it easy for someone to look at your poster. Others should be able to identify what you've done and what you found out. If you don't think you ran a fair test as you had planned, your poster should also have a report on how you would change your procedure if you had a chance to run the experiment again.

Sometimes scientists make posters when they present their investigations and results. They set up their poster in a large room where other scientists have also set up their posters. Then other scientists walk around the room. They look at the posters and talk to the scientists who did the investigations. Another way scientists share results is by making presentations. For presentations, they stand in front of a room of scientists. They talk about their investigations and results. They usually include visuals (pictures) showing all the important parts of their procedures and results. They talk while they show the visuals. Then other scientists ask them questions.

Your *Investigation Expos* will combine these practices. Sometimes, each group will formally present their results to the class. Sometimes, each group will put their poster on the wall for everyone to walk around and read. In this *Expo*, because you investigated only two variables, every group will put their posters on the wall. The class will look at all the posters. Then two groups will make presentations to the class. One will present for each variable investigated.

> *Investigation Expo*: a presentation of the procedure, results, and interpretations of results of an investigation.
>
> **fair test**: things that are being compared are being tested under the same conditions, and the test matches the question being asked.

TEACHER TALK

"A fair test is when you compare things under the same conditions. For example, if I were to drop a single coffee filter and seven stacked coffee filters to see how mass affects the time it takes the coffee filters to fall, then I would have to drop them from the same height and at the same time. It would not be a fair test if I dropped the single filter from a higher or lower position. Similarly, I would want to be sure that I measured the time of flight in the same way. But, it would be really difficult for me to make sure that there were not air currents or that they were the same at all times."

TEACHER TALK

"So, what I need to do is make sure the doors and windows are closed and the air conditioning and/or heating is not on so that I can minimize the effect of air currents. Then, although it might change, it is so small that it does not significantly affect my measurements. Of course, when I write up my results I'll have to mention all of this."

○ Get Going

Tell students that each group will be making a poster for the *Investigation Expo* and that they should keep in mind the bulleted list in their books (page 49). Show students an example of the poster sheet and point out the spaces for the investigative question, predictions, procedure and what makes it a fair test, results and how confident you are in them, interpretations of the results and how confident you are of these interpretations, and your claims which are statements about what a trend means.

Also point out the bulleted list of ideas the audience will be listening for about their investigation so they can keep these in mind as they prepare.

Distribute poster materials.

Investigation Question:	
Predictions:	
Procedures: **Is your experiment a fair test? If so, what makes it a fair test?** **If not, what would make it a fair test?**	
What you measured and how good your measurements are	**Trends in your data**
Interpretation of your results and how good you think they are	
Claims	

△ Guide

As groups are working on their posters and preparing for their presentations, assist them as needed. Some issues that may arise are listed below.

- Students might have trouble deciding on how to determine the confidence in their results. They can base this on the quality of their experiment (how consistently they ran their procedures, how they controlled variables, how much variation was in their data, and if the procedure answered the experiment question).

- Students might not completely understand a fair test. You could describe it as only allowing two variables in their experiment to change: the variable they intentionally change (manipulated variable) and the one they measure in response to it (responding variable).

- Students might include opinions in their interpretations or claims. Ask them if the claim is directly supported by their data or if something more is in their claim.

- Students might be using science knowledge incorrectly or incorrect information that they think is accepted science knowledge.

Remind groups that everything they show on their poster or say in their presentation will have to be clear so that others can understand and follow their thinking.

NOTES

....

....

....

....

....

....

....

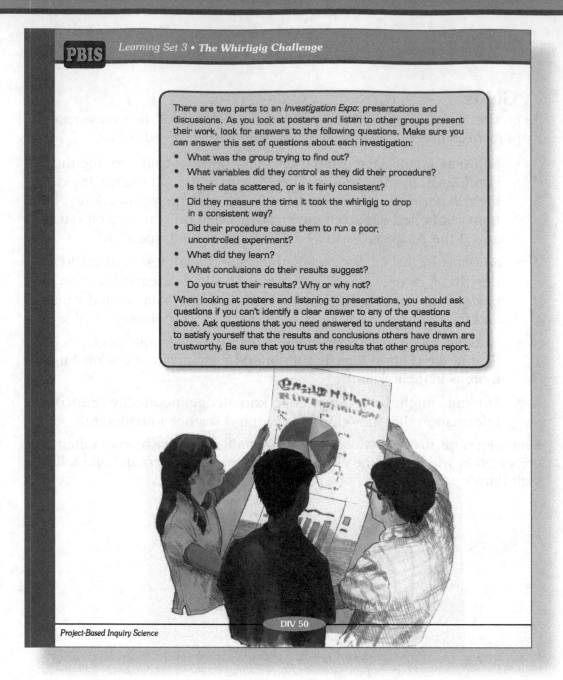

There are two parts to an *Investigation Expo*: presentations and discussions. As you look at posters and listen to other groups present their work, look for answers to the following questions. Make sure you can answer this set of questions about each investigation:

- What was the group trying to find out?
- What variables did they control as they did their procedure?
- Is their data scattered, or is it fairly consistent?
- Did they measure the time it took the whirligig to drop in a consistent way?
- Did their procedure cause them to run a poor, uncontrolled experiment?
- What did they learn?
- What conclusions do their results suggest?
- Do you trust their results? Why or why not?

When looking at posters and listening to presentations, you should ask questions if you can't identify a clear answer to any of the questions above. Ask questions that you need answered to understand results and to satisfy yourself that the results and conclusions others have drawn are trustworthy. Be sure that you trust the results that other groups report.

☐ Assess

As you are visiting groups, decide on which two groups from each experiment you wish to present. You may want to choose the groups that did not present their experiment plan in the previous section or you may want to pick groups that have very good examples or that have difficulties with fair tests or variables identification.

◇ Evaluate

Before moving on, check to see if groups have completed the items required for their poster and ask them if they are ready for presentations. For the posters, students should describe what makes or what would make their experiment a fair test. They should note if their measurements are good based on how clustered their trials are and on the trend in their data. Their interpretation of results should agree with the trend in their data. Their claims should be supported by the data and contain no opinions and nothing that the data does not explicitly and directly support. If they are using science knowledge in their interpretations it must be correct.

⬡ Get Going

Now that students have prepared their posters and presentations, they are ready to review each other's posters. Remind the class that for each poster they will need to look for what claims are being made and if they are believable. They can use the bulleted lists (pages 49 and 50) to help them ask questions. While viewing posters they should record questions they have for each group. They will have an opportunity to ask questions when groups present their experiment results.

Have each group display their posters around the room (see *Activity Setup and Preparation*), and allow everyone to view each poster for a minute or so to become familiar with each groups' work.

Let students know that they will have about one minute to review each plan.

As students are viewing posters, review the plans and choose two groups from each question to present their poster to the class.

△ Guide a Class Discussion

Transition the class to a whole-class discussion.

Remind students that during the presentations they should be listening for descriptions of the investigation and claims. If they are unclear about the investigation or the claim they should ask questions of the presenting group. Emphasize that they should pay particular attention to consistent procedures and whether or not the experiment is a fair test.

Inform the two groups you selected for each experiment that they will be presenting. You should have the groups doing the blade experiment present first, followed by the groups doing the paper clip experiment. Remind students to provide their reasoning, describing why their experiment is or is not a fair test, and whether their results are in agreement or disagreement with the other results that have already been presented.

META NOTES

There will be a class discussion after each group presents. The first two groups presenting should have the same experiment question so that you can compare the two plans for the same experiment. After all four groups present, you should compare experiment plans across experiments.

△ Guide Presentations and Discussions

Begin a short discussion after each presentation. Students should have an easier time leading the discussion since they have practiced discussions in the last section. Assist students with some of the language needed by modeling it for them or asking questions that guide them.

TEACHER TALK

" • Do you agree with what ... said? Why or why not?

• I agree with .... because....

• I don't understand the reasoning behind your interpretation of your results. Could you start from showing the data and the trend?

• Why is this a fair test? What things did you change deliberately? What did you measure? Did anything else vary? What things did you make sure stayed the same?"

After the **first pair** of groups presents (same experiment question), ask questions to compare and contrast the experiment results and procedures.

TEACHER TALK

"These two experiments are asking the same question. Do the results indicate the same thing? That is, do they both show the same trend? Do they follow the same procedures? How are they the same? How are they different? Are they fair tests? "

Then ask the class if they had questions about any of the posters involving this experiment question. Encourage discussion between groups while noting areas of difficulty students are having.

Point out that sometimes you cannot trust results because the procedures were not done in the same way, or because the experiment was not a fair test.

Be a Scientist

Different Kinds of Variables

As you designed and ran your experiment, there were several kinds of variables you worked with:

- One you changed or varied in your experiment. This is called the **independent variable** (or **manipulated variable**).

- Some were ones you worked hard to keep the same (constant) during every trial. These are called **control variables**.

- Some were ones that you measured in response to changing the manipulated variable. These are called **dependent variables** (or **responding variables**). Their value is dependent on the value of the independent or manipulated variable.

Experiments are a very important part of science. When scientists design experiments, they think about the things that might have an effect on what could happen. Then they identify the one thing they want to find out more about. They choose this thing as their independent (manipulated) variable. This is the one they change to see what happens. They must keep everything else in the procedure the same. The variables they keep the same, or hold constant, are control variables. Finally, there is a set of things that they measure. This is the dependent (responding) variable. If they have designed a fair test, then they can assume that changes in the dependent (responding) variables result from changes made to the independent (manipulated) variable.

When you ran your whirligig experiments to find out the effects of the number of paper clips on how a whirligig falls, your independent (manipulated) variable was the number of paper clips attached to the stem. Your dependent (responding) variable was the time it took a whirligig to fall. Everything else, including the shape of the blades, the length of the stem, the height from which the whirligig was dropped, and the way the time to the ground was measured were the control variables. To be sure that what was measured (the dependent or responding variable) was dependent on what was changed (the independent or manipulated variable), it was important to keep the controlled variables exactly the same every time the whirligig was dropped.

independent (manipulated) variable: in an experiment, the variable that the scientist intentionally changes.

control variables: in an experiment, the variables that are kept constant (not changed).

dependent (responding) variables: in an experiment, the variables whose values are measured. Scientists measure how these variables respond to changes they make in a manipulated variable.

META NOTES

Students often have a difficult time distinguishing between the types of variables. Often times they think the manipulated (independent) variable is a controlled variable because they control its values.

DIV 51

DIVING INTO SCIENCE

TEACHER TALK

"As I walked around while you were working, I noticed that group X was running their experiment like …. I noticed that they made sure they ran their experiment the same way each time. How do you think that affected their results? What would have happened if they hadn't worked that way?"

This is a good time to talk about the types of variables. Using one of the presented experiments, point out the manipulated variable (blade length) and the responding variable (time of fall). Then point out all of the control variables that could have been changed but were not (height, paper clips, etc.).

Then discuss the claims made by the groups and how confident they are of their claims. Students should be confident if their claims are based on the trends of their data and if their data results from a fair test in which procedures were followed consistently. Compare the claims of both groups. Although groups will not have identical data, they should see similar trends in their data resulting in similar claims.

META NOTES

When changing the blade length, the mass of the whirligig changes, but this is negligible.

TEACHER TALK

"Let's consider the claims. How do we determine if the claim is good? Do you trust the claims the groups made? Why or why not? Do you think we can make a claim based on both experiments?"

Then point out that scientists call claims valid if many different groups see similar trends when they are investigating the same variables (e.g., blade length and time of fall).

After the **second pair** of groups present, ask questions to compare across all four experiments. This is a good time to re-examine fair test, variables, and believable claims.

Point out to students that there are two claims that were made today because there were two fair tests conducted. The first claim is about blade length: Increasing the whirligig's blade length increases the time it takes the whirligig to reach the ground. The second claim is about the number of paper clips: Increasing the number of paper clips on the whirligig decreases the time it takes a whirligig to reach the ground.

Students can also begin to use some of the new language, specifically *independent (manipulated) variable, dependent (responding) variable,* and *control variable.* At this point students should have a good idea of what these variables mean, but they still will be unfamiliar with the scientific terminology. Remember knowing the terminology is not as important as understanding the meaning.

PBIS | *Learning Set 3 • The Whirligig Challenge*

Reflect

Answer the following questions. Then discuss your answers and how they may help you better achieve the *Whirligig Challenge* with your class.

1. What variable were you investigating in your experiment? What were you investigating about that variable? How did you vary it to determine its effects?

2. List all of the variables you tried to hold constant in your experiment.

3. How many trials did you perform? Explain why you performed that number of trials. Was this a good number of trials?

4. How consistent was your set of data? Why is consistency in repeated trials important in an experiment?

5. Do you think that the data set you collected was useful in determining the effect your variable had on the fall of the whirligig? Explain why or why not.

6. What do you think you now know about how things fall that would allow you to design a better whirligig than the one you started with? Do you know enough to explain your results?

What's the Point?

You have just investigated how a variable affects the time it takes a whirligig to fall to the ground. You then presented your results in an *Investigation Expo*. In your experiment, you only investigated one possible variable. You needed to rely on other groups to get the data you needed for the other variable. This is the way scientists work. Presenting results of investigations to other scientists is one of the most important things they do. This lets other scientists build on what they learned.

You interpreted the data from your investigation. The trends you found and the claim you made will help you in achieving the *Whirligig Challenge*.

Reflect

15 min.

Wrap up the class discussion by having students reflect on their own experiments, fair tests, and believable claims and how their claims will help answer the Whirligig Challenge.

△ Guide

Transition students to rethink their individual investigations and the challenge.

TEACHER TALK

"In our *Investigation Expo* we reviewed everyone's results on posters, listened to four presentations, and discussed some important ideas like consistent results and fair tests. Now it's time to think about how all you know now pertains to your own experiments and to the challenge.**"**

○ Get Going

Ask groups to come up with their best group responses to the six questions.

Let groups know how much time they have for answering the questions. You should give no more than 10 minutes.

☐ Assess and Guide

Hold a discussion using the information provided below and guide students using questions that lead them to the essential part of the answer. Answers to some or all of questions 1-4 might have come up during the post-presentation discussion. Use these questions and responses to lead students to think about questions 5 and 6. Spend most of the discussion time focused on why their data is useful (question 5) and how they might now be able to design a better whirligig (question 6).

Reflect

Answer the following questions. Then discuss your answers and how they may help you better achieve the *Whirligig Challenge* with your class.

1. What variable were you investigating in your experiment? What were you investigating about that variable? How did you vary it to determine its effects?

2. List all of the variables you tried to hold constant in your experiment.

3. How many trials did you perform? Explain why you performed that number of trials. Was this a good number of trials?

4. How consistent was your set of data? Why is consistency in repeated trials important in an experiment?

5. Do you think that the data set you collected was useful in determining the effect your variable had on the fall of the whirligig? Explain why or why not.

6. What do you think you now know about how things fall that would allow you to design a better whirligig than the one you started with? Do you know enough to explain your results?

Assess student understanding of what they were investigating, the variables involved, and what made their results trustworthy. Then use these to assist students in recognizing how their experiments will help them solve the challenge of building a slow-falling whirligig. Student responses should contain the following:

1. Either blade length or number of paper clips and how it affected the time of fall, increased it or decreased it from ... to ....

2. Both experiments could list the following: blade width, height dropped from, procedures, stem length, and stem width. The blade length experiment could also list the number of paper clips. The paper clip experiment could also list the blade length.

3. The number of trials (at least three) should be enough to show consistency in their measurement of time. If a lot of trials are taken and the results are not consistent, it indicates a problem with the procedures or measuring tools.

4. It is important that there be consistency in repeated trials to ensure that the measurements are reliable.

5. If the experiment was a fair test and the trials were consistent for each measurement, then the data set is useful. There should be a trend showing an increase in time of fall for increased blade length, and a decrease in time of fall for increased number of paper clips.

   It may help students if you generalize this: If data shows a trend increasing, decreasing, or staying the same, those all indicate a relationship between the manipulated variable and the responding variable and that information is useful for the challenge.

6. This is the key part of the reflection. For the first part (designing a better whirligig) Students should note that the paper clips are needed for stability of the fall. If no paper clips are added, the whirligig turns sideways and falls quickly. Now they have evidence that as the paper clips increase, the whirligig falls faster. This indicates that they need to decrease the number of paper clips. Also, as the blade length increases the whirligig falls more slowly, so they will want to increase the blade length as much as possible.

   For the second part (explaining results) students' answers will vary. They have not formally learned how to construct an explanation, but they should try.

Be sure to wrap up the discussion with tying in the social practices. For example, tell students that they now know more because they shared like scientists.

Point out to students that what they have learned (their claims) is limited to their observations based on just two experiments. In the next section they will learn some science, based on many experiments that have been done, that will either support their ideas, or help them to refine their ideas.

What's the Point?

5 min.

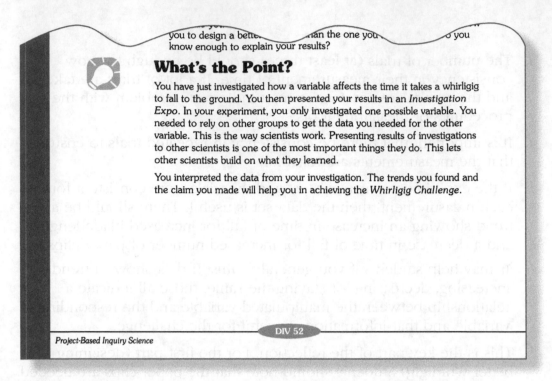

you to design a bette ~~~~~~~ han the one you ~~~~~~~ o you know enough to explain your results?

What's the Point?

You have just investigated how a variable affects the time it takes a whirligig to fall to the ground. You then presented your results in an *Investigation Expo*. In your experiment, you only investigated one possible variable. You needed to rely on other groups to get the data you needed for the other variable. This is the way scientists work. Presenting results of investigations to other scientists is one of the most important things they do. This lets other scientists build on what they learned.

You interpreted the data from your investigation. The trends you found and the claim you made will help you in achieving the *Whirligig Challenge*.

Project-Based Inquiry Science　　　　　　　　DIV 52

It is important for students to realize that they needed to depend on each other to gather information on the whirligig and that scientists depend on each other to build their information bank. Students also need to realize the importance of interpreting data by finding trends and making claims and that claims must be supported by evidence. These are essential to achieving the *Whirligig Challenge*.

NOTES

....

....

....

....

....

....

Assessment Options

Targeted Concepts, Skills, and Nature of Science	How do I know if students got it?
Scientists often work together and then share their findings. Sharing findings makes new information available and helps scientists refine their ideas and build on others' ideas. When another person's or group's idea is used, credit needs to be given.	**ASK:** What information did you obtain from the *Investigation Expo* that you did not have before? **LISTEN:** Students' responses should include that they have information about the results of the experiment they did not do. **ASK:** How will the new information you have help you? **LISTEN:** Students' responses should contain the idea that they can now apply this information to solving the challenge.
Scientists make claims (conclusions) based on evidence obtained (trends in data) from reliable investigations.	**ASK:** What is a scientific claim or conclusion? **LISTEN:** Students should be able to define a claim or conclusion as a statement that is backed up by their data. Students should also be able to give an example, referring back to question 6 of the *Reflect* segment.

Teacher Reflection Questions

- What difficulties are your students having with determining if an experiment is a fair test? What difficulties did students have in making claims and determining if claims were trustworthy? What ideas do you have for next time?

- What difficulties did students have with either running the experiment or preparing their presentations? How did you assist them? What ideas do you have for assisting them next time?

- How did you manage the *Investigation Expo* and the discussions involved with it? What would you like to do the same next time? What would you like to do differently?

SECTION 3.4 INTRODUCTION

3.4 Read

1 class period* ▶

Whirligig Science

Overview

Students read about the gravitational force pulling down and the air resistance force pushing up on objects as they fall. Students then consider how they are changing the forces on their whirligig in their experiments. Students see how established science knowledge about gravitational forces and drag forces affirms their experimental results from the last section and can provide the basis for new ideas about how to make the whirligig fall more slowly. Finally, students focus on columns 3 and 4 as they update the *Project Board* with their claims and evidence.

**A class period is considered to be one 40 to 50 minute class.

Targeted Concepts, Skills, and Nature of Science	Performance Expectations
Scientists often work together and then share their findings. Sharing findings makes new information available and helps scientists refine their ideas and build on others' ideas. When another person's or group's idea is used, credit needs to be given.	Students should be able to describe and apply information they read about gravity and air resistance to their experimental observations and to solving the *Whirligig Challenge*.
The way an object falls through air depends on its mass, surface area, and other factors.	Students should be able to describe the different forces that affect an object falling through the air.
Earth's gravity pulls things toward Earth.	Students should be able to describe how gravity affects the motion of the whirligig.
Air resistance is a force opposing the motion of an object moving through air.	Students should be able to describe what causes air resistance or drag and how it affects the motion of the whirligig.

Materials

1 per class   class *Project Board*

Activity Setup and Preparation

Read the *Understanding for Teachers* segment at the beginning of this *Learning Set* for a deeper understanding of the force due to gravity and the drag force.

Homework Options

Reflection

• **Science Content:** Summarize what you know about the force of gravity and the force of air resistance and how they affect the whirligig. Draw a diagram of how these forces act on the whirligig. *(The force of gravity on the whirligig is caused by Earth pulling the whirligig toward it. The air particles hitting the whirligig and pushing up on it are the cause of the drag force or the force due to air resistance. Gravity pulls down the whirligig, air resistance pushes up on the whirligig.)*

Preparation for 3.5 and the Challenge

• **Science Process:** Based on what you know now, make a recommendation to the cereal company on how to design the whirligig and explain why you made this recommendation. *(Students should try to optimize the effects so that the whirligig falls slowly.)*

NOTES

....

....

....

....

....

....

1 class period ▶

3.4 Read

Whirligig Science

5 min.

Lead students through the reading with demonstrations of falling, resistance to falling, and changing these pushes and pulls.

3.4 Read

Whirligig Science

Many times you know what will happen in a situation without knowing why. For example, you know that you will not float away as you walk across the floor. What you may not have known is the science behind it. You now know that the science behind why you stay on the floor is gravity pulling you toward Earth. In this section, you will read about the science of why the paper clips and blade length have the effects they do on the way a whirligig falls.

People use scientific information to explain how and why things happen the way they do. But scientific information does more than tell people why a particular thing happens the way it does. Accurate information also helps you predict what will happen in new situations. You now know how paper clips and blade length affect how much time it takes a whirligig to fall. After learning the science behind these phenomena, you will probably be able to predict things that you didn't investigate. For example, you could predict what will happen if you make the blades of a whirligig wider.

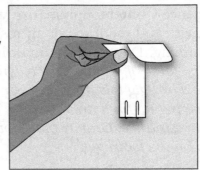

Gravity

You probably know why your whirligig falls toward the ground. It is because of gravity – the same force that you had to consider in the *Book-Support Challenge*. Just as Earth pulled the book toward it, Earth also pulls the whirligig toward it. This pull is called gravity.

Gravity is the pull between Earth and the whirligig. Even when the whirligig is in your hand, Earth is pulling on it. Your hand and fingers create a pull up on the whirligig. This pull up opposes the pull down of gravity. Therefore, the whirligig does not fall toward the ground. When you release the whirligig, however, your hand is not there to oppose the pull down. The whirligig falls towards Earth.

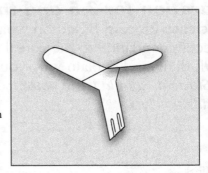

DIV 53

DIVING INTO SCIENCE

○ Engage

Begin by briefly reminding the class of the demonstrations you did at the start of this Unit with the book, paper, and coffee filters. Then ask students what they learned from their experimental results. Students should state their claims. *(Increasing the blade length increases the time to reach the ground. Increasing the number of paper clips on the stem decreases the time to reach the ground.)* You may want to drop the whirligig again.

Then point out that scientists not only try to explain how and why things happen, they also try to make predictions. Scientists use information from the scientific community as well as from their own experiments. Tell students that they, like scientists, will now learn how pushes and pulls affect the whirligig as it falls.

TEACHER TALK

TEACHER TALK

"Scientists learn from experiments or investigations but they also use knowledge from the scientific community. From the demonstrations we have done in class with the coffee filters and from the two different experiments the class did, you have some information about what affects the time of flight of a whirligig. There is more information available from experiments scientists have done. Scientists try to explain how and why things happen the way they do, and they try to make predictions based on what they know. Scientists have studied the pushes and pulls that act on objects as they fall. We are going to learn about two of these pushes and pulls now so we can better understand how the whirligig falls."

△ Guide

Remind students of what they learned in the *Book-Support Challenge*. Objects with mass attract each other, but the attraction between them is not noticeable unless one of the objects is very massive, like Earth. Earth pulls all things with mass toward it. This pull is called the force due to gravity.

Explain how Earth attracts the whirligig at all times, even when it is being held. When the whirligig is in your hand, your hand provides an opposite push up that opposes the pull down on it by Earth. When you let go of the whirligig, Earth pulls the whirligig toward it causing the whirligig to fall toward Earth.

NOTES

....

....

....

....

....

....

....

Gravity

10 min.

Discuss how the gravitational force affects the whirligig.

META NOTES

This information will help students write an explanation in the next section about their observations of how and why the whirligig falls.

A Push against Gravity

10 min.

Discuss the drag force arising from the air, which is also called air resistance. This force acts on the object in the direction opposite to the object's motion.

META NOTES

The purpose of this PBIS Unit is to introduce students to PBIS, the nature of science, the social practices of scientists, and along the way learn some concepts about how things fall so that they can learn how to design an experiment and construct an explanation. The sciences of addition of forces, balancing forces, acceleration, or terminal velocity are explored in later Units. The *Understanding for Teachers* segment contains information about the topics not covered in this Unit to help you address student questions if they arise.

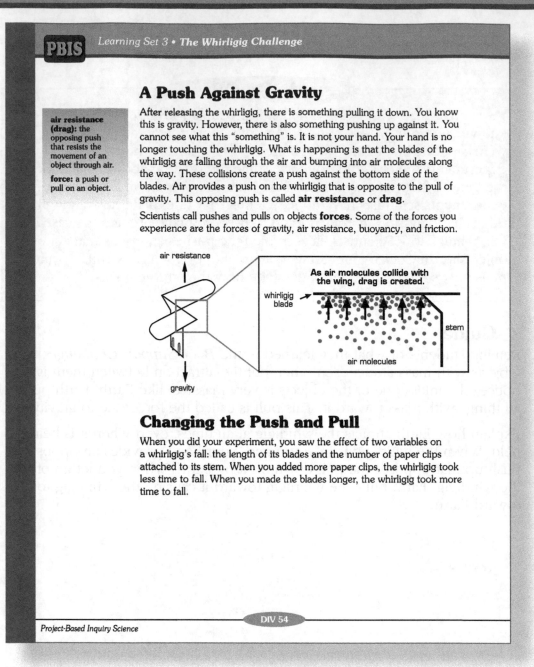

A Push Against Gravity

air resistance (drag): the opposing push that resists the movement of an object through air.

force: a push or pull on an object.

After releasing the whirligig, there is something pulling it down. You know this is gravity. However, there is also something pushing up against it. You cannot see what this "something" is. It is not your hand. Your hand is no longer touching the whirligig. What is happening is that the blades of the whirligig are falling through the air and bumping into air molecules along the way. These collisions create a push against the bottom side of the blades. Air provides a push on the whirligig that is opposite to the pull of gravity. This opposing push is called **air resistance** or **drag**.

Scientists call pushes and pulls on objects **forces**. Some of the forces you experience are the forces of gravity, air resistance, buoyancy, and friction.

air resistance

As air molecules collide with the wing, drag is created.

whirligig blade

stem

air molecules

gravity

Changing the Push and Pull

When you did your experiment, you saw the effect of two variables on a whirligig's fall: the length of its blades and the number of paper clips attached to its stem. When you added more paper clips, the whirligig took less time to fall. When you made the blades longer, the whirligig took more time to fall.

DIV 54

Project-Based Inquiry Science

△ Guide

Ask students to hold their hand with their palm facing to the right or left. Then ask students to move their hand rapidly through the air. Ask students to describe what they are feeling and why they think it is happening. Ask students to compare how it feels when they hold their hand still. Students should notice that they feel the air as they move their hand rapidly through the air. Students may describe this as wind.

Tell students that the air is made up of particles and that our hand, or any object moving through the air, collides with these particles and has to move them out of the way. That is what they feel. And the faster you move through the air, the more you feel this because you are colliding with particles at a faster rate. Tell students that wind is when the air particles are moving, collide with us, and move past us. When we move through the air, we collide with the air particles and we have to move the particles out of the way. This is called air resistance or drag.

Then ask students to compare how it feels to move their hand right and left when their palm is facing the floor and when it is perpendicular to the floor. Students should feel more collisions with the air (they may describe this as wind) when their hand is perpendicular to the floor. Ask them why they think this is. Again, emphasize that the air is made up of particles that collide with their hand and have to be moved out of the way. When their hand is perpendicular they collide with, and have to push out of the way, more air particles than when their hand is parallel to the floor. The air resistance increases as the surface area moving through the air increases.

Emphasize that when we collide with the air, there is a push from the air on our hand that points opposite to the direction we are moving in. This push, known as the force due to air resistance or drag, always pushes opposite the direction of motion. Provide an example of this such as moving your hand so that your palm is moving to the right, left, upward, or downward and notice how the air flows past.

META NOTES

Students often have a difficult time understanding that air is made up of particles and that air resistance is caused by these particles colliding with an object moving through it. Exploring what they feel when they move their hand in various ways through the air should help students to understand that the air is made of something. It should also help them to understand some of the properties of air resistance.

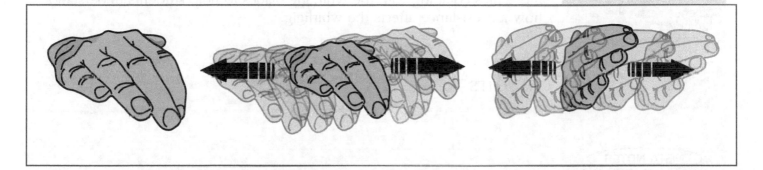

TEACHER TALK

❝What difference did you feel when you moved your hand parallel to the floor compared to perpendicular to the floor? You probably noticed more push against you from the air when your hand was perpendicular to the floor. This is because more air particles have to be pushed out of the way by your hand. This also means more air particles hit your open hand. Why? *(More particles hit your hand and have to be pushed or moved out of the way because there is more surface area for the particles to hit.)*❞

A Push against Gravity
(continued)

META NOTES

Students may wonder if the drag force ever gets bigger than gravity and things start moving upward — it doesn't. They may confuse air resistance with lift, which is a different force. For an object falling toward Earth, the air resistance or drag force acting on the object never gets larger than the force of gravity. It actually increases from zero strength until it is equal to the force of gravity. When these forces are equal, they balance each other and the object falls with a constant speed known as the *terminal velocity*. This is discussed in a later Unit.

META NOTES

Some students may wonder about how things can stay up in the air such as planes and gliders. The upward force balancing the force of gravity is called lift and arises from a difference in air pressure that is created above and below the wings.

Remind students then of the demonstration you did in the first lesson where you dropped seven stacked coffee filters and seven filters in a floral pattern. Ask students which they thought had more collisions with air particles and had to move more air out of the way: the floral pattern. Ask which felt a greater push upward from air resistance. (*The floral pattern.*) Then ask students what they think this means for the whirligig blades? (*Longer blades have more surface area so more collisions occur with the air.*)

TEACHER TALK

"When the air particles hit your hand they push your hand. This push from the air particles on your hand is opposite to the direction your hand is moving in. If you are moving your hand to the right, air resistance pushes on your hand to the left. And if you are moving your hand up, air resistance pushes on your hand downward."

Ask students to describe how air resistance affects the whirligig as it falls. Students should describe air particles colliding with the whirligig blades, pushing upward on the whirligig. Use the diagram in the student text of air molecules colliding with the whirligig blades to help students understand how air resistance affects the whirligig.

NOTES

....

....

....

....

....

....

....

....

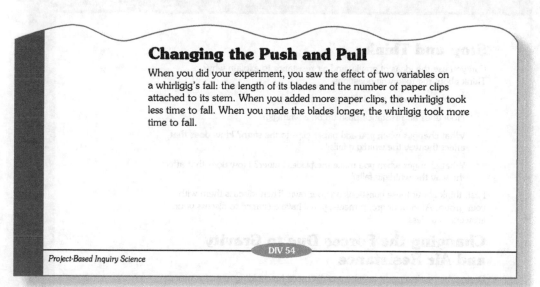

Changing the Push and Pull

When you did your experiment, you saw the effect of two variables on a whirligig's fall: the length of its blades and the number of paper clips attached to its stem. When you added more paper clips, the whirligig took less time to fall. When you made the blades longer, the whirligig took more time to fall.

Project-Based Inquiry Science

DIV 54

Changing the Push and Pull

5 min.

Remind students of their experimental results with changing the push and pulls of falling objects.

△ **Guide**

Remind students of the experiments they did. Ask them what claims they made for each experiment, i.e., when they added more paper clips to the stem of the whirligig it took less time to fall. When they made the whirligig's blade longer it took more time to fall. Tell students that they are going to answer four questions to try to explain this using the ideas of gravity and air resistance.

Stop and Think

20 min.

Lead a class discussion linking the science of falling with the Whirligig Challenge.

Stop and Think

Can you use the ideas of gravity and air resistance to explain why? Think about the following questions:

- How does gravity pull down on a whirligig?

- How does air resistance push up on a whirligig?

- What changes when you add paper clips to the stem? How does that affect the way the whirligig falls?

- What changes when you make the blades longer? How does that affect the way the whirligig falls?

First, think about these questions on your own. Then, discuss them with your group. After your group meets, you'll have a chance to discuss your answers as a class.

Changing the Forces Due to Gravity and Air Resistance

During the book-support activity you discussed how adding mass (or more matter) to an object increases the force due to gravity that Earth exerts on the object. That is, when you add more matter to an object, there is more stuff for Earth to pull on. The pull on the object is larger.

When you add paper clips to the stem, you add matter to the whirligig. There is more whirligig matter for Earth to pull on, so the pull of gravity is greater. However, the push up of air resistance does not change. Therefore, the overall pull down is larger. You probably saw the whirligig fall in less time as you added more paper clips to the stem.

How does the opposing air resistance affect the time for the whirligig to fall when the length of the blades increases? When you increased the length of the blades, you increased the size, or surface area, of the blades. This increase in surface area results in a greater number of collisions between the air molecules and the blades. A greater number of collisions creates a larger push upward on the bottom of the blades. Thus, increasing the blade size creates larger air resistance. You probably observed this during the experiments. Increasing the blade length increased the time it took the whirligig to fall toward Earth.

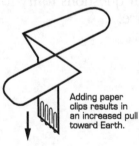

Adding paper clips results in an increased pull toward Earth.

DIV 55

DIVING INTO SCIENCE

⬡ Get Going

Let students know that they should first answer the questions on their own. Then they should discuss their answers with their group and come up with their best group answer. If group members cannot agree on an answer then they should list all their answers. Tell students that groups will be sharing their answers during a class discussion. Let students know how much time they have (no more than 10 minutes) to answer the questions.

△ Guide

Then begin a class discussion of how gravity, air resistance, and their data are related to how the whirligig falls.

- Students should say that the force of gravity between Earth and the whirligig pulls the whirligig straight down toward Earth. Guide students by relating what they learned about gravity from the book challenge, what they read about gravity earlier, and what they observed with the whirligig.

TEACHER TALK

"What did you learn about the force of gravity during the book challenge and how this force affects things near Earth? *(If something above Earth is not supported then it will fall toward Earth because of the gravitational pull between Earth and the object.)* What does this mean for the whirligig? *(When I'm holding the whirligig above the ground my hand is supporting it, but when I let go the whirligig falls toward Earth because of the gravitational pull between the whirligig and Earth.)* **"**

- Students' responses should include that as the whirligig falls through the air toward Earth, it collides with the particles of air. Most of the collisions occur with the blades of the whirligig. These collisions cause an upward push on the whirligig. Air resistance pushes opposite to its downward motion. Guide students by reminding them of moving their hand through the air and asking them how the air affects the whirligig as it moves through the air.

TEACHER TALK

"Move your hand through the air again. Why does it feel the way it does? What is your hand interacting with? How does the air interact with the whirligig as it moves through the air?**"**

TEACHER TALK

"When you add paper clips to the stem of the whirligig, the mass of the whirligig increases. This increase in mass results in an increase in the pull between Earth and the whirligig. We observed that when we increased the number of paper clips (mass), the whirligig reached the ground in less time.**"**

- Students should include ideas about how adding paper clips increases the mass of the whirligig and changes the results from their experiments. Some students may say it falls more quickly — you may want to ask them what this means as far as their measurements. Ask if they are measuring quickness or something else. Guide students by reminding them that mass attracts mass and that the attraction between masses increases (and becomes noticeable) when one of the objects is very massive. Then try to lead them to realizing that the force due to gravity increases with increasing mass.

TEACHER TALK

"Remember mass attracts mass. But we don't notice this unless one of the masses is very massive, like Earth. That is because the attractive pull between the objects increases as the mass increases. We don't notice the gravitational pull between the desk and the chair because their masses are not so large, but we notice the gravitational pull between objects and Earth because Earth is so massive. As the mass of the falling object increases, so does the gravitational pull between it and Earth. So what happens when we add paper clips to the whirligig? *(When you add paper clips to the stem, the mass of the whirligig increases. This increases the force between Earth and the whirligig).* And what did you observe when you added mass to the whirligig? *(As the mass increased, the time to reach Earth decreased.)*"

- Students should describe that when the blades get longer there is more surface for the air particles to collide with, causing a greater push upwards on the whirligig. Students should also include their observations from their experiment. As the blade length (surface) increased, the time it took to reach Earth decreased. Guide students by asking them questions about how the air and whirligig interact as the whirligig falls through the air.

TEACHER TALK

"Remember moving your hand through the air. When your palm was facing the floor you didn't notice so much air resistance, but when your palm was facing the direction you were moving your hand in, you noticed the air going around your hand. Why? *(Increased surface area means an increase in number of collisions with air particles and more air to move out of the way.)* What does this imply for the whirligig? *(Longer blades increases the surface area going through air, and more collisions with air.)* What did you observe in your experiments and does the science you learned support your observations?"

194

◇ Evaluate

Make sure students know the following ideas before continuing.

- Things fall because gravity pulls them toward Earth.
- Objects moving through air collide with air molecules, causing a push on the object opposite to the direction it is moving in.
- Adding paper clips adds mass to the whirligig, resulting in the whirligig falling more quickly.
- Adding blade length increases the surface area resulting in the whirligig falling more slowly.

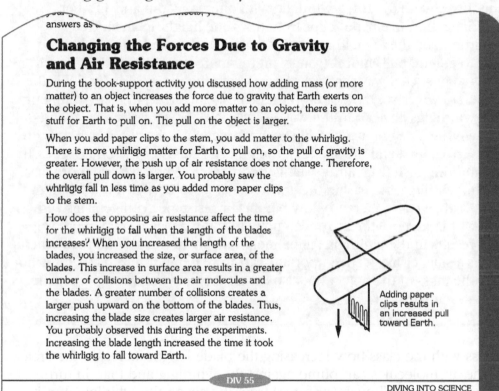

Changing the Forces Due to Gravity and Air Resistance

During the book-support activity you discussed how adding mass (or more matter) to an object increases the force due to gravity that Earth exerts on the object. That is, when you add more matter to an object, there is more stuff for Earth to pull on. The pull on the object is larger.

When you add paper clips to the stem, you add matter to the whirligig. There is more whirligig matter for Earth to pull on, so the pull of gravity is greater. However, the push up of air resistance does not change. Therefore, the overall pull down is larger. You probably saw the whirligig fall in less time as you added more paper clips to the stem.

How does the opposing air resistance affect the time for the whirligig to fall when the length of the blades increases? When you increased the length of the blades, you increased the size, or surface area, of the blades. This increase in surface area results in a greater number of collisions between the air molecules and the blades. A greater number of collisions creates a larger push upward on the bottom of the blades. Thus, increasing the blade size creates larger air resistance. You probably observed this during the experiments. Increasing the blade length increased the time it took the whirligig to fall toward Earth.

Adding paper clips results in an increased pull toward Earth.

DIV 55

DIVING INTO SCIENCE

Changing the Forces due to Gravity and Air Resistance

5 min.

Now guide the discussion to how the forces of gravity and air resistance are affected by the variables of blade length and number of paper clips in the whirligig experiments.

△ Guide

Lead from the last two questions about the whirligig falling more quickly or more slowly and transition students to think about how these variables affect the forces on the whirligig.

TEACHER TALK

❝We know that longer blade length results in the whirligig taking more time to reach the ground and that more paper clips results in the whirligig reaching the ground in less time. Now let's think about how the variables we tested (blade length and paper clips) affect the forces acting on the falling whirligig.❞

Discuss with the class that increasing the number of paper clips increases the mass of the whirligig and hence, the force of gravity acting on the whirligig.

META NOTES

The more massive whirligig takes longer to reach its terminal velocity because it can reach higher terminal velocities. *See Understanding for Teachers* for more information.

META NOTES

Here the drag force reaches is maximum value (and its terminal speed) quickly because of the large surface area. See *Understanding for Teachers* for more information.

TEACHER TALK

❝When you add paper clips to the whirligigs you are increasing the whirligig's mass. What happens when the mass gets bigger? *(There is a greater pull between Earth and the whirligig.)*

❝How does this affect the time of flight? Some of the science involved is beyond the scope of this Unit, so I'm going to tell you just a little about this. If we were to drop a whirligig with one paperclip and another whirligig with five paper clips from the same height in an air-free environment, they would reach the ground at the same time. The force due to gravity pulls more strongly on the more massive whirligig, but it does so in such a way that the rate at which the two whirligigs fall is the same. However, we did not drop the whirligig in an air-free environment: our whirligigs have air in the way of their fall. The air resistance acting on the whirligig can only get as big as the force of gravity and it depends on the surface area and the speed of the object. The faster the object goes, the greater the push from air resistance acting on it. When we add more mass to the whirligig, increasing the gravitational force between the whirligig and Earth, we also increase how big the air resistance can get. This allows the whirligig more time to speed up before it reaches its maximum value and results in the whirligig falling more quickly to the ground than when it has a smaller mass. The important part to remember here, is that it is not just the mass of the object but also the air it is moving through that affects how fast it falls.❞

Discuss with the class how increasing the blade length increases the area that the air molecules can bump against the whirligig and that, in turn, increases the overall push (or force) from the air on the whirligig, but it does not increase the maximum drag force that the whirligig can experience.

TEACHER TALK

"Think about the different ways you moved your hand through the air. Now think about the whirligig. When we increase the blade length of the whirligig, what is it about the whirligig we are increasing? (*The surface area increases.*)

Why does changing the surface area of the whirligig affect how it falls? (*Increasing the surface area increases the air resistance because there are more collisions with the surface.*) Increasing the surface area does not increase the maximum drag force, rather it decreases the time it takes the drag force to reach its maximum value. This results in the whirligig reaching its maximum value more quickly and hence, it falls longer distances at slower constant speeds (it doesn't speed up for a long time during its fall)."

META NOTES

The force due to air resistance (drag force) can only be as large as the gravitational force. If the mass is not increasing, the maximum drag force cannot increase. Increasing the whirligig's blade length only minimally increases its mass, so the maximum drag force for longer blade lengths is about the same. However, increasing the blade length increases the rate at which the drag force reaches its maximum value and decreases its maximum speed (terminal velocity). The longer the blade, the more surface area, the smaller the terminal velocity.

◇ **Evaluate**

Make sure students know the following ideas.

- Adding paper clips adds mass and increases the pull due to gravity acting on the whirligig.

- Adding blade length increases the push due to air resistance acting on the whirligig.

Update the Project Board

10 min.

Introduce students to columns 3 and 4 (claims and evidence) of the Project Board.

Update the *Project Board*

What are we learning? and *What is our evidence?*

Earlier you began a *Project Board* centered on the idea of learning more about how things fall. Now you've done some experiments and read some whirligig science. You know more about the factors that affect how things fall. You are now ready to fill in the *Project Board* more completely.

Up to now, you've only recorded information in the first two columns of the *Project Board*. You'll focus on the next two columns now. These are the *What are we learning?* and *What is our evidence?* columns. When you record what you are learning in the third column, you will be answering some questions in the *What do we need to investigate?* column. You will describe what you learned from an investigation you just did. But you cannot just write what you learned without providing the evidence for your conclusions. Evidence is necessary to answer scientific questions. You will fill in the evidence column based on data and trends you found in your investigations. You will also include your understandings of the science readings and your discussions with each other. You may use the text in this book to help you write about the science you've learned. However, make sure to put it into your own words. The class will fill in the large *Project Board*. Make sure to record the same information on your own *Project Board* page.

The *Project Board* is a great place to start discussions. You may find that you disagree with other classmates about what you've learned and the evidence for it. This is a part of what scientists do. Such discussions help participants identify what they or others still don't understand well and what else they still need to learn or investigate.

○ Engage

Remind students of the *Big Challenge* — designing a whirligig that fits on the back of a cereal box and falls slowly.

⬡ Get Going

Display the class's *Project Board* and remind students that the *Project Board* is a way to organize their ideas and questions and helps them see how their ideas change as they gather more information.

Then remind students what they have already recorded, and remind them of what the five columns are: *What do we think we know?*, *What do we need to investigate?*, *What are we learning?*, *What is our evidence?* and *What does it mean for the challenge or question?*

Next, tell students that they will be updating their *Project Board* with the results from their experiments and with the science knowledge they have just read about and that this information will go primarily into the third (*What are we learning?*) and fourth (*What is our evidence?*) columns. Point out that they may also have new questions they want to investigate that can be added to column 2.

△ Guide

First, model for students how to fill out columns 3 and 4 by emphasizing that columns 3 and 4 are directly linked. Remember to draw arrows directly linking the claim and evidence on the *Project Board*. You may want to use the example below:

TEACHER TALK

"Column 3: *What are we learning?* **Claim:** Objects fall toward Earth. Column 4: *What is our evidence?* **Evidence:** We learned that mass attracts mass and that objects with mass are attracted to the Earth, this is called the force due to gravity. We also observe this in our daily experiences when dropped objects (such as the whirligig) fall toward Earth."

META NOTES

If claims cannot be supported by evidence then an investigative question should be developed and placed in column 2.

Then begin the discussion by asking students what else they know based on what they read today and what they learned from their experiments. Update the, of the *Project Board* as requested by the class. Remember to draw arrows indicating the flow of ideas and to date the entries.

TEACHER TALK

" • What did you learn from your experiments? What is the evidence that supports that idea?

• What did you learn about gravity/air resistance that is not on the board? What should we write as evidence?

• What did you learn about how gravity/air resistance affects the whirligig? What should we write as evidence? "

◇ Evaluate

Make sure students include the claims and evidence below, written in their own words. Note that it is O.K. if they do not understand all of the science knowledge.

- **Claim:** The force of gravity between Earth and the whirligig causes the whirligig to fall to Earth.
  Evidence: This is supported by accepted science knowledge and our everyday experiences.

- **Claim:** The force of gravity has to do with mass attracting mass. It is this force that causes objects to fall toward Earth when dropped near Earth.

  Evidence: Accepted science knowledge from the student text.

- **Claim:** Increasing the number of paper clips decreases the time of fall.

  Evidence: Experimental data showing this trend and accepted science knowledge. (Science knowledge = increasing gravitational force results in a greater maximum value for the drag force resulting in reaching its maximum value and a higher terminal speed in a longer amount of time.)

- **Claim:** Increasing blade length increases the time it takes the whirligig to fall.

  Evidence: Experimental data showing this trend and accepted science knowledge. (Science knowledge = increasing surface area causes drag force to reach its maximum value and reach a smaller terminal speed in a shorter amount of time.)

Teacher Reflection Questions

- What difficulties did students have understanding the force of gravity, the drag force, and/or how it connects to the whirligig? How did you help guide them? What ideas do you have for next time?

- How did you guide students through the discussion updating the *Project Board*? What ideas would you like to try out?

- During the discussion updating the *Project Board*, what techniques did you use to maximize student participation? What ideas do you have for next time?

SECTION 3.5 INTRODUCTION

3.5 Explain

Create an Explanation

◀ *1 class period* *

Overview

Students are introduced to scientific explanations and how to create one. They practice creating explanations for the whirligig based on their observations and the science knowledge from the last section. Students then share their explanations with the class. Hearing others' explanations will help students to refine their own in the next section.

Targeted Concepts, Skills, and Nature of Science	Performance Expectations
Scientists often work together and then share their findings. Sharing findings makes new information available and helps scientists refine their ideas and build on others' ideas. When another person's or group's idea is used, credit needs to be given.	Students should be able to describe how their ideas are changing.
Scientists make claims (conclusions) based on evidence obtained (trends in data) from reliable investigations.	Students should be able to make claims based on trends in their data and in the class's data. This could be part of their explanation.
Explanations are claims supported by evidence, accepted ideas and facts.	Students should be able to create an explanation of why the whirligig falls the way it does based on the results of all the class experiments and based on what they learned in the previous section.

Materials

1 per student   *Create Your Explanation* page

*A class period is considered to be one 40 to 50 minute class.

Homework Options

Reflection

- **Science Process:** Write an explanation for the experimental question you did not investigate. *(Look for claims, evidence, and science knowledge backing up the explanation. They should be logical and contain no opinions.)*

- **Science Process:** Explain why things fall and point out the components of your explanation that make it a scientific explanation. *(Explanations contain a claim backed up by evidence and science knowledge in a logical way and no opinions should be included.)*

Preparation for 3.6

- **Science Process:** Revise your explanation for the investigation you carried out in Section 3.3 based on what you now know about scientific explanations. *(Look for explanations that contain claims that are backed up by evidence and science knowledge, are logical, and do not contain opinions.)*

NOTES

SECTION 3.5 IMPLEMENTATION

3.5 Explain

Create an Explanation

After scientists get results from an investigation, they try to make a claim. They base their claim on what their evidence shows. They also use what they already know to make their claim. They explain why their claim is valid. The purpose of a science explanation is to help others understand the following:

- what was learned from a set of investigations
- why the scientists reached this conclusion

Later, other scientists will use these explanations to help them explain other phenomena. The explanations will also help them predict what will happen in other situations.

You will do the same thing now. Your claim will be the trend you found in your experiment. You will use data you collected and science knowledge you have read to create a good explanation. This will help you decide whether your claim is valid. You will be reporting the results of the investigation to your classmates. With a good explanation that matches your claim, you can convince them that your claim is valid.

Because your understanding of the science of forces is not complete, you may not be able to fully explain your results. But you will use what you have read to come up with your best explanation. Scientists finding out about new things do the same thing. When they only partly understand something, it is impossible for them to form a "perfect" explanation. They do the best they can based on what they understand.

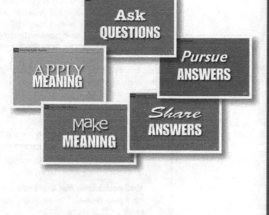

DIV 57

DIVING INTO SCIENCE

◄ *1 class period*

3.5 Explain

Create an Explanation
15 min.

Introduce scientific explanations, which students will be constructing throughout the PBIS curriculum.

META NOTES

Many students will already have ideas about what an explanation is. In science and PBIS an explanation has specific components: a claim backed up by evidence and science knowledge in a logical way.

⃝ Engage

Remind students that they now have evidence and science knowledge about what happens when a whirligig falls. Tell students that when they make a recommendation to the cereal company they will need to explain how to make a slow-falling whirligig. The cereal company will want a scientific explanation.

TEACHER TALK

"Now that you have some evidence from your investigations and you know more about how things fall, you need to explain to the cereal company how to make a slow-falling whirligig. They will want to know why your recommendation will make a whirligig fall slowly. They will want a scientific explanation."

As scientists learn more, they make their explanations better. This is what you will do now and what you will be doing throughout PBIS. You will explain your results the best you can based on what you know now. Then, after you learn more, you will make your explanations better.

evidence: data collected during investigations and trends in that data.

science knowledge: knowledge about how things work gathered from reading or research, or discussion that helps you understand why a claim is true.

Be a Scientist

What Do Explanations Look Like?

Making claims and providing explanations are important parts of what scientists do. An explanation is made up of three parts:

- **Claim** – a statement of what you understand or a conclusion that you have reached from an investigation or set of investigations

- **Evidence** – data collected during investigations and trends in that data

- **Science knowledge** – knowledge about how things work. You may have learned this through reading, talking to an expert, discussion, or other experiences.

An explanation is a statement that connects the claim to the evidence and science knowledge in a logical way. A good explanation is provided in a way that can convince somebody that the claim is valid.

For example, suppose you live in a city in the USA that gets cold and has snow in the winter. It is fall. You see a lot of birds flying past your home. You wonder why so many birds are flying by. You have learned that many birds cannot live in cold places. They fly to warm places (usually south) to spend the winter. You wonder if these birds are flying by your home on their way to a warmer place. You take out your compass and observe that the direction they are flying is south. You conclude that the birds are flying past your home to a warmer place where they will spend the winter. Look at how you can form an explanation.

Your claim: The birds flying past my house are flying south for the winter.

Your evidence: The birds are flying in a southern direction. (You've observed and measured that using a compass.)

Your science knowledge: Birds that can't live in cold weather fly to warm climates and stay there for the winter.

Your explanation (for why there are so many birds flying south past your house): The birds are flying south to find a warmer place to spend the winter.

An explanation is what makes a claim different from an opinion. When you create an explanation, you use evidence and science knowledge to back up your claim. Then people know your claim is not simply something you think. It is something you've spent time investigating. You have found out things that show your claim is likely to be correct.

DIV 58

Project-Based Inquiry Science

△ Guide

Then describe a scientific explanation by first telling students that an explanation is a statement that connects a claim to the evidence and science knowledge supporting the claim, and that connection has to be done in a logical way.

"When scientists make explanations they are answering a question about a situation or phenomenon. They use evidence and science knowledge to make a claim. They also use logic to connect their evidence and science knowledge to their claim. An explanation is not based on opinions. It is O.K. not to have complete or perfect explanations if you do not have complete or perfect understanding. Just like scientists, you should explain things as well as you can, based only on what you know.

For example, after you completed your experiment you had a claim you could support with evidence and you could partially support it with science knowledge.

Increasing the blade length of the whirligig decreases the time it falls. This is supported by my data that showed when the blade length increased from short, to medium, to long, the time it took to reach the ground also increased. The whirligig falls because of the pull due to gravity between Earth and the whirligig. I don't have enough information yet to explain why it falls more slowly.

This explanation does not state why it falls more slowly, but it does state why it falls.

Then you learned some science knowledge and you may now have some idea of why it falls more slowly. The explanation could be revised to include this information."

Begin by reviewing claims, evidence, and science knowledge. Emphasize that a claim is a statement or conclusions reached from one or more investigations. Evidence is the data from the investigations. And science knowledge is knowledge about how things work based on what experts have previously investigated. Use examples from the whirligig investigation and the previous reading to illustrate each component and to remind students of information they will use to create their own explanations.

"Lets consider what is the claim, evidence, and science knowledge from the example we did earlier involving changing the blade length.

Claim: Increasing the blade length decreases the time it takes to reach the ground.

Evidence: This is supported by my data that showed when the blade length increased from short, to medium, to long, the time it took to reach the ground also increased.

Science Knowledge: The whirligig falls because of the pull due to gravity between Earth and the whirligig.

I don't have enough information yet to explain why it falls more slowly."

Next, use the example explanation below about birds flying south to point out how each component (claim, evidence, and science knowledge) is connected in a logical way. Also, point out that when students say their explanation they may just say the first line, but when they write their explanation they should connect all the parts together to support the claim. Be sure to write the explanation below on the board and have students copy it. Explanations should contain their reasons. The explanation in the student edition should contain the supporting information in it.

Explanation for why there are so many birds flying south past your house: The birds are flying south to find a warmer place to spend the winter because birds that can't live in cold weather fly to warm climates and stay there for the winter.

Below is an additional example illustrating an explanation of falling.

"**Claim:** All things with mass fall to the ground when they are dropped.

Evidence: Everything I have seen dropped in class (the book, the piece of paper, the coffee filters, the whirligig) and fell to the ground.

Science Knowledge: I have read about the force due to gravity. Mass attracts mass and this attraction increases as the mass increases. The effect of this force is not easily observed unless one of the objects is very massive, like Earth.

Explanation: Dropped objects fall because the force due to gravity between the object and Earth pulls the object towardEarth. Everything I have seen dropped in class (a book, a piece of paper, coffee filters, and whirligigs) support this."

Explain

Creating an Explanation

Here is an example from the *Book-Support Challenge*. It might make what an explanation is clearer. When you worked on that challenge, you saw that bundling several hollow cylinders together to make a single cylinder for under a part of a book seemed more sturdy than using a few cylinders, each made out of a single index card, under that part of the book. You then read about how cylinders distribute forces over their whole perimeter, pushing up on what they are holding all the way around. Look at the claim and explanation created by a group of students who worked in the *Book-Support Challenge* and how they derived it.

Solid cylinders, like the columns shown, distribute forces over the entire cross-sectional surface area.

DIVING INTO SCIENCE

Explain

5 min.

First walk through the steps of constructing an explanation for the Book-Support Challenge*, then have students construct their own explanations for the whirligig.*

⚠ Guide

First, remind students of their evidence and science knowledge about cylinders as support structures from the *Book-Support Challenge*. Note that the explanation in the student edition is a recommendation. A recommendation is a type of claim based on evidence and science knowledge. Students will learn more about recommendations in *Section 3.7*.

Then walk through the example of constructing an explanation describing the thought or reasoning behind each step. Emphasize that there are no opinions in explanations.

DIVING INTO SCIENCE

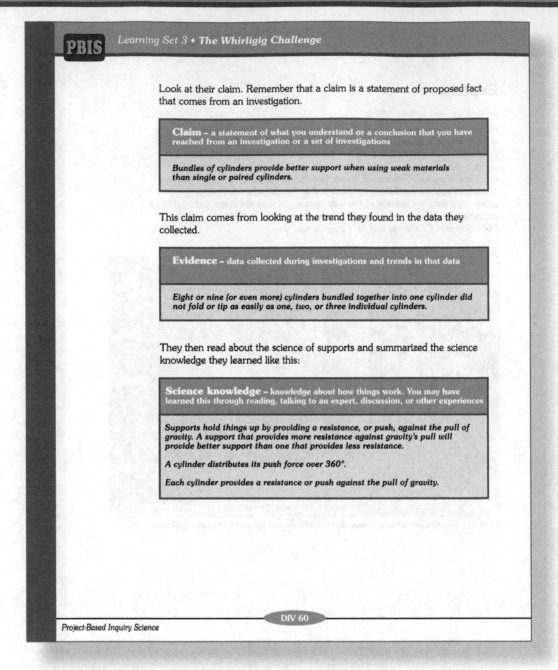

Look at their claim. Remember that a claim is a statement of proposed fact that comes from an investigation.

> **Claim** – a statement of what you understand or a conclusion that you have reached from an investigation or a set of investigations

> *Bundles of cylinders provide better support when using weak materials than single or paired cylinders.*

This claim comes from looking at the trend they found in the data they collected.

> **Evidence** – data collected during investigations and trends in that data

> *Eight or nine (or even more) cylinders bundled together into one cylinder did not fold or tip as easily as one, two, or three individual cylinders.*

They then read about the science of supports and summarized the science knowledge they learned like this:

> **Science knowledge** – knowledge about how things work. You may have learned this through reading, talking to an expert, discussion, or other experiences

> *Supports hold things up by providing a resistance, or push, against the pull of gravity. A support that provides more resistance against gravity's pull will provide better support than one that provides less resistance.*
>
> *A cylinder distributes its push force over 360°.*
>
> *Each cylinder provides a resistance or push against the pull of gravity.*

◯ Get Going

Next, have students work in groups to construct their own explanations for the whirligig investigation they did using their claims, data, and the science knowledge presented so far in this Unit. Students should use their *Create Your Explanation* pages.

Let groups know that they will be presenting their explanations to the class.

☐ Assess

As groups are constructing their explanations, assess how they are doing, paying particular attention to see if they have included opinions and if they are making logical connections. They should use phrases like, "...this follows" and "because..."

They came up with this explanation:

> *We recommend using bundles of cylinders to build a book support when using weak materials. Our data showed that eight or nine (or even more) cylinders bundled together did not fold or tip as easily as one, two, or three individual cylinders. We know that cylinders distribute force over 360°, which prevents folding and compression. Also, each cylinder helps hold the book up by providing a resistance or "push against" the pull of gravity. In a bundled cylinder, each cylinder distributes force over 360°. Each resists the pull of gravity on the book. The more cylinders in a bundle, the less gravity each cylinder in the bundle has to resist. Because each cylinder in the bundle has to resist only some of the pull of gravity, the bundle of cylinders is less likely to fold or tip over than individual cylinders, even if a lot of individual cylinders are used.*

This is a long explanation. Long explanations are not always needed. However, seeing this explanation might help you as you try to write explanations. You will also have a *Create Your Explanation* page, similar to the one shown, to help you with explanations. It will give you space to write your claim, your evidence, and your science knowledge. It will also remind you what each of these is.

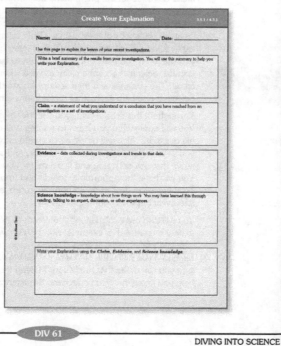

△ Guide

While groups are working on their explanations, assist individual students and groups as needed. If you notice the majority of the class having difficulty in constructing a particular part of an explanation, then stop the class and hold a class discussion.

Communicate

5 min.

Hold a class discussion on explanations presented by groups.

META NOTES

Hearing their classmates' explanations will help students to refine their own. Consider creating a class list of explanations to refer back to later.

Communicate

Share Your Explanation

When everyone is finished, you will share your explanations with the class. As each group shares theirs, record the explanation. You might also create a poster for the classroom that has the full set of explanations on it. You will have an opportunity to revise your explanations after you learn more about how whirligigs work and how things fall.

What's the Point?

Science is about understanding the world around you. Scientists gain understanding by investigating and explaining. The results of investigations are useful in making sense of and organizing the world. To help others better understand what they have learned through their investigations, scientists must communicate their results and understandings effectively. Scientists make claims about the phenomena they investigate. They support their claims with evidence they gather during investigations. They also read science that others have written about. They combine all of that together to create explanations of their claims. Other scientists carefully examine these explanations. They discuss them with each other. They try to decide if the explanation is complete enough for them to be sure about whether the claim is **valid**. Scientists accept a claim as valid when many different scientists agree. The evidence and their science knowledge must justify the claim. Scientists also help each other make their claims and explanations better.

valid: has a solid justification

Throughout this school year, you will investigate a variety of phenomena. You will apply what you learn to solving unit challenges and answering big questions. You will be asked to create explanations. Every explanation you write will include a claim, evidence, and science knowledge. As you move through each unit and learn more, you will create new explanations. You will have the opportunity to edit and improve the explanations you created earlier. Just as you iteratively improved your book supports, you will iteratively improve your explanations.

You will also use explanations you create to help you predict what will happen in new situations. For example, now you know why blade length affects a whirligig's fall the way it does. Therefore, you can probably predict what will happen if you make the blades of a whirligig wider or more narrow. Make sure you can make that prediction. Making that prediction successfully will help you know that you understand the science you've been learning.

DIV 62

⬡ Get Going

Let the class know that if they are in the audience (not presenting) then they should be looking for the parts of an explanation (claim(s) backed by experimental evidence and science knowledge in a logical way with no opinions) and model for them how to ask for clarification.

> **TEACHER TALK**
>
> "I don't understand how the science knowledge backs up your claim. Could you walk me through it?"

Let the class know which set of groups (pertaining to a particular investigation question) will be presenting first and then begin the presentations.

△ Guide

After each group presents, hold a class discussion on their explanation. You may want to have the class pick out what the claim, the evidence, and the science knowledge is or describe them, if the presenting group is not getting many questions.

Encourage the presenting group to answer the person asking the question.

At the end of the presentations and discussion, let students know that they will have a chance to revise their explanations during the next section. Then summarize the parts of an explanation.

Below are example explanations that you can use as a reference for yourself and to help guide students. Some of the science content is not in the reading so students may have a difficult time incorporating it in their explanations. This is O.K. because the focus of this Unit is the practices of PBIS and the content will be visited again in a later Unit.

META NOTES

You may only want to have two groups from each investigation question present. Pick two groups that have not presented before.

Example Explanations

Explanation 1: As the whirligig's blade length increases, its time to reach the ground decreases. This is supported by data we obtained during our investigation. We observed that as we increased the blade length from small to medium to large, the time it took the whirligig to fall from the same height increased. We learned that the air resistance is what pushes up on the whirligig. It is caused by the air particles colliding with the whirligig blade. As the length of the blade increases, more particles collide with the blade, creating a bigger initial push upward after it is dropped. The end result of this is that the whirligig falls to Earth in less time.

Explanation 2: As the number of paper clips increases, the whirligig falls to Earth from the same dropped height in less time. This is supported by data we obtained during our investigation. We observed that as we increased the number of paper clips from ... to ... the fall time decreased. We learned that the downward pull of gravity increases as the mass of the whirligig increases. The added mass to the whirligig increases the gravitational force on the whirligig. This results in the whirligig spending more time speeding up during its fall and so it reaches the ground in less time.

☐ Assess

Assess students' ability to construct and pick out claims, evidence, and science knowledge and their ability to construct explanations. Remember that it is not expected for students to master this yet.

What's the Point?

5 min.

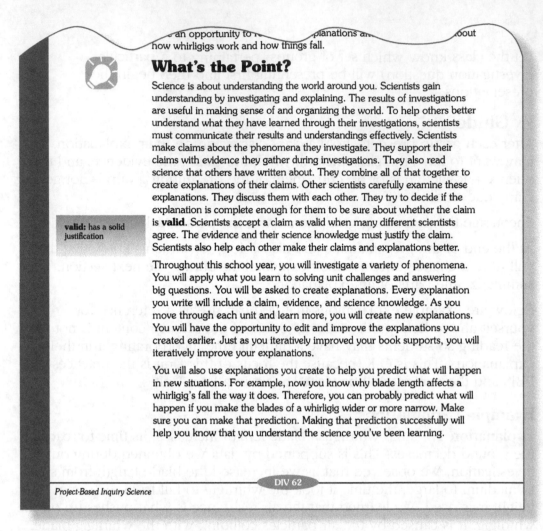

...e an opportunity to r...... .planations a............ .bout how whirligigs work and how things fall.

What's the Point?

Science is about understanding the world around you. Scientists gain understanding by investigating and explaining. The results of investigations are useful in making sense of and organizing the world. To help others better understand what they have learned through their investigations, scientists must communicate their results and understandings effectively. Scientists make claims about the phenomena they investigate. They support their claims with evidence they gather during investigations. They also read science that others have written about. They combine all of that together to create explanations of their claims. Other scientists carefully examine these explanations. They discuss them with each other. They try to decide if the explanation is complete enough for them to be sure about whether the claim is **valid**. Scientists accept a claim as valid when many different scientists agree. The evidence and their science knowledge must justify the claim. Scientists also help each other make their claims and explanations better.

valid: has a solid justification

Throughout this school year, you will investigate a variety of phenomena. You will apply what you learn to solving unit challenges and answering big questions. You will be asked to create explanations. Every explanation you write will include a claim, evidence, and science knowledge. As you move through each unit and learn more, you will create new explanations. You will have the opportunity to edit and improve the explanations you created earlier. Just as you iteratively improved your book supports, you will iteratively improve your explanations.

You will also use explanations you create to help you predict what will happen in new situations. For example, now you know why blade length affects a whirligig's fall the way it does. Therefore, you can probably predict what will happen if you make the blades of a whirligig wider or more narrow. Make sure you can make that prediction. Making that prediction successfully will help you know that you understand the science you've been learning.

Project-Based Inquiry Science

DIV 62

Students will be writing explanations throughout PBIS because writing good explanations is a key part of doing science. It is important for them to understand the parts of an explanation and to be able to construct one. Writing explanations is not an easy task. They will have a chance to revise their explanations during the next section.

Highlight the term *valid*. Scientists say a claim or a test is valid if there is repeatable evidence supporting it, no evidence against it, and if it is logical.

Teacher Reflection Questions

- What difficulties did students have understanding what a scientific explanation is? Students will revisit explanations in the next section. What ideas do you have for guiding their understanding during the next section?

- Would modeling another explanation be beneficial for the students? What ideas do you have for modeling explanations?

- How did you use the student text? How could you assist students in their reading ability as well as their comprehension?

SECTION 3.6 INTRODUCTION

3.6 Iterate

More Science and More Explanation

◀ *1 class period**

Overview

A demonstration of a whirligig falling with no paper clips is used to challenge the logical idea that if fewer paper clips results in the whirligig falling more slowly, then zero paper clips will be the slowest. The demonstration also reinforces the ideas of iteration and the evolution of ideas as new information is obtained. The demonstration leads into a discussion revisiting ideas of stability and center of mass. Groups revise their explanations of falling whirligigs, incorporating new science knowledge — that the paper clips are needed to introduce stability to the whirligig, otherwise it does not fall properly. Reflecting their experience with other falling objects, groups extend their knowledge of how the forces of gravity and air resistance affect other objects. Groups then organize and connect ideas while updating the class *Project Board*.

*A class period is considered to be one 40 to 50 minute class.

Targeted Concepts, Skills, and Nature of Science	Performance Expectations
Scientists often work together and then share their findings. Sharing findings makes new information available and helps scientists refine their ideas and build on others' ideas. When another person's or group's idea is used, credit needs to be given.	Students should be able to revise their explanations based on new information they have, and update their *Project Boards* based on what they now know.
The way an object falls through air depends on its mass, surface area, and other factors.	Students should be able to describe how other factors affect the way the whirligig falls such as: The orientation of the whirligig (sideways, right side up) affects the amount of air resistance, and the number of paper clips affects the location of its center of mass and its stability.
Earth's gravity pulls objects toward Earth.	Students should be able to describe how gravity affects the motion of the whirligig.

DIVING INTO SCIENCE

Targeted Concepts, Skills, and Nature of Science	Performance Expectations
Air resistance is a force opposing the motion of an object moving through air.	Students should be able to describe what causes air resistance or drag and how it affects the motion of the whirligig.
Explanations are claims supported by evidence, accepted ideas, and facts.	Students should be able to create an explanation of why the whirligig falls the way it does based on the results of all the class experiments and science knowledge they have learned in this and previous sections.

Materials

2 per student	*Create Your Explanation* sheet
1 per class	class *Project Board*
1 or 2 per classroom	whirligig for demonstration

Activity Setup and Preparation

- Review the class *Project Board* so that during *Implementation* you can quickly point out how their ideas have changed since they started this Unit and prepare them for completing the *Whirligig Challenge*.

- Create a whirligig of basic blade length to demonstrate how it falls when no paper clips are added to it. You should do the demonstration before students open their books. You may want to try dropping a whirligig with no paper clips and a whirligig with two paper clips at the same time. Try this out first to make sure the difference in flight is noticeable. If you cannot notice a big difference in flight, you should at least notice that the whirligig with no paper clips falls in an inconsistent way, sometimes having short fall times and sometimes having long fall times.

Homework Options

Reflection
Science Content and Process: Write an explanation of why the whirligig falls as it does when no paper clips are attached to it. *(Students should use information about stability and air resistance in student text on pages 63 and 64 along with their observations.)*

Preparation for 3.7

- **Science Process:** Based on what you know now, make a recommendation to the cereal company on how to design the whirligig and explain why you made this recommendation. *(Students should try to optimize the effects so that the whirligig is stable and falls slowly.)*

NOTES

_____

_____

_____

_____

_____

_____

_____

_____

_____

_____

_____

_____

_____

_____

1 class period ▶

3.6 Iterate

More Science and More Explanation

10 min.

Challenge the idea that no paper clips on the whirligig is best, with a demonstration.

3.6 Iterate

More Science and More Explanation

Your experiments showed you that the fewer paper clips on the stem of the whirligig, the more slowly it falls. That is because with more paper clips there is more gravity pulling down on the whirligig. With fewer paper clips, there is less gravity pulling down on it, allowing it to fall more slowly.

What happens when there are no paper clips attached to the stem of a whirligig? You may wish to try this out.

The whirligig probably turned itself upside down and came down quickly.

The reason why is that the paper clips have two effects on the whirligig. They add mass, which results in the whirligig falling more quickly. They also add stability. To understand stability, think back to the *Book-Support Challenge*. You saw that if an object is not balanced, it will tip over. When the whirligig comes down in a vertical (up and down) position, its blades collide with air molecules. In a vertical position, air collides with the blades evenly. This creates a balanced and stable-falling whirligig.

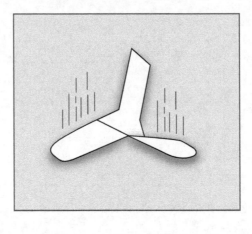

DIV 63

DIVING INTO SCIENCE

Students should not open their books yet!

○ Engage

Tell students not to open their books yet. Remind the class of their results for increasing the number of paper clips on the whirligig (it took less time to fall). Then ask students what they think would happen with no paper clips added to the whirligig's stem.

TEACHER TALK

❝What do you think will happen when I drop this whirligig without any paper clips on it? Why? Base your reasoning on the experiments the class has conducted and on what we read about how air resistance and gravity affect how something falls.❞

Next, demonstrate how a whirligig falls when no paper clips are added to it (it tilts to the side and falls in very little time since the blade edge is going through the air rather than the blade face). Consider having students describe how it is falling and elicit students' ideas of why it falls the way it does. Demonstrate the whirligig falling with two paper clips on its stem and ask students what causes the difference. Consider dropping the whirligig with no paper clips at the same time and from the same height as the whirligig with two paper clips so students can observe the differences side-by-side. Note that the whirligig with no paper clips, will fall inconsistently so drop it a few times. Sometimes it will fall more slowly than the whirligig with two paper clips, and sometimes it will fall more quickly.

△ Guide

Ask students what they think is happening to the whirligig. Then ask them how the push up from air resistance is affected when the whirligig is on its side.

Introduce the science content using the student text and emphasize the need for stability and the role air resistance plays.

> **META NOTES**
>
> When the whirligig is on its side, very little surface of the whirligig hits the air particles and hence, very little air resistance pushes up on the whirligig.

NOTES

....

....

....

....

....

....

....

....

....

Explain

15 min.

Have students revise their explanations using the new information and then discuss their new explanations with the class.

The paper clips on the stem puts the center of mass of the whirligig in a place that keeps the whirligig vertical when it falls. With nothing to keep it vertical as the whirligig falls through the air, it turns downward. When it turns, the blade surfaces no longer collide evenly with the air. There is very little air resistance. Because there is so little air resistance when it turns upside-down, it falls very quickly.

Explain

Sometimes, when you try to apply an explanation in a new situation, you find it doesn't work as expected. This is what happened when you tried to predict what would happen if you took all of the paper clips off of the stem of a whirligig. When you try to use an explanation to design a new solution or make a prediction and you get poor results, it generally means that your understanding of the science is not complete.

This is common in science. Scientists are trying to understand why things work the way they do. They make the best explanations they can as they investigate. But it takes a long time to understand anything completely. Scientists are constantly learning more. They are always revising explanations to make them more accurate and complete.

You have a chance now to do the same thing. Look at the explanations you have created so far as a class. These are the ones about blade length and the ones about paper clips. Work with your group to make those explanations better. Work on your own explanation, and work on one from a group that investigated the other variable. When you revise an explanation, sometimes you will revise the science and the reasoning included in it. Other times you will want to add new evidence or even revise the claim. It is important that all the parts of your explanation work together with each other. Make sure when you revise one part that the whole explanation still makes sense.

If you think an additional claim and explanation is needed based on what you have just learned, spend time in your group working on that too. Use a new *Create Your Explanation* page for each explanation you create.

When you are finished, you will share your revised explanations with the class and discuss the wording, so make sure it is clear and complete.

△ Guide

Assist students in making connections between how scientists must revise their explanations as they gather new information and how they need to revise their old explanations based on what they now know.

○ Get Going

Tell students to revise their old explanations using the old *Create Your Explanation* page, and write their new explanation on new sheets. Tell students how much time they have (five minutes) to complete their explanations.

☐ Assess

Check how students are updating their claims, writing explanations, and working within their groups. Listen for what types of difficulties students are having and that need to be addressed in the class discussion.

△ Guide

First, ask a couple of students to present their explanations, and with the class, assess these explanations making sure they have a claim backed by evidence and science knowledge. Then guide students by encouraging them to point out when an explanation contains an opinion, does or does not make logical sense, and when the evidence supporting it is reasonable or lacking something. An example is provided below:

Example Explanation: Stable whirligigs that do not tip fall more slowly. We observed that the whirligig with no paper clips often turned to its side and when it did it fell quickly. We learned that surface area affects the time it takes to fall. If the whirligig turns to its side, then there is not a lot of surface for the air particles to collide with and this results in a shorter fall time. We also observed that the whirligig with no paper clips often turned to its side during its fall and the whirligigs with paper clips did not tip. We learned that adding paper clip's on the stem, leads to the center of mass being located in a place that allows the whirligig not to tip over during its fall. Adding paper clips to the stem of the whirligig makes the whirligig more stable and it will consistently fall more slowly because it doesn't tip over, so the surface area of the blades will collide with more air particles decreasing the time of flight.

> **META NOTES**
>
> Examples of explanations pertaining to the experiment questions are provided in the *Implementation* notes for *Section 3.4*.

☐ Assess

Check to see if students' explanations include the need for stability during the fall of the whirligig and that a paper clip provides this by changing the location of the center of mass so the whirligig does not tip over. Also, check if students include the idea that objects fall more slowly in air when they have a larger surface area.

◇ Evaluate

Make sure that students can describe what an explanation is and pick out the parts. Students should have some ability of writing explanations, claims that are backed up by evidence and science knowledge, in a logical way and without opinions. They may not master explanations until the next Unit.

Reflect

15 min.

Help students make connections between other experiences with falling objects and what they have learned about explanations.

Reflect

Answer the following questions. Discuss your answers and how they may help you better achieve the *Whirligig Challenge* with your class.

1. What are some other objects that use air resistance to change how they fall or travel? What pull or push is air resistance opposing in your example?

2. The book support uses opposing pulls and pushes to keep the book in place. Here, the whirligig has opposing pulls and pushes, but it does not stay in one place. What would have to happen to keep the whirligig in one place when you released it?

3. Why do you think it was important to return to your explanation to review and possibly edit it? Why might your explanation be a better one by returning to it?

Update the *Project Board*

If the first four columns of the *Project Board* are out of date, spend some time as a class updating it before moving on to address the *Whirligig Challenge*.

What's the Point?

You have learned how to create explanations. You made claims about factors that affect how a whirligig falls. You supported your claims with evidence from your investigations. You also used science that you read about to back your claims. These explanations should help you and others predict what will happen in a new situation.

Sometimes, however, when you apply an explanation to a different situation, it does not work. That is usually because your understanding is not complete. In that case, you need to revise your explanation.

DIV 65

DIVING INTO SCIENCE

◯ Get Going

Inform groups that they should come up with their best answer to the three questions in the student text in the next five minutes. These questions will help students to complete the *Whirligig Challenge*. The class will be going over the responses.

△ Guide

1. If students have a hard time answering this, ask them about what objects they have seen that fall very slowly through the air. Objects students may have seen include: parachutes, seeds (as from a maple tree or dandelion), airplane, helicopter, Frisbee®, etc. Ask students

what is common about these items and what makes them fall slowly. They should note that air resistance plays a role in all of these items. Air resistance is the force that acts against the force due to gravity, pulling the object to Earth and these items have features such as large surface area and stability due to the location of their center of mass. The location of the center of mass may not be easy to realize for many items so you may want to point out that a dandelion seed has fluffly material of little mass at the top and a seed at its stem. The seed contains most of the mass so the center of mass is near the stem of the complete dandelion seed. This allows it to stay airborne and travel with the wind. Airplanes and helicopters stay airborne for different reasons. With a helicopter, the rotors are pushing air, creating an upward push from the air on the rotors that balance gravity and allows the helicopter to hover. An airplane must travel forward to stay in the air. The shape of the airplane is designed to create a difference in pressure below the wing and above it. This difference in pressure produces a force called lift that acts opposite to the force due to gravity.

META NOTES

The concepts of balanced and unbalanced forces is developed in another Unit. There is no need to go into depth of these concepts here.

2. To keep a whirligig in one place when you release it would require a force equal in size but opposite in direction to the downward pull of gravity acting on the whirligig, and it would have to be acting on the whirligig as soon as you released it. A support force like a table under the whirligig would do this, or a string attached to the whirligig and the ceiling that does not allow it to fall.

   Some may suggest air resistance, but air resistance is zero unless the object is moving through the air. Air resistance cannot be a support force at zero speed. The drag force is a force that increases as the surface area increases, and it increases as the speed increases. Air resistance is initially zero when you drop an object and then increases as the object moves through the air, colliding with the air particles. The drag force reaches its maximum value when it equals the force due to gravity acting on the falling object. At this point the object reaches what is called its terminal speed or maximum speed. It can no longer speed up because the overall force acting on the object is zero (the drag force and force due to gravity add up to zero since they are of the same size and opposite direction). The drag force can never be equal to the gravitational force when the object is not moving because the drag force is zero when the object has zero speed.

3. As you get more information, your explanation will be more complete, making it better. It is important to return to your explanation and edit it whenever you have more information or understanding of the phenomenon you are interested in. Prompt

students to think about how they changed their explanations. Students should realize that their explanations can now include information about stability and how that is needed in order for the whirligig to fall slowly through the air.

Update the Project Board

10 min.

Guide the class as they update their Project Board *based on what they now know.*

Update the *Project Board*

If the first four columns of the *Project Board* are out of date, spend some time as a class updating it before moving on to address the *Whirligig Challenge*.

⬡ Get Going

Remind the class of what the first four columns of the Project Board are: *What do we think we know? What do we need to investigate? What are we learning?* and *What is our evidence?* Remind students also of what has already been recorded on the Project Board.

Ask students to use information on the *Create Your Explanation* pages to update the class's *Project Board*. Students should focus on columns 3 and 4 since they have been introduced to more science knowledge. Students may have additions to columns 1 and 2 as well.

◇ Evaluate

As students are updating the project board make sure the following are on the *Project Board*:

- Claims made about how the paper clips on the stem of the whirligig affect the stability of the whirligig and the effect they have on how the whirligig falls, as well as the evidence supporting this (columns 3 and 4). You might ask students what they learned about the stability of the whirligig today and what claims they can make about it based on their observations. Their observations are evidence supporting the claims and should be described in column 4 and linked to the claims in column 3.

- Questions recorded in column 2 referring to how to make the whirligig fall as slowly as possible by optimizing the variables of the number of paper clips and the blade length (surface area). You might ask what new questions students have about how to construct the whirligig so it meets the challenge of falling as slowly as possible and being made from the back of a cereal box and paper clips.

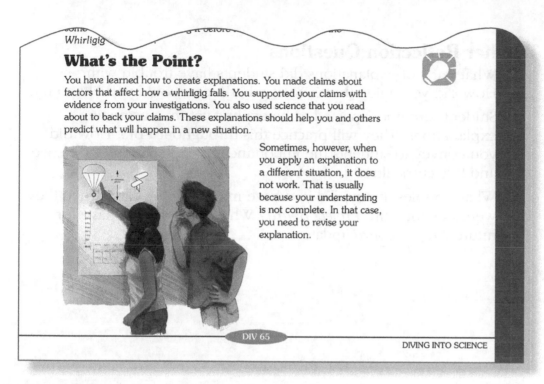

What's the Point?

You have learned how to create explanations. You made claims about factors that affect how a whirligig falls. You supported your claims with evidence from your investigations. You also used science that you read about to back your claims. These explanations should help you and others predict what will happen in a new situation.

Sometimes, however, when you apply an explanation to a different situation, it does not work. That is usually because your understanding is not complete. In that case, you need to revise your explanation.

DIV 65

DIVING INTO SCIENCE

What's the Point?

5 min.

◇ Evaluate

It is important that students understand that a scientific explanation is a statement where a claim(s) is backed up by evidence and science knowledge in a logical way. Students will be constructing explanations throughout PBIS.

Assessment Options

Targeted Concepts, Skills, and Nature of Science	How do I know if students got it?
Explanations are claims supported by evidence, accepted ideas, and facts.	**ASK:** Students should tell you what an explanation is and why it is O.K. to revise it. **LISTEN:** Students should be able to state that an explanation is a statement made up of a claim or claims supported by evidence and science knowledge in a logical way, and explanations should be revised as new information becomes available.

Teacher Reflection Questions

- What parts of explanations did students have trouble with? How did you guide them? What other ideas would you like to try?

- Students are not expected to be experts yet in constructing explanations. They will practice this throughout PBIS. How did you convey to students the importance of explanations in science and this curriculum?

- What troubles, if any, did you have managing the class when they were updating the *Project Board?* What ideas do you have for future *Project Board* updates?

NOTES

....

....

....

....

....

....

....

....

....

....

....

....

BACK TO THE CHALLENGE INTRODUCTION

Back to the Challenge

The Whirligig Challenge

Overview

While the class records their explanations in the last column of its *Project Board*, they are organizing and connecting all they learned during this Unit that is related to completing the *Whirligig Challenge*. Students are introduced to recommendations and then each student completes the challenge by writing a letter recommending to the cereal company how they should design the whirligig and why they should design it that way. Writing the letter of recommendation helps to develop students' clarity of reasoning and expression.

Targeted Concepts, Skills, and Nature of Science	Performance Expectations
Explanations are claims supported by evidence, accepted ideas, and facts.	Students should be able to write a good recommendation based on their explanations containing claims, evidence from their investigations, and science knowledge.
Scientists make claims (conclusions) based on evidence obtained (trends in data) from reliable investigations.	
The way an object falls through air depends on its mass, surface area, and other factors.	
Earth's gravity pulls Objects toward Earth.	
Air resistance is a force opposing the motion of an object moving through air.	

Materials

1 per class   class *Project Board*

DIVING INTO SCIENCE

Homework Options

- **Science Content and Process:** Complete the letter of recommendation to the cereal company. *(Letters should contain good explanations supporting their recommendations and should include ideas of how stability, gravity, and air resistance affect the whirligig's fall time.)*

- **Science Content and Process:** Construct a whirligig based on your letter of recommendation to the cereal company. *(Students' whirligigs should embody their recommendations. Consider having a class challenge where students vote on the best and slowest whirligig.)*

NOTES

Back to the Challenge

The Whirligig Challenge

You have raised questions about how a whirligig works and how it could be made better. You then designed and did experiments to begin to find out answers to those questions. Afterwards, you interpreted your results and made some claims. You also read some science that helped you understand more about the whirligig and how it works. Finally, you created and revised explanations to go with each of your claims. You have talked a lot about what affects how things fall. It is time now to identify your answers to how things fall and to apply what you have learned to the *Whirligig Challenge*. What will you tell the president of the cereal company? You will need to make recommendations and justify your recommendations with science. The last column of the *Project Board* is where you record the things that will help you answer your question and address your challenge.

Updating the *Project Board*

What does it mean for the challenge or question?

The last column on the *Project Board* helps you pull together everything you have learned. You can then use this to answer the driving question or address the challenge. Each investigation you do is like a piece of a puzzle. You must then fit the pieces together to help you address the challenge. Each piece provides you with a critical factor that must be addressed to answer the question. Your question was, *What affects how an object falls toward Earth?* The last column is the place to record what you have learned about the roles air resistance and gravity in affecting how things fall.

recommendation: a claim that suggests what to do in certain situations.

This column is also the place to record **recommendations** about how to address the challenge. Each of the sets of investigations you carried out told you some different things about how to make a slower-falling whirligig. The experiments with paper clips told you about the effects of extra mass or matter on how quickly a whirligig will fall. The experiments with blade length gave you ideas about how they might better shape the blades so that it will fall more slowly. You will pull them together now to make recommendations.

With your class, compose recommendations about how to design a better whirligig. Put them in the last column of the *Project Board*.

DIV 66

◯ Engage

First review with the class what they have done so far: investigated two variables that affect the time it takes the whirligig to fall, learned science knowledge pertaining to how the whirligig falls, and learned how to construct an explanation. Then ask students what kinds of things they would write in their letter of recommendation to the president of the cereal company.

Tell students they will use the *Project Board* to organize all the information and ideas they have so that they can come up with good recommendations.

Updating the Project Board

20 min.

Guide the class in recording their explanations in the Project Board, *focusing on the last column, which will contain students' explanations and recommendations.*

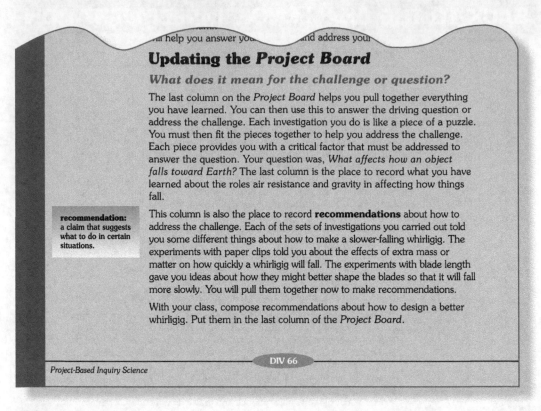

...ill help you answer yo... ...nd address you...

Updating the *Project Board*

What does it mean for the challenge or question?

The last column on the *Project Board* helps you pull together everything you have learned. You can then use this to answer the driving question or address the challenge. Each investigation you do is like a piece of a puzzle. You must then fit the pieces together to help you address the challenge. Each piece provides you with a critical factor that must be addressed to answer the question. Your question was, *What affects how an object falls toward Earth?* The last column is the place to record what you have learned about the roles air resistance and gravity in affecting how things fall.

recommendation: a claim that suggests what to do in certain situations.

This column is also the place to record **recommendations** about how to address the challenge. Each of the sets of investigations you carried out told you some different things about how to make a slower-falling whirligig. The experiments with paper clips told you about the effects of extra mass or matter on how quickly a whirligig will fall. The experiments with blade length gave you ideas about how they might better shape the blades so that it will fall more slowly. You will pull them together now to make recommendations.

With your class, compose recommendations about how to design a better whirligig. Put them in the last column of the *Project Board*.

DIV 66

Project-Based Inquiry Science

◯ Get Going

Let students know that they are now ready to record their explanations in the last column of their class *Project Board*. First they will answer the *Big Question What affects how things fall?* The answer to this question will be composed of information they have already put in columns 3 *What are we learning?* and 4 *What's is our evidence?* Let students know that after they have completed answering this question then they will learn how to write a formal recommendation and put these in the *Project Board*.

△ Guide

Ask students for their answers on what affects how things fall and edit their ideas until the class agrees that it likes the explanation. Then put their explanations in the fifth column. Examples are provided below:

What affects how things fall?

Gravity affects how things fall. Gravity arises because of an attraction between two objects with mass. It's a small force and you don't notice it unless one of the objects is very massive — like Earth. Objects fall to Earth because of the gravitational attraction between Earth and the object.

Air resistance affects how things fall. When something falls through air it collides with the particles of air and has to move the air out of the way. This causes an upward push on an object falling down. This upward push is sometimes called *drag*.

The shape of the object affects how it falls in air. When the object has a larger surface going through the air (like the flower-patterned coffee filters, or the whirligig with longer blades), it collides with more air particles resulting in the object falling more slowly then an object with a smaller surface area.

The mass of the object affects how it falls in air. When the object has a greater mass (same surface/shape), it tends to fall in less time.

The stability of an object (or where its center of mass is) affects how an object falls. For example, the whirligig tumbles and falls inconsistently and on the average more quickly if it has no paper clips on its stem.

Transition students to recommendations by letting them know that not only do their explanations go into the fifth column of the *Project Board*, but their recommendations about how to address the challenge also go into this column. Their recommendations will be based on the evidence they have in columns 3 and 4.

Then describe for students the parts of a recommendation using the student text. Emphasize that recommendations are a kind of claim that take the form: "When some situations occurs, then do or try or expect something." Sometimes recommendations can be in the form: "If something then something."

○ Get Going

Ask students to work in groups to come up with their best group recommendation. Remind them to review their explanations and to make sure their recommendations connect to columns 3 and 4 of the *Project Board*. (About five minutes.)

△ Guide

Hold a class discussion asking a group to provide their recommendation and allowing other groups to comment on their recommendation. Display each recommendation in a place where the class may edit it before it is placed on the *Project Board*. Group similar recommendations together so that they may be combined before writing them on the *Project Board*.

Assist the class in making recommendations based on single ideas, by asking students to support their recommendations with evidence from column 4, and their explanations of how things fall from column 5. Write the recommendations the class makes in column 5. Let students know that they will put together all the recommendations when they construct the letters of recommendation to the cereal company.

Here are examples of the three main recommendations students should make and why. Look for these ideas and guide students to them if they are having trouble. Remember that students wording may be very different from these examples.

META NOTES

The surface area affects the drag force and this is what affects the time of fall. The larger the surface area the lower the terminal speed of the object.

META NOTES

The mass affects the maximum drag force and results in the object reaching a higher terminal speed. This is what affects the time of fall.

META NOTES

Some students might say that increasing surface area affects the drag force acting on the object and this in turn decreases the time of flight.

- If you want to make a consistently slow-falling whirligig then you need to make sure it is stable. To do this you should place at least one paper clip on the stem, otherwise the whirligig will tumble and fall on its side rather quickly. This was verified by a demonstration we observed. If the whirligig tumbles to its side it will fall rapidly to Earth.

- If you want to build a slow-falling whirligig that fits on the back of a cereal box, then you should add as few paper clips as possible. This is based on the investigation we did in which we observed that as the mass of the whirligig increased (by increasing the number of paper clips) the time of fall decreased. The whirligig falls because of the force of gravity between Earth and the whirligig. As this force increases it affects the drag force in such a way that the whirligig takes less time to fall.

- If you want to build a slow-falling whirligig then you should have its blade as long and wide as possible. This is based on our investigations in which we observed that as the blade length increased the time of fall decreased, and on the science knowledge that as the surface area falling through air increases, the object will fall more slowly to the ground.

◇ **Evaluate**

Before students move on, make sure they have made recommendation based on the stability (need at least one paper clip), mass (number of paper clips), and surface area (blade length).

NOTES

Be a Scientist

Making Recommendations

A recommendation is a kind of claim that suggests to someone what to do when certain kinds of situations occur. It can have this form:

When some situation occurs, **do** or **try** or **expect** something.

For example, if you want to make a recommendation for crossing the street you might say the following:

When you have the right of way, **expect** that some cars will not have time to stop in time.

When you have the right of way, look **(do)** both ways to make sure the traffic has stopped.

Recommendations might also begin with *if*. For example,

If you have the right of way, and the traffic has stopped, **then** you can cross the street.

For each recommendation, make sure to identify the evidence and science knowledge that support it (from columns 3 and 4).

Address the Challenge

Your challenge from the cereal company was to create a whirligig that would fall more slowly than the one they have on boxes now. Write a short letter addressed to the president of the company explaining how and why you would change the whirligig. Use what is on the *Project Board* to write your letter – the questions you answered, what you found out, your evidence for those things, the science that helps you explain why you got the results you did, the science that helps you answer the question, and the recommendations about whirligig design that you pulled from your experience. Your letter should spell out specific recommendations you are making about how to change the basic whirligig design to make it fall more slowly. For each of your recommendations, be sure to include the evidence you have that this is a good recommendation and the science you've learned that backs up your recommendation.

DIV 67

DIVING INTO SCIENCE

Address the Challenge
15 min.

Begin students on writing their letter of recommendations to the president of the cereal company using the information in the class's Project Board.

◯ Get Going

Review the expectations of the challenge: the whirligig must fit on the back of a cereal box and fall as slowly as possible. The only materials are the cereal box and paper clips. Assume the customer has scissors.

Have students write their recommendations individually. Emphasize that for the recommendations to be good, they must include the evidence from their observations and the science that backs up their recommendations.

Consider having students read their letters of recommendation to the class, trade their letters and giving each other feedback, or collecting their letters and providing individual feedback to the students.

◇ Evaluate

Evaluate students' letters of recommendation. They should contain suggestions on what the cereal company should do based on the evidence they collected during their investigations and the science knowledge presented to them. Look specifically for a description of stability (why you should have at least one paper clip), keeping the mass as low as possible (effect of increased mass on time of flight), and increasing the surface of the blade (effect of surface area on time of flight.)

NOTES

_____

_____

_____

_____

_____

_____

_____

_____

_____

_____

_____

_____

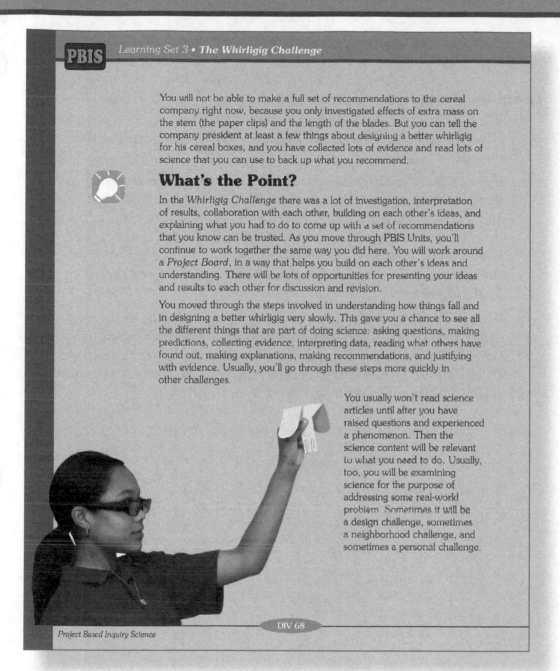

You will not be able to make a full set of recommendations to the cereal company right now, because you only investigated effects of extra mass on the stem (the paper clips) and the length of the blades. But you can tell the company president at least a few things about designing a better whirligig for his cereal boxes, and you have collected lots of evidence and read lots of science that you can use to back up what you recommend.

What's the Point?

In the *Whirligig Challenge* there was a lot of investigation, interpretation of results, collaboration with each other, building on each other's ideas, and explaining what you had to do to come up with a set of recommendations that you know can be trusted. As you move through PBIS Units, you'll continue to work together the same way you did here. You will work around a *Project Board*, in a way that helps you build on each other's ideas and understanding. There will be lots of opportunities for presenting your ideas and results to each other for discussion and revision.

You moved through the steps involved in understanding how things fall and in designing a better whirligig very slowly. This gave you a chance to see all the different things that are part of doing science: asking questions, making predictions, collecting evidence, interpreting data, reading what others have found out, making explanations, making recommendations, and justifying with evidence. Usually, you'll go through these steps more quickly in other challenges.

You usually won't read science articles until after you have raised questions and experienced a phenomenon. Then the science content will be relevant to what you need to do. Usually, too, you will be examining science for the purpose of addressing some real-world problem. Sometimes it will be a design challenge, sometimes a neighborhood challenge, and sometimes a personal challenge.

Project Based Inquiry Science

DIV 68

What's the Point?

5 min.

It is important that students recognize the process they have been using to answer questions — they have been working together to investigate, interpret results, constructing explanations, and make recommendations. They have worked in small groups and then shared their ideas with the class and built on each other's ideas.

META NOTES

If you have already introduced the student letter at the beginning of the student text (page x) then refer back to it during this time. Otherwise, introduce the student letter after students complete this Unit.

Teacher Reflection Questions

- What difficulties did students have constructing a recommendation? How did you address these? What ideas do you have for the future?

- In PBIS the challenge acts to motivate and engage students in goals of the *Learning Set* and the *Big Challenge* acts to motivate and engage students in the goals of the Unit. How could you tell if your students were motivated by the challenge and reached the goals of the *Learning Set?* What ideas do you have to motivate students to reach the goals of the Unit by the end of the next *Learning Set?*

- What difficulties with group work are you noticing in the class? How can you resolve these issues? (You may want to Google "cooperative learning" online or refer to some books on collaborative groups such as: *The Nuts and Bolts of Cooperative Learning* (Johnson, Johnson, & Holubec, 1994).

NOTES

4.0

LEARNING SET 4 INTRODUCTION

Learning Set 4
The Parachute Challenge

◀ $9\frac{1}{2}$ *class periods**

Students work in groups and practice design and investigation skills as they build parachutes that fall as slowly as possible, using coffee filters, string, tape, and washers.

Overview

Students design, construct and investigate a coffee-filter parachute as they continue to research how things fall. Their goal is to figure out how to make the parachute fall as slowly as possible. Students design and run experiments to find out how various variables affect the way a parachute falls while applying what they have learned in previous *Learning Sets*. Based on their experimental results from investigating the parachute and on science knowledge, students create and present explanations of what affects how the parachute falls. Students also create recommendations for how to design a slow-falling parachute and groups begin an iterative process of designing a parachute. Groups present their design ideas to get feedback from the class on their parachute plans and in the end to share their final designs and solutions. Throughout the *Learning Set*, students organize their questions, ideas, and solutions on the class *Project Board*. Finally, the class compares the performance of the different parachutes and interprets the results.

*A class period is considered to be one 40 to 50 minute class.

Targeted Concepts, Skills, and Nature of Science	Section
Criteria and constraints are important in design.	4.1
Identifying factors that lead to variation is an important part of scientific investigations.	4.1
Scientists often work together and then share their findings. Sharing findings makes new information available and helps scientists refine their ideas and build on others' ideas. When another person's or group's idea is used, credit needs to be given.	4.1, 4.3, 4.5, 4.6
Scientists must keep clear, accurate, and descriptive records of what they do so they can share their work with others, consider what they did, why they did it, and what they want to do next.	4.2, 4.6

235

Targeted Concepts, Skills, and Nature of Science	Section
Scientific investigations and measurements are considered reliable if the results are repeatable by other scientists using the same procedures.	4.2
In a fair test, only the manipulated (independent) variable, and the responding (dependent) variable change. All other variables are held constant.	4.2
Scientists make claims (conclusions) based on evidence (trends in data) from reliable investigations.	4.2, 4.3, 4.7
Explanations are claims supported by evidence, accepted ideas and facts.	4.4, 4.7
The way an object falls through air depends on its mass, surface area, and other factors.	4.4, 4.7
Earth's gravity pulls things toward Earth.	4.4, 4.7
Air resistance is a force opposing the motion of an object moving through air.	4.4, 4.7

Students' Initial Conceptions and Capabilities

- Students may have trouble evaluating a design or applying knowledge from other contexts during the design process (McCormick et al, 1993).

- Students are often quick to infer causality (Kuhn et al, 1988), and they may accept conclusions based on weak evidence.

- Even when students have a notion of how to make a fair comparison, they may have trouble applying this to novel investigations (Wollman, 1977a, 1977b; Wollman and Lawson, 1977).

- They may not see the need to actively identify variables that should be controlled (Linn and Swiney, 1981; Linn et al, 1983).

- Students also may not distinguish between explanations, claims, evidence, and prior knowledge (Allen, Statkiewitz, and Donovan, 1983; Kuhn, 1991, 1992; Roseberry, Warren, and Conant, 1992).

- Students may have difficulty understanding the interaction of forces, such as the interaction of gravity and the drag or air resistance on a parachute's canopy (Gunstone and Watts, 1985).

- Students may believe that a constant velocity requires a constant force (Gunstone and Watts, 1985).

Understanding for Teachers

The two forces that affect the parachute as it falls are gravity and drag (air resistance). Please refer to the *Understanding for Teachers* in *Learning Sets 1* and *3* for information on these forces and how they affect a falling object.

NOTES

....

....

....

....

....

....

....

....

....

....

....

....

....

....

NOTES

LEARNING SET 4 IMPLEMENTATION

Learning Set 4

The Parachute Challenge

You have learned a bit about how things fall. You will continue learning about how things fall, but this time you will be designing parachutes.

The cereal company took your advice about the whirligig changes. The changes to the whirligig made the toy more fun for children. As a result, the company sold more cereal. Now the company is back again for advice because they trust your input. They want to place another fun toy inside the cereal box. This toy also involves something falling slowly to the ground – a parachute.

The toy is free. Therefore, the cost of the toy to the cereal company must be very low. They want you to make the parachutes out of simple materials. They suggest coffee filters. Also, the slower the parachute falls, the more fun the toy will be. Your challenge is to design, test, and construct a parachute from coffee filters that will fall as slowly as possible.

In groups, you will investigate several variables. You will look at what affects the time it takes a parachute to fall to the ground. Each group will investigate a different variable. You will then present, explain, and defend your work and results to other groups.

DIV 69

DIVING INTO SCIENCE

1 class period ▶

Learning Set 4

The Parachute Challenge

10 min.

Introduce students to the challenge — to design a parachute made of coffee filters, string, and a washer, that falls as slowly as possible.

⭕ Engage

Begin by telling students about the cereal company and its goals. Then discuss why a parachute might be a fun toy to put in a cereal box. You can point out the ways a parachute is similar to the whirligig, and how the things that made the whirligig fun might also make a parachute fun.

META NOTES

Students might suggest that a colorful parachute or a parachute with a load shaped like a certain animal would be fun. Features such as these might make the parachute more interesting but that won't necessarily affect the speed at which the parachute falls.

"The cereal company now wants to put a parachute in their cereal boxes. It has to be made out of simple materials—coffee filters, string, and washers. Remember they wanted to put the whirligig in their cereal boxes because they thought it would help sell cereal and they thought that if it fell more slowly it would be more fun. Similarly, the parachute will be more fun if it falls slowly. You'll have to figure out what affects the way a coffee-filter parachute falls, design a coffee-filter parachute, and then test your parachute. Then you'll have to make recommendations to the cereal company on how they should design their parachute."

NOTES

....

....

....

....

....

....

....

....

....

PBIS   *Learning Set 4 • The Parachute Challenge*

As before, you will do this in an *Investigation Expo*. You will then make recommendations for designing and building parachutes. You will explain your recommendations using the data you collect and the science content you learn. With the lessons you learn, you will design and build your best parachute. Then, as a final activity, everyone will drop and time their parachutes. You will see which one falls the slowest and discuss why. This is probably the design you will suggest to the company. Everyone will write a letter to the company suggesting this design and why it is the right one.

This time, you'll move through the steps much more quickly than before. You now know the basics of working together, doing science, and making recommendations. You will use what you have learned before in meeting this challenge.

DIV 70

Project-Based Inquiry Science

META NOTES

The *Parachute Challenge* of this Learning Set has students apply what they have learned in previous *Learning Sets*. Some students may find this difficult, however, keep in mind that the model used for the *Whirligig Challenge* is the same as that used for the *Parachute Challenge*. Students should find this *Learning Set* easier to move through since no new skills or processes are required and most of the content is the same. Students should use their ideas about falling, testing ideas, design, and sharing and explaining ideas from the whirligig experience.

Then remind students of what they've done so far in this Unit (planning and constructing a design, designing an investigation, investigating how objects fall, and how to construct explanations and recommendations). Let students know that in this *Learning Set* they will be pulling together and applying what they have learned from the previous *Learning Sets*.

SECTION 4.1 INTRODUCTION

4.1 Understand the Challenge

Thinking about the Parachute Challenge

◀ *1 class period**

*A class period is considered to be one 40 to 50 minute class.

Overview

Students are challenged to design a slow-falling toy parachute that can be put inside a cereal box. They explore the materials they will use to build the parachutes and identify the criteria and constraints of the challenge, as well as the variables they need to investigate to design a slow-falling parachute. They update the same *Project Board* they used in the *Whirligig Challenge* with what they now think they know about how things fall and with questions they have about what makes a parachute fall slowly.

Targeted Concepts, Skills, and Nature of Science	Performance Expectations
Criteria and constraints are important in design.	Students should identify the criteria and the constraints for the challenge.
Identifying factors that lead to variation is an important part of scientific investigations.	Student groups should be able to identify variables that could affect the time it takes a parachute to fall and discuss these when the class updates the *Project Board*.
Scientists often work together and then share their findings. Sharing findings makes new information available and helps scientists refine their ideas and build on others' ideas. When another persons or group's idea is used, credit needs to be given.	Students should be able to describe the benefits of working in small groups and then sharing ideas as a class.

Materials

5	per group	coffee filters
1	per class	250 ft spool of cotton string
4	per group	washers (outer diameter 1")
5	per class	safety scissors
5	per class	roll of transparent tape
1	per student	*Messing About Observations* page
1	per group	metric ruler
1	per group	stopwatch
1	per class	class *Project Board*

Students should be careful not to swing around string with washers attached to it.

Because students will be dropping the parachute at heights greater than 6 ft, take precautions to ensure that the area from which students drop their parachutes will not endanger anyone or any property. Students must be supervised as they drop their parachutes.

Activity Setup and Preparation

- Consider whether you want to change student groups or keep the same groups as in *Learning Set 3*. Groups should be composed of three to four students. There should be at least five groups and no more than eight.

- Decide how you want to arrange the classroom. Keep in mind that students will need to drop their parachutes from a height greater than 6 ft., and they will need an area clear of obstacles that could interfere with the fall of the parachute.

- Create a materials station so groups may select what they wish to investigate or have the materials separated and ready to hand out at the beginning of class.

- Construct a model parachute (as in the image) to help in describing the parts and demonstrating how it falls to the class.

- Cut two pieces of string so that they are about equal to the diameter of the coffee filter.

- Tie the washer to the midpoint of both strings.

- Tape the ends of the string to four equidistant places on the rim of the coffee filter. You may fold the coffee filter in quarters and unfold it. The creases will be equidistant.

Homework Options

Reflection

- **Science Process:** Sketch and describe your first parachute. What do you plan to do differently next time and why? *(Students' plans should take account of the variables that were found, as well as the criteria and constraints.)*

- **Science Content:** List all the variables you think affect the time it takes the parachute to fall and why. Which two do you think most affect the time of flight? *(Students' answers should include the features of the parachute that they can change, such as the area of the canopy, the length of the string, and the weight of the load.)*

Preparation for 4.2

- **Science Process:** Pick one of the variables you identified. How would you investigate the effects of that variable? *(Students should plan to control other variables while they change each variable they identified in some way.)*

- **Science Process:** Do you think a parachute will fall faster if it falls straight down than if it drifts or sways back and forth? Why? How could you test for this? *(To test for this, students first have to determine what makes parachutes drift and sway back and forth. They may not be able to give a good answer at this point, but this is something they should start thinking about.)*

SECTION 4.1 IMPLEMENTATION

4.1 Understand the Challenge

Thinking about the Parachute Challenge

Mess About with Parachutes

To better understand the challenge, you are going to *Mess About* with parachutes. Afterward, you will gather around the *Project Board* to discuss what you observed. You will identify the criteria and constraints of the challenge. You will also develop questions you need to answer to address the challenge and to better understand how things fall.

The parachute has several parts. Look at the diagram. Be sure to use the correct names when you talk about these parts.

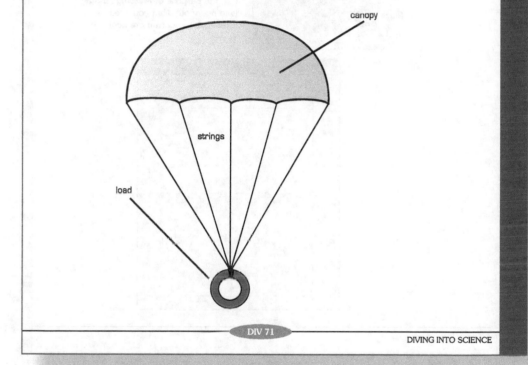

canopy

strings

load

DIV 71

DIVING INTO SCIENCE

4.1 Understand the Challenge

Thinking about the Parachute Challenge

Mess About with Parachutes

15 min

Get students thinking about the variables they need to investigate by having them Mess About *with parachutes.*

△ Guide

Begin by briefly describing the parts of a parachute (canopy, strings, and load), pointing out the diagram in the student text on page 71 and in an example parachute that you will demonstrate. Demonstrate your model parachute. Make sure students understand that your model parachute is not necessarily the ideal parachute.

Next, ask students what they think they might want to know about parachutes before they design one. You can write students' ideas on the board for later reference. Students should identify features of a toy parachute that they can change and that might affect how the parachute falls, such as the size of a canopy, the weight of the load, and the length of the strings.

Materials
- coffee filters
- string
- washers
- transparent tape
- stopwatch
- ruler
- scissors

Obtain the materials to make a basic parachute. These include coffee filters, strings, tape, and washers. Look at the model parachute presented by your teacher. You will have about ten minutes to construct a similar parachute and drop it several times. Remember, *Messing About* means exploring how something looks or works. You will have a chance to figure out the structure, behavior, and mechanisms of the parachute. In this case, you are *Messing About* to try to figure out what variables might affect how quickly or slowly a parachute falls.

Use a *Messing-About Observations* page. Record your observations, ideas, and questions. Then list the variables that you think you might be able to test to determine their effect on a parachute's fall. Remember that the purpose of *Messing About* is to figure out what you need to investigate or learn more about.

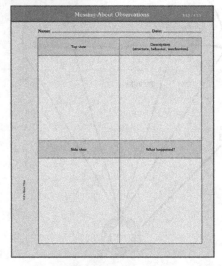

Project-Based Inquiry Science

Project-Based Inquiry Science

> ### TEACHER TALK
>
> **"**You've seen what the coffee-filter parachute looks like, and we discussed the parts of a parachute. What else might you want to know to build a slow-falling parachute? What do you think will affect the time it takes the parachute to reach the ground?**"**

Show students their class *Project Board* and ask students if they learned anything about the way things fall in the *Whirligig Challenge* that they could apply to the *Parachute Challenge*.

> ### TEACHER TALK
>
> **"**When you designed whirligigs, you thought a lot about what affects how an object falls toward the ground. What did you learn while designing the whirligigs that you can use in designing the parachutes? What makes things fall faster or slower? We recorded everything you learned on the *Project Board*. Take a look.**"**

After students have suggested a few things that might have an effect on how a parachute falls, remind them that *Messing About* is a good way of exploring how something works. In this case, they will *Mess About* with parachutes to identify the variables that they will need to know more about before they design their parachutes.

○ Get Going

Tell students they are now going to *Mess About* for a short time with the parachute materials. They should explore many different variables like they did with the whirligig. Then distribute the materials.

> ### TEACHER TALK
>
> **"**Now you're going to get to explore the parachute to see what variables affect the time it takes the whirligig to reach the ground. You'll want to try out a lot of different things to learn as much as you can.**"**

☐ Assess

As students are exploring the parachute, check to see that groups are making observations and identifying variables. Ask for some of the variables they have identified. They might identify canopy size or shape, string length, load weight, or number of strings. If any students are confused about variables, take a moment to review the concept of variables with the class. Page 44 in *Learning Set 3* is where variables were introduced.

> **META NOTES**
>
> Students might think they already know everything about falling. Encourage them to explore to see if there is anything yet to learn.

> **META NOTES**
>
> The science of parachutes is basically the same as the science involved in describing and explaining how a whirligig falls through air. The difference is that the parachute has different variables that affect how it falls. A description of what affects how the parachute falls is in *Section 4.4*.

Identify Criteria and Constraints

5 min.

Lead students in a discussion to identify the criteria and constraints of the Parachute Challenge.

Identify Criteria and Constraints

Criteria are what you need your parachute to be able to do. Constraints are the limitations you have to keep in mind as you design it. It is always a good idea to identify criteria and constraints when working on a design challenge. That way, you have a way of checking which of your ideas are worth spending more time on. You can also identify which ideas are not worth spending time on. List and discuss the criteria and constraints.

Revise the *Project Board*

When you were designing your whirligigs, you raised the question: *What affects how an object falls toward Earth?* You already know some things about the answer to this question. You wrote them on the *Project Board* you used for the *Whirligig Challenge*. You will be addressing the same question for this challenge. Therefore, you will continue to use the same *Project Board*.

There will be some things on the board that are specific to whirligigs. You won't use them in this challenge. But, you will find that much of what is on the board is relevant to designing your parachutes. Now that you've messed about with parachute materials, you probably have some new ideas about how to answer this question. You also may have some smaller questions you need to answer to determine what affects how a parachute falls toward Earth. Now is a good time to return to the *Project Board*.

To begin, as you did before, you will review what you think you know about falling objects. As a result of your work with whirligigs, you know more now than you did a week ago. You should also include in the *What do we think we know?* column what you think you know about parachutes and how they fall.

As you noticed while working on the *Whirligig Challenge*, some of your observations might have confused you. These questions go into the *What do we need to investigate?* column. Now that you know about variables, try to write some of these questions so that they ask about the effects of variables on how something falls. For example, you have probably seen parachutes in the movies or on TV. They are not all the same shape. You might want to ask one of these questions (or both):

- *How does the shape of the parachute's canopy affect how fast a parachute falls?*
- *How does the shape of the parachute's canopy affect the path it takes as it falls?*

DIV 73

DIVING INTO SCIENCE

△ Guide

Begin with ideas from students' exploration of the parachute to determine the criteria and constraints of the *Parachute Challenge*. Students may include criteria such as a minimum number of strings, a minimum load, as few materials as possible (to reduce costs). Students may include criteria more specific to their observations while exploring the parachute, and should support these criteria with their observations. The constraints are the materials (coffee filters, tape, string, and washers).

Record the list of criteria and constraints for the class to see.

◇ Evaluate

The class list of criteria should include "the parachute must fall slowly" and "the parachute must carry a load." They may also include a criterion about the stability of the parachute, requiring it to fall nearly straight down. In their list of constraints, they should list the materials they have to use (coffee filters, tape, string, and washers). They may also say that the parachute must fit in a cereal box.

⬡ Get Going

After the class has completed its list of criteria and constraints, ask them to take out their class *Project Board* pages and write on the top "The *Parachute Challenge*" and a third question: "What affects the time it takes a parachute to reach the ground?"

△ Guide

Then ask students what they think they know about what affects how a parachute falls to the ground and list these ideas in column 1 of the class's *Project Board*. Students might have ideas about how the weight of the parachute, the balance of the parachute, or the shape of the parachute affects how it falls.

TEACHER TALK

"Did you see anything new about how things fall when you were exploring how a parachute falls? We'll put that in column 1 of the *Project Board*.

Think about the structure of the parachute and what you observed when you explored the parachute. What do you think you know affects how the parachute falls? Let's put that in column 1 too."

Finally, help students put together a list of things they need to investigate. Their questions should take the form of: "How does ... affect how slowly a parachute falls?" All of the variables students identify should be addressed in this list. The two questions provided in *Revise the Project Board* can be used to guide students' thinking.

TEACHER TALK

"What parts of the parachute do you think affect the time it takes to fall? What else might affect the time it takes the parachute to fall?"

Revise the Project Board
15 min.

Transition the discussion to what they know and what they need to find out about how parachutes fall.

META NOTES

Students will record their ideas in columns 1 and 2 of the *Project Board*. The remaining columns will be filled out after students do their investigations. Remember that the 3rd and 4th columns are discussed together: the 3rd lists the claims and the 4th lists the evidence that backs up the claims. The 5th column contains explanations and recommendations to the *Big Questions* of the *Project Board*, for example, *What affects how a parachute falls?*

META NOTES

Listen for any disagreement between students or uncertainty in this discussion; if students disagree about something they've learned, this is a good indicator that it belongs in column 2.

META NOTES

Remember to keep track of when items were posted on the *Project Board*. That way, students can monitor changes in their ideas and their progress on the challenge. You should date the entries and link related entries across columns with arrows that connect them.

☐ Assess

With students, look over the ideas and questions on the *Project Board*. Make sure everyone has had the opportunity to contribute and that all contributions are represented on the *Project Board*.

Some features of parachutes that students might identify as things to investigate are:

- Canopy: size, weight, and placement
- Holes: size and placement
- Strings: length, number, placement
- Load: weight
- Height dropped from
- How the parachute is dropped
- Vents in the canopy

◇ Evaluate

Make sure ideas or questions about the mass of the load and the surface area are included.

NOTES

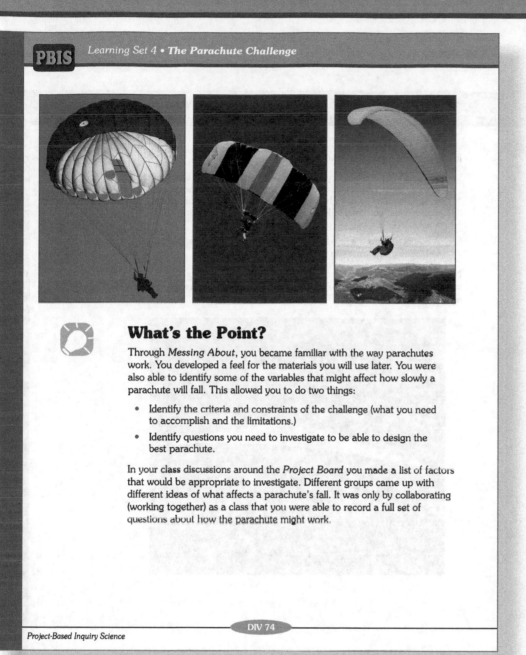

Learning Set 4 • *The Parachute Challenge*

What's the Point?
10 min.

What's the Point?

Through *Messing About*, you became familiar with the way parachutes work. You developed a feel for the materials you will use later. You were also able to identify some of the variables that might affect how slowly a parachute will fall. This allowed you to do two things:

- Identify the criteria and constraints of the challenge (what you need to accomplish and the limitations.)
- Identify questions you need to investigate to be able to design the best parachute.

In your class discussions around the *Project Board* you made a list of factors that would be appropriate to investigate. Different groups came up with different ideas of what affects a parachute's fall. It was only by collaborating (working together) as a class that you were able to record a full set of questions about how the parachute might work.

DIV 74

Project-Based Inquiry Science

△ Guide

Emphasize that by *Messing About* and identifying the variables involved in a parachute's fall, students were able to identify the criteria and constraints of the challenge and to identify the questions they need to investigate to design the best parachute.

It is important to remember two earlier lessons:

- *Messing About* can help you understand the problem you are trying to solve or the question you are trying to answer. It is important to begin to understand a problem before trying to solve it. You should identify exactly what you need to learn more about before attempting a solution or answer.

- A *Project Board* is a good tool to use to keep track of what you need to be doing and what you are learning.

Now that you've identified the questions you need to answer, you know what you need to do next. You need to investigate to find the answers to some of those questions.

Assessment Options

Targeted Concepts, Skills, and Nature of Science	How do I know if students got it?
Criteria and constraints are important in design.	**ASK:** Which criteria and constraints are due to the materials that you are using? **LISTEN:** Students should only identify constraints that are due to the materials they are using.
Identifying factors that lead to variation is an important part of scientific investigations.	**ASK:** What are some of the factors that affected how long it took the parachute to fall?
Scientists often work together and then share their findings. Sharing findings makes new information available and helps scientists refine their ideas and build on others' ideas. When another person's or group's idea is used, credit needs to be given.	**ASK:** How is the way you're working with your classmates similar to the way scientists work together? **LISTEN:** Students should recognize that scientists also work in groups and then share their findings with the larger community.

Teacher Reflection Questions

- What variables did students identify? Did they identify all of the variables you expected them to identify?

- *Messing About* activities are very student centered. How did you guide students?

- What did you do differently in managing the *Messing About* segment in this section compared to that in *Learning Set 3*? What effect did it have? What would you change?

$1\frac{1}{2}$ *class periods* ▶

SECTION 4.2 INTRODUCTION

4.2 Investigate

Investigate Parachutes

Overview

Student groups first design and run experiments testing the effects of the variables they identified in 4.1 on how a parachute falls, and then use *Investigation Expos* to share and evaluate their results with the class. Each group designs a specific experiment procedure to test the effects of one of the variables and records their findings on the *Project Board*. Following the *Investigation Expos*, some groups revise and rerun their experiments, while others investigate new variables from the *Project Board*, until groups have answered all the class questions about what affects how parachutes fall.

Targeted Concepts, Skills, and Nature of Science	Performance Expectations
Scientists must keep clear, accurate, and descriptive records of what they do so they can share their work with others and consider what they did, why they did it, and what they want to do next.	Students should be able to keep descriptive and accurate records of their experiment plans on their *My Experiment Planning* sheets and present this information clearly during their presentations.
Scientific investigations and measurements are considered reliable if the results are repeatable by other scientists using the same procedures.	Although students conducted different experiments, their trials should be repeatable in the sense that the results of the trials are clustered.
In a fair test only the manipulated (independent) variable, and the responding (dependent) variable change. All other variables are held constant.	Students should be able to describe what a fair test is and what the manipulated, responding, and control variables are in their experiment.
Scientists make claims (conclusions) based on evidence obtained (trends in data) from reliable investigations.	Students should be able to distinguish between claims and evidence.

Materials

1	per class	class *Project Board*
1	per group	stopwatch
5	per group	coffee filters
1	per class	250 ft spool of cotton string
4	per group	washers (outer diameter 1")
1	per group	safety scissors
5	per class	transparent tape
1	per student	*Parachute Experiment Planning Guide* page
1	per student	packet of *Parachute Experiment Results Guide* pages equal to the number of groups in the class.
1	per group	poster paper and markers
1	per group	metric ruler

Activity Setup and Preparation

Set up a materials station as you did in *Section 3.1*, including the handouts with the other materials, or have the materials separated and ready to hand out at the beginning of class.

Determine which investigative questions students will be answering. Ideally, students should investigate all the questions they listed on their class *Project Board*. Assume each group has enough time to run two experiments. Some groups may investigate a second question and some may need to revise their original experiment plan and rerun their experiment. If the class has more questions than twice the number of groups you will have to determine which questions to include. Be sure to include questions that test how the features of the parachute affect the **mass, surface area, and stability** of the parachute such as string length, canopy size, mass of the load, number of strings, placement of strings. If you have fewer investigative questions than groups, you should assign multiple groups the same question.

Homework Options

Reflection

- **Science Process:** How might changing the variable you are studying change some of the other variables you identified? Could you change the variable you are studying and control those other variables? If not, do you think the other variable changes in a significant way? (*Students should think about ways to compensate*

DIVING INTO SCIENCE

and ensure that this is a fair test. In most cases, changing one variable—such as canopy size—will have negligible effects on other variables—such as the parachute's weight—when compared with their direct effects on how fast the parachute falls, but students should be aware of all the factors that could prevent a fair test.)

- **Science Content:** Based on the results of the class, give a brief description of the parachute design that you think would be best and explain your reasons. *(Student answers should cite specific evidence from the* Investigation Expos. *For instance, the class might have found that a parachute doesn't open properly if the strings are too long. In this case students' answers should specify shorter strings and that longer strings prevent the parachute from opening properly.)*

- **Science Process:** If you could change any of the constraints of your investigation to get more reliable results, what constraint would you change? *(Look for things that could lead to design ideas. For instance, if students would use a heavier material for the canopy if they could, this could lead to the idea that they could use two stacked coffee filters instead of one.)*

Preparation for 4.3

- **Science Content:** Describe what evidence, claims, explanations, and recommendations are. What is the relationship between them? *(Responses should reflect what students learned in* Learning Set 3*).*

- **Science Content:** Write an explanation for a claim you can make based on the observations you have made and heard about during the *Investigation Expo. (Look for a claim backed up by evidence and logical reasoning and any science knowledge they could apply.)*

SECTION 4.2 IMPLEMENTATION

4.2 Investigate

Investigate Parachutes

You have just identified variables that might make a difference in the way a parachute will fall. You've also recorded questions about the effects of those variables on the *Project Board*. Now it is time to find the answers.

Design Your Experiment

Each group will investigate the effects of a different variable on how a parachute falls. In your group, discuss and then design a good experiment to investigate the effects of your variable on a parachute's fall. You will want an answer to your question that you can trust. Therefore, it is important to remember the lessons you learned while experimenting with the whirligig. Here is a list of reminders to help you organize your thinking.

Materials
• coffee filters
• string
• washers
• transparent tape
• stopwatch
• ruler
• scissors

Question
What question are you investigating and answering with this experiment?

Prediction
What do you think the answer is, and why do you think that?

Variable Identification
• Which part of the parachute will you be changing in your experiment?
• Which variable will you manipulate (change) in your experiment to test the effects of that parachute part?
• What conditions and procedures will you keep the same (hold constant or control) in your experiment?
• What will you measure?
• How many trials will you do for each value of your manipulated variable?

Procedure and Data
Write detailed instructions for how to conduct the experiment.
Include the following:
• how you set up the parachute
• how you drop it
• how you measure its performance
• how you record the data
• how many trials you will do

⚠️ Have your teacher check your plan before you run your experiment.

DIV 76

4.2 Investigate

Investigate Parachutes
5 min.

Give each group the question they will investigate.

◯ Get Going

Using the *Project Board* assign groups a question to investigate. Pick questions that involve aspects of the parachute that affect the mass, surface area, or stability of the parachute such as string length, canopy size, mass of the load, number of strings, and placement of strings.

META NOTES

Many students will keep in mind that each group may do two investigations. Make sure essential questions are investigated first and reserve the other questions for the second investigation. See *Activity Setup and Preparation* suggestions on this.

Design Your Experiment

15 min.

Get student groups started designing experiments to answer their questions about how parachutes fall.

...ou have just identified ...might make a di... ...ay a parachute will fall. You've also recorded questions about the effects of those variables on the *Project Board*. Now it is time to find the answers.

Design Your Experiment

Materials
- coffee filters
- string
- washers
- transparent tape
- stopwatch
- ruler
- scissors

Each group will investigate the effects of a different variable on how a parachute falls. In your group, discuss and then design a good experiment to investigate the effects of your variable on a parachute's fall. You will want an answer to your question that you can trust. Therefore, it is important to remember the lessons you learned while experimenting with the whirligig. Here is a list of reminders to help you organize your thinking.

Question
What question are you investigating and answering with this experiment?

Prediction
What do you think the answer is, and why do you think that?

Variable Identification
- Which part of the parachute will you be changing in your experiment?
- Which variable will you manipulate (change) in your experiment to test the effects of that parachute part?
- What conditions and procedures will you keep the same (hold constant or control) in your experiment?
- What will you measure?
- How many trials will you do for each value of your manipulated variable?

Procedure and Data
Write detailed instructions for how to conduct the experiment. Include the following:
- how you set up the parachute
- how you drop it
- how you measure its performance
- how you record the data
- how many trials you will do

Have your teacher check your plan before you run your experiment.

DIV 76

△ Guide

Now that students know what question they will investigate, review what is important to keep in mind while designing and running an experiment (there is a good list of reminders in *Design Your Experiment*). Students should be clear about what question they are trying to answer, which variable they are intentionally changing and which variable they are measuring in response to this change, as well as variables they are trying to keep constant. Students should make a prediction, and they should write detailed instructions for how to conduct the experiment.

TEACHER TALK

❝As you design your experiment, you will need to keep in mind a number of things. These are listed on page 76 if you need to look at them. These include the question you're trying to answer, what you think is going to happen, the variable you will intentionally change and the one you will measure in response to this change, and which variables you will hold constant. You should also be very clear about what you will measure and how many trials you will run.**❞**

If students are not sure how to begin, you can review one of the whirligig investigations as an example. You can also tell students to think about their whirligig investigation as they work on their parachute investigation.

⬡ Get Going

Now have student groups begin designing investigations of their questions. Make sure that each student has a copy of the *Parachute Experiment Planning Guide* and the *Parachute Experiment Results Guide*. Let groups know how much time they have (about 10 minutes) and have them start designing their experiments.

△ Guide

If a group is having trouble getting started, ask them to think about what variable they need to change to be able to answer the question. Often students will have trouble identifying the variables. Assist them by asking questions about the manipulated, responding, and control variables. Use the whirligig investigation as an example to remind a group about variables.

> **TEACHER TALK**
>
> ❝What are you intentionally changing? What are you measuring in response to this change? What other things could change that you will have to keep constant? How did you control variables in the *Whirligig Challenge?*❞

As groups design their experiments, check with each group to see how they are progressing on identifying the manipulated, responding, and control variables.

See how groups are determining what procedure to use, how many trials to take, and if they are making detailed plans. Encourage brainstorming by asking them about ideas they have discussed and what other ideas they have.

If a group thinks they are finished but aren't, help them see what they haven't done yet. For example, some groups may not have accounted for all the control variables necessary, or they may not have explicitly described each step of their procedure. Ask if everybody in the group agrees about the procedure.

> **TEACHER TALK**
>
> ❝Tell me about your procedure. What are you going to do? What are you going to do with ...(pick something students have omitted in their plan such as, how they drop the parachute or a variable that needs to be controlled.)❞

META NOTES

Some students may wonder whether the class needs to control variables across groups. That is, should all groups use the same values for each of the control variables? Do all groups have to drop from the same height? Variables must be controlled, but when experiments are independent of each other, because they are asking different questions and are being investigated separately, there is no need to control variables across experiments.

META NOTES

Some groups may need help identifying how many trials they should run. In general, they should run at least five trials of a given value of their manipulated variable, and they should test at least three different values of their manipulated variable.

META NOTES

Listen for areas where students are having trouble and use these as points to discuss during the *Investigation Expo*. Students often have difficulties picking out the manipulated and responding variables, and taking into account all the variables that need to be held constant (control variables).

After someone answers, ask the others in the group how that sounds to them and if they want to add anything else.

◇ Evaluate

As groups complete their experiment designs, have those that have finished show you their plans. Groups will have the opportunity to revise and rerun their experiments, so it is all right if there are some problems in their experiment plans. However, make sure that experiment plans are specific enough to be replicable, and that they plan for multiple trials. Also, look for areas in groups' plans that could be safety issues.

NOTES

Use the *Parachute Experiment Planning Guide* and *Parachute Experiment Results Guide* to help you plan and organize your experiment.

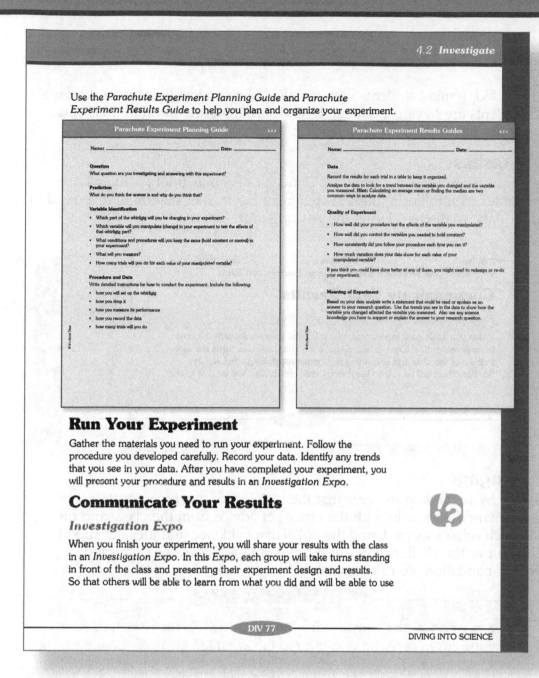

Run Your Experiment

Gather the materials you need to run your experiment. Follow the procedure you developed carefully. Record your data. Identify any trends that you see in your data. After you have completed your experiment, you will present your procedure and results in an *Investigation Expo*.

Communicate Your Results

Investigation Expo

When you finish your experiment, you will share your results with the class in an *Investigation Expo*. In this *Expo*, each group will take turns standing in front of the class and presenting their experiment design and results. So that others will be able to learn from what you did and will be able to use

Run Your Experiment

5 min.

Have groups begin their experiments.

> **META NOTES**
>
> Groups may begin at different times. Make sure the class knows at what time everyone should be finished with their experiments.

⬡ Get Going

Once groups have completed their experiment plan and passed your safety check, let them get started on running their experiment. Emphasize that they should record their results.

△ Guide

As students work on their experiments, check their progress on collecting the evidence they need to answer their question. You might ask if they think will be able to answer their question when they complete their experiments. If not, ask what they would need to correct to answer the question. Do they think their experiment is a fair test? Remind groups, as necessary, to follow their procedure, run multiple trials, monitor controlled variables, and record their data.

If needed, remind students how to calculate the average value of their trials. If students are having a difficult time determining the trend in their data, consider having them plot it.

☐ Assess

As groups are working, listen for difficulties such as troubles identifying variables, controlling variables, creating a fair test, or determining a trend in their data, to discuss during the *Investigation Expos*.

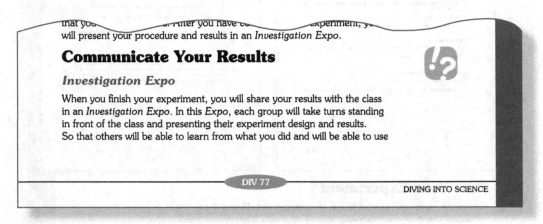

Communicate Your Results

20 min.

Lead student in their Investigation Expo *to share their experimental results, interpretations, and claims on posters.*

that you ~~will. After you have co~~ ~~experiment, y~~ will present your procedure and results in an *Investigation Expo*.

Communicate Your Results

Investigation Expo

When you finish your experiment, you will share your results with the class in an *Investigation Expo*. In this *Expo*, each group will take turns standing in front of the class and presenting their experiment design and results. So that others will be able to learn from what you did and will be able to use

DIV 77

DIVING INTO SCIENCE

○ Engage

Begin by reminding students that the purpose of the *Investigation Expo* is to share their results with the class, get advice from the class, and build on each other's ideas. Using the collective evidence and ideas is important to achieve the challenge because the more we know, the better the recommendation we can provide.

TEACHER TALK

"The reason you're doing an *Investigation Expo* is that we all need to know the answers to the questions about what affects how the parachute falls so we can make a good recommendation to the cereal company. If we don't have the answer yet, we need to know that too. So if you're not sure you've got the answer yet, you should say so in this *Investigation Expo*.

By sharing our results we can build on each other's ideas, like scientists do.**"**

△ Guide

Before students make their posters, briefly review the objectives of *Investigation Expos*. The presentations should clearly and honestly communicate the question they are trying to answer, how groups ran their experiments, the results of the experiments, if it was a fair test, and their confidence in their results. You may want to review what a fair test is.

your results when they design their best parachute, you will make a poster that includes the procedure you followed, your data, and the meaning of your results. Your poster should include five kinds of information:

- questions you were trying to answer in your investigation;
- your predictions;
- the procedure and what makes it a fair test;
- your results and how confident you are about them; and
- your interpretation of the results and how confident you are of it.

You might find out after running your experiment that you did not control variables well enough. If you find that, don't worry right now. You will have another chance. But do be honest about it. If you think the test you ran was not as fair as you had planned, say so. Then explain how you would change your procedure if you had a chance to run the investigation again.

Now you should be ready to discuss your results. Use your poster to present your experiment and results to the class. Like you did in the whirligig activity, take notes as others present. Look for answers to these questions in each presentation:

- What was the group trying to find out?
- What variables did they control as they did their procedure?
- Is their data scattered, or is it fairly consistent?
- Did they measure the time it took the parachute to drop in a consistent way?
- Did their procedure cause them to run a poor, uncontrolled experiment?
- What did they learn?
- What conclusions do their results suggest?
- Do you trust their results? Why or why not?

Each group in the class investigated effects of a different variable. Therefore, each group will have a chance to present their experiment and results to the class. Make sure you can answer these questions for each presentation. If you cannot, ask questions of the group that is presenting. It will be important for you to trust the results of other groups in the class. You will need these results to fully address the *Parachute Challenge*.

DIV 78

◯ Get Going

Distribute the poster materials and emphasize that that each poster should address the five bulleted items in *Communicate Your Results*. Let students groups know how much time they have to complete their posters (no more than 10 minutes).

Consider displaying one of the *Investigation Expo* posters from the *Whirligig Challenge* to give students an example.

Once students have completed their posters, have each group present their experiment and results to the class using their poster.

△ Guide

Remind students that as each group presents, they should be taking notes of each presentation on the extra *Parachute Experiment Results Guide* sheets you provided and in their notebooks. Emphasize that they will need everyone's results to achieve the challenge.

As each group presents, the class should be taking notes and asking questions when something isn't clear. Remind them to look for answers to the questions on the bottom of page 78. Model the participation you expect by asking questions of the presenting group when anything isn't clear. You may need to ask a question or two to begin the discussion on whether the group ran a fair test and if their results were reliable and whether the group answered their investigative question. Then ask a student to ask a question.

TEACHER TALK

❝What variable did you change? Which one did you measure? Which variables did you control?

Is the experiment a fair test? *(The conclusion should answer the experiment question, the only variables that should change are the manipulated and responding, all other variables should be held constant.)*

How do your results compare with your prediction?

How confident are you of your results? *(Students should support their confidence level by describing how clustered the trial values are for a given measurement and how consistent the overall trend in the data is.)*❞

META NOTES

Assess students' skills in sharing ideas, asking questions, and responding to peers. Students' questions should effectively evaluate whether or not groups are running their investigations properly.

If the discussion stalls or loses focus, ask students whether all of the questions on page 78 have been answered. Make sure the presenters respond to the student who asks the questions.

*After **every** presentation lead the class to evaluate if the experimental results were trustworthy and what this means for the* Parachute Challenge.

Point out the importance of determining if the experimental results are trustworthy and can be used when constructing the recommendation to the cereal company. If they are not, then the experiment will need to be redone. If the results were not trustworthy, then discuss why they were not and how the experiment needs to be revised and rerun.

❝How do we know if experimental results are trustworthy? Are these experimental results trustworthy? *(If the experiment is not a fair test or if the results are not reliable, then the experiment should be revised and rerun.)*

What do the results of this experiment indicate for the challenge of designing a slowly-falling parachute? *(Students should indicate if the manipulated variable should be increased, decreased, or has no affect on the time it takes the parachute to fall.)*

Do you think this experiment is tied in to the science knowledge you were introduced to while working on the *Whirligig Challenge?* *(Students should indicate if their variable somehow affects the mass, surface area, or stability of the parachute and relate this with the science knowledge they were introduced to in Learning Set 3.)*❞

META NOTES

If students decide that a group didn't run a fair test or didn't use replicable procedures, the group will need to revise their procedure to better control variables or to be more specific. If students decide that a group didn't answer the question they were investigating, the group will need to look again at what variable they were investigating, and revise their experiment plans to make sure they are testing at least three variations of that variable while controlling other variables.

◇ **Evaluate**

Make sure students can recognize a fair test.

NOTES

....

....

....

....

....

....

....

....

NOTES

4.2

Revise Your Experiment

Do you trust all of the results that were presented? Probably not. Why do you not trust every groups' results? Some groups might not have managed variables well and some groups might have run their procedures inconsistently. Maybe some measured in a way that was inconsistent across trials. What made you think you could not trust some groups' results? Their data were probably too scattered or inconsistent.

What should you do now if the class does not trust every groups' results? Remember why you are running these experiments. Every group is running an experiment to investigate the effects of one variable on a parachute's fall. If you cannot trust results about a variable's effects, then you will not know what to do about that variable when you design *your* best parachute. For example, if a group that investigated the effects of the surface area of the canopy did not produce results you trust, then how will you know what size the canopy on your parachute should be?

DIV 79

DIVING INTO SCIENCE

Revise Your Experiment
5 to 15 min.

Have students revise their experiments or test a new question with their groups.

◯ Get Going

Then have the groups whose results were not trustworthy revise their experiments and run them again. While they are revising their experiments, have the other groups pick questions from the *Project Board*, or else assign them questions from the *Project Board*, and have them design experiments to answer them.

◇ Evaluate

Make sure that students are using ideas and feedback they got from the class in revising their experiment plans.

After groups have completed their second experiment, have them present their results in another *Investigation Expo*. Follow the same procedures as described in the previous *Investigation Expo*, again discussing how trustworthy the results are and making claims (conclusions) based on the data.

META NOTES

The claims (conclusions) for all the investigations will be used in the next section when students write explanations and recommendations based on their observations and the science introduced during the *Whirligig Challenge*.

Reflect
10 min.

Lead a discussion on what students think may help achieve the Parachute Challenge *based on their experimental results.*

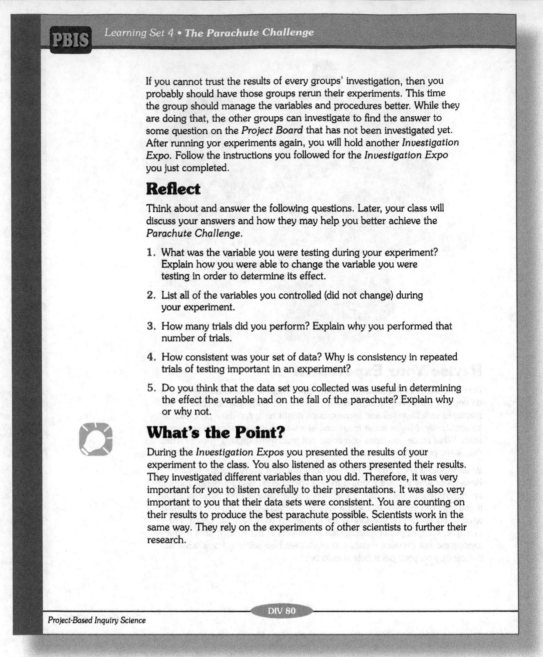

If you cannot trust the results of every groups' investigation, then you probably should have those groups rerun their experiments. This time the group should manage the variables and procedures better. While they are doing that, the other groups can investigate to find the answer to some question on the *Project Board* that has not been investigated yet. After running yor experiments again, you will hold another *Investigation Expo.* Follow the instructions you followed for the *Investigation Expo* you just completed.

Reflect

Think about and answer the following questions. Later, your class will discuss your answers and how they may help you better achieve the *Parachute Challenge.*

1. What was the variable you were testing during your experiment? Explain how you were able to change the variable you were testing in order to determine its effect.

2. List all of the variables you controlled (did not change) during your experiment.

3. How many trials did you perform? Explain why you performed that number of trials.

4. How consistent was your set of data? Why is consistency in repeated trials of testing important in an experiment?

5. Do you think that the data set you collected was useful in determining the effect the variable had on the fall of the parachute? Explain why or why not.

What's the Point?

During the *Investigation Expos* you presented the results of your experiment to the class. You also listened as others presented their results. They investigated different variables than you did. Therefore, it was very important for you to listen carefully to their presentations. It was also very important to you that their data sets were consistent. You are counting on their results to produce the best parachute possible. Scientists work in the same way. They rely on the experiments of other scientists to further their research.

DIV 80

⬡ Get Going

When the class has finished its investigations, have groups answer the *Reflect* questions to review students' understanding of manipulating and controlling variables in experiments, why they run multiple trials, and how their results assist them in achieving the *Parachute Challenge.* Then lead a brief discussion of students' responses focusing on question 5.

☐ Assess

Listen for the following:

1. Groups should display an understanding of the manipulated (independent) variable for the variable they intentionally change and

responding (dependent) variable for the variable they measure that is responding to the change. This is usually part of the experiment question: *If I change* manipulated variable, *what happens to* responding variable?

2. Groups should display an understanding that all variables, other than the manipulated and responding variable, should be kept the same or held constant. These are the control variables. There are some variables students may not be able to control; these should have a negligible affect on the outcome, otherwise the experiment is not a fair test.

3. Groups should have at least three trials as an absolute minimum although five or more is better. The reasons for having the trials are to assure that the measurements are reliable and to determine something of the precision of the measurements. The results are more precise and there is less variation in the trials.

4. Groups should discuss not only the consistency in the repeated trials but also the trend and the consistency in the trend. The results are more precise and there is less variation in the trails.

5. Groups should determine what information they got out of their investigation and determine how it helps them in determining the final design of the parachute. Note: flight times, cost effectiveness, and ideas on what to do and what not to do for the final design are all useful information. Further guide students by asking them if the variable they tested ties in with the science knowledge they were introduced to during the *Whirligig Challenge*. Students should determine if the variable they manipulated affected the mass, surface area, or stability of the parachute and how that might attribute to the change in fall time they measured. *(If the mass increases, the fall time decreases due to an increased maximum value of the drag force. If the surface area increases, the fall time increases due to the drag force reaching a lower terminal velocity. If the parachute is not stable, the results will be inconsistent, with large variations in the time of fall and the average fall time will be shorter.)*

> **META NOTES**
>
> The science content for the parachute challenge parallels the science content introduced in the *Whirligig Challenge*.

What's the Point?

5 min.

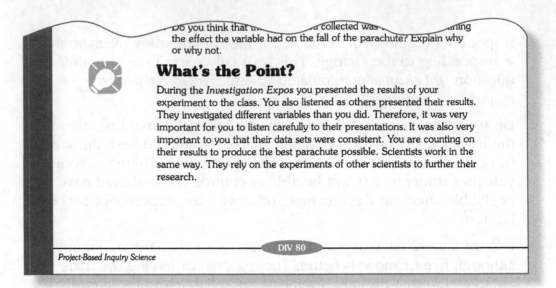

...Do you think that th... ...a collected was ...ning the effect the variable had on the fall of the parachute? Explain why or why not.

What's the Point?

During the *Investigation Expos* you presented the results of your experiment to the class. You also listened as others presented their results. They investigated different variables than you did. Therefore, it was very important for you to listen carefully to their presentations. It was also very important to you that their data sets were consistent. You are counting on their results to produce the best parachute possible. Scientists work in the same way. They rely on the experiments of other scientists to further their research.

DIV 80

Project-Based Inquiry Science

◇ Evaluate

Make sure students understand the importance of sharing their results in order for the class to achieve the challenge and the need for experimental results to be consistent to be considered reliable.

NOTES

Assessment Options

Targeted Concepts, Skills, and Nature of Science	How do I know if students got it?
Scientists must keep clear, accurate, and descriptive records of what they do so they can share their work with others and consider what they did, why they did it, and what they want to do next.	**ASK:** What are some important things to record in your investigations? **LISTEN:** Answers should include something about what the researchers did, the reasons for what they did, and the results.
Scientific investigations and measurements are considered reliable if the results are repeatable by other scientists using the same procedures.	**ASK:** How can you determine if the results of an experiment are reliable? **LISTEN:** Students should say that results that can be repeated are reliable.
In a fair test only the manipulated (independent) variable, and the responding (dependent) variable change. All other variables are held constant.	**ASK:** What are the differences between the manipulated variable, the responding variable, and the control variable? **LISTEN:** Students should understand that the manipulated variable is changed in experiments, the responding variable is observed, and the control variable is held constant.
Scientists make claims (conclusions) based on evidence obtained (trends in data) from reliable investigations.	**ASK:** What is required to make a good claim? **LISTEN:** The claim should be based on the evidence (trends in data) that they obtained from reliable investigations.

Teacher Reflection Questions

- What ideas about science or investigations from *Learning Sets 2* and *3* did you see students applying in their experiments? How are they building on what they learned in *Learning Sets 2* and *3*?

- How did you guide and encourage students to direct their own investigations? What ideas do you have for next time?

- What worked well during the *Revise Your Experiment* segment? What didn't work well? What would you do differently?

NOTES

....

....

....

....

....

....

....

....

....

....

....

....

....

4.3 Explain and Recommend

Explanations and Recommendations about Parachutes

◀ $\frac{1}{2}$ *class period* *

Overview

Students create explanations for their experimental results and make recommendations about how to design a slow-falling parachute based on their results. Working with their groups, students first make claims and use their data as evidence for their claims. Then groups create a recommendation based on their evidence, science knowledge, and explanation. Finally, they share their explanations and recommendations with the class, and keep track of the explanations and recommendations of other groups.

Targeted Concepts, Skills, and Nature of Science	Performance Expectations
Scientists often work together and then share their findings. Sharing findings makes new information available and helps scientists refine their ideas and build on others' ideas. When another person's or group's idea is used, credit needs to be given.	Students work with their groups and then share their results with the class.
Scientists make claims (conclusions) based on evidence obtained (trends in data) from reliable investigations.	Students support their claims with evidence.

Materials

1 per student per investigation	*Create Your Explanation* page

*A class period is considered to be one 40 to 50 minute class.

Activity Setup and Preparation

Consider reviewing *Section 3.5*, which introduced scientific explanations, before class.

Homework Options

Reflection

- **Science Content:** What is the claim and what is the evidence in the following explanation? A set of seven coffee filters taped together in a floral pattern will fall to the ground more slowly than a single coffee filter because as the surface area increases, the object falls more slowly, as demonstrated by our experiments in *Learning Set 3*. *(The claim is that the greater air resistance on the set of coffee filters slows it down, and the evidence is that this was demonstrated by the experiments in* Learning Set 3.)

- **Science Process:** What claim did you make in your explanation of the parachute? What was your evidence? *(Students' claims should be supported by their experimental evidence.)*

Preparation for 4.4

- **Science Process:** What do you need to do if you use evidence that comes from your classmates' work? *(Students should state the need to credit other researchers if they use ideas or evidence that comes from their work.)*

SECTION 4.3 IMPLEMENTATION

4.3 Explain and Recommend

Explanations and Recommendations about Parachutes

As you did after your whirligig experiments, you will spend some time now explaining your results. You will also try to come up with recommendations. Remember that explanations include your claims, the evidence for your claims, and the science you know that can help you understand the claim. A recommendation is a special kind of claim where you make a statement about what someone should do. The best recommendations also have evidence, science, and an explanation associated with them. In the *Whirligig Challenge*, you created explanations and recommendations separately from each other. This time you will work on both at the same time.

Create and Share Your Recommendation and Explanation

Work with your group. Use the hints on the *Create Your Explanation* pages to make your first attempt at explaining your results. You'll read about parachute science later. After that, you will probably want to revise your explanations. Right now, use the science you learned during the *Whirligig Challenge* for your first attempt.

Write your recommendation. It should be about designing a slow-falling parachute. Remember that it should be written so that it will help someone else. They should be able to apply what you have learned about the effects of your variable.

Create Your Explanation
Name: _____ Date: _____
Use this page to explain the lesson of your recent investigations.
Write a brief summary of the results from your investigation. You will use this summary to help you write your Explanation.
Claim – a statement of what you understand or a conclusion that you have reached from an investigation or a set of investigations.
Evidence – data collected during investigations and trends in that data.
Science knowledge – knowledge about how things work. You may have learned this through reading, talking to an expert, discussion, or other experiences.
Write your Explanation using the *Claim*, *Evidence*, and *Science knowledge*.

DIV 81

DIVING INTO SCIENCE

◀ $\frac{1}{2}$ *class period*

4.3

4.3 Explain and Recommend

Explanations and Recommendations about Parachutes

5 min.

Review explanations and recommendations with the class.

△ Guide

Begin by reminding the class of how they created explanations after their whirligig experiments and then made recommendations based on their evidence and science knowledge. Then point out they will make claims (conclusions) based on the evidence from their recent experiment.

META NOTES

Explanations consist of a claim or claims backed by evidence and science knowledge in a logical way. Explanations were introduced in *Learning Set 3* on page 58.

META NOTES

Recommendations were introduced on page 67 in *Learning Set 3*.

TEACHER TALK

"Your group has investigated at least one question about what affects how a parachute falls. This allows you to make a claim. For example, in the whirligig experiments you could make the following claim: "As you increase the mass of the whirligig the time it takes to fall decreases." And you used the *Create Your Explanation* page to help you to organize the information and construct your explanations. We will used these pages for the parachute challenge too. Your explanations should contain science knowledge you learned during the *Whirligig Challenge*."

Remind students that a recommendation is a special type of claim where you make a suggestion about what should be done based on evidence and science knowledge. Inform students that they will also be working on recommendations while they work on their explanations.

◇ **Evaluate**

Make sure students realize an explanation contains a claim supported by evidence and science knowledge in a logical way, and that no opinions should be included in an explanation or claim.

Create and Share Your Recommendation and Explanation

25 min.

Guide students through creating and sharing their recommendations and explanations.

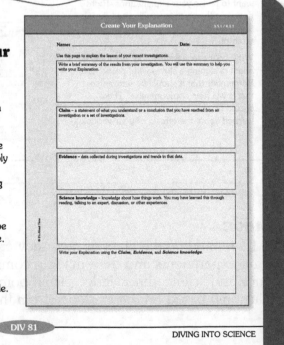

and recommendations separately from each other. This time you will work on both at the same time.

Create and Share Your Recommendation and Explanation

Work with your group. Use the hints on the *Create Your Explanation* pages to make your first attempt at explaining your results. You'll read about parachute science later. After that, you will probably want to revise your explanations. Right now, use the science you learned during the *Whirligig Challenge* for your first attempt.

Write your recommendation. It should be about designing a slow-falling parachute. Remember that it should be written so that it will help someone else. They should be able to apply what you have learned about the effects of your variable.

DIV 81

DIVING INTO SCIENCE

Guide students through creating and sharing their recommendations and explanations.

⬡ Get Going

Let students know that they should fill out one *Create Your Explanation* page for each investigation they did and that they should write their recommendations on the bottom of the *Create Your Explanation* pages. Let groups know how much time they will have to complete their explanation pages (no more than 10 minutes).

△ Guide and Assess

As groups are constructing their explanations, see if they need assistance making claims (conclusions based on the trend in their data), stating the evidence, or the science knowledge. If you see someone has opinions written down, remind them that opinions are not part of a scientific explanation and ask them where they have written something that is not backed by evidence or science knowledge. Students may not remember the science knowledge from *Learning Set 3* that applies to this situation. Encourage them to review it, or to review the class's *Project Board*. Students' recommendations and explanations for the parachute's fall should contain science knowledge from the *Whirligig Challenge* pertaining to how changing the mass, changing the surface area, and changing the stability affect the fall of an object.

⬡ Get Going

When groups have finished, let the class know that each group will be presenting their explanations and recommendations to the class. While a group is presenting, the rest of the class should be keeping track of their presentation, using a new *Create Your Explanation* page for each investigation done.

△ Guide

Guide the discussion by modeling questions students could ask. These questions should help students to understand how claims are supported by the evidence and science knowledge in an explanation. They should also verify that the group has not included any unfounded opinions in their explanations and that the science knowledge they use is correct. You can also ask if a group's recommendations are supported by the evidence and science knowledge they used in their explanations. Do they follow from the explanations? Will they help get a slow-falling parachute?

TEACHER TALK

"I'm not sure where this idea is supported. What was the evidence for it?

Can you go over how this fact leads to this idea?

I don't see how this recommendation is going to make the parachute fall slowly. Can you show me how you got this from your explanation?**"**

◇ Evaluate

Make sure that groups have written claims based on the trends in their data and that their explanations contain science knowledge and evidence to support their claims and that no opinions are included. Also, make sure that students' recommendations clearly state ways in which a parachute can be designed to fall slowly.

NOTES

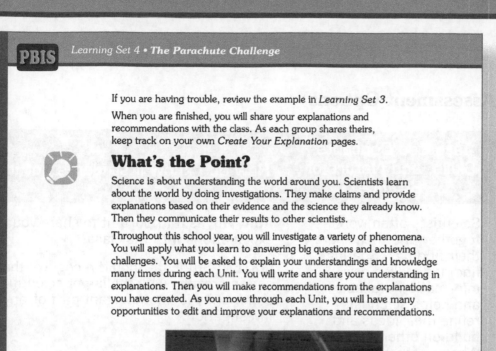

PBIS   *Learning Set 4 • The Parachute Challenge*

If you are having trouble, review the example in *Learning Set 3*.

When you are finished, you will share your explanations and recommendations with the class. As each group shares theirs, keep track on your own *Create Your Explanation* pages.

What's the Point?

Science is about understanding the world around you. Scientists learn about the world by doing investigations. They make claims and provide explanations based on their evidence and the science they already know. Then they communicate their results to other scientists.

Throughout this school year, you will investigate a variety of phenomena. You will apply what you learn to answering big questions and achieving challenges. You will be asked to explain your understandings and knowledge many times during each Unit. You will write and share your understanding in explanations. Then you will make recommendations from the explanations you have created. As you move through each Unit, you will have many opportunities to edit and improve your explanations and recommendations.

DIV 82

Project-Based Inquiry Science

What's the Point?

5 min.

◇ Evaluate

Before moving on to *Section 4.4*, make sure that students have applied what they have learned in this investigation, as well as previous ones, to creating their explanations and recommendations. They should have used what they learned about gravity, air resistance, and stability in *Learning Set 3* to support their claims. And they should have applied what they learned in *Learning Set 3* about supporting claims with data they have gathered and with accepted facts to creating persuasive explanations.

Assessment Options

Targeted Concepts, Skills, and Nature of Science	How do I know if students got it?
Scientists often work together and then share their findings. Sharing findings makes new information available and helps scientists refine their ideas and build on others' ideas. When another person's or group's idea is used, credit needs to be given.	**ASK:** Why is it important to share your explanations with the class? **LISTEN:** Students should recognize that sharing results with the larger scientific community is an important part of any investigation.
Scientific investigations and measurements are considered reliable if the results are repeatable by other scientists using the same procedures.	**ASK:** What are some claims you made in your explanations? **LISTEN:** Students should separate the claims they made from the evidence they used.

Teacher Reflection Questions

- What evidence do you have that students understand the difference between claims, explanations, and recommendations? What areas do they need further guidance to understand these concepts?

- When engaging students it is important to make a connection to the students' lives. How have you made connections so far with the PBIS curriculum and your students' lives?

- What worked well during the presentations? What didn't work well? What would you like to do during the next presentations?

4.4 Read

How Parachutes Work

◀ $1\frac{1}{2}$ *class periods**

Overview

Students learn more science of parachutes that will help them understand the factors that affect how a parachute falls. Using what they've learned, they revise their recommendations and explanations and present their revisions to the class. Finally, they add what they've learned to the *Project Board* and discuss it, building upon what they learned in the *Whirligig Challenge*.

Targeted Concepts, Skills, and Nature of Science	Performance Expectations
The way an object falls through air depends on its mass, surface area, and other factors.	Students should include heaviness or mass and surface area in their explanations of why things fall the way they do.
Earth's gravity pulls things toward it.	Students should be able to explain that gravity causes the parachute to fall.
Air resistance is a force opposing the motion of an object moving through air.	Students include air resistance in their explanations of what slows the fall of a parachute.

Materials

1 per class	class *Project Board*
2 per student	*Create Your Explanation* pages
variable per class	large flat-bottomed coffee filters for optional demonstrations
variable per class	cotton string for optional demonstrations
variable per class	washers for optional demonstrations (1" outside diameter)
1 per class	scissor for optional demonstrations
1 per class	roll of transparent tape for optional demonstrations

*A class period is considered to be one 40 to 50 minute class.

Activity Setup and Preparation

You may wish to review *Introducing the Project Board* in *Section 3.1* for use of the columns in the *Project Board*. Students will be updating column 3 (*What have we learned?*) and column 4 (*What is our evidence?*) during this section.

Below, a number of optional demonstrations are listed. Students have probably investigated these variables. If students did not investigate these variables then it is strongly suggested that you demonstrate how the parachute's fall is affected by changing that variable.

Optional demonstration of adjusting the canopy size: Construct two parachutes, one with a single canopy as described in the *Activity Setup and Preparation* of *Section 4.1*, the other with a three or more coffee filters taped together, or a floral pattern of coffee filters as described in *Section 3.1*. Each parachute should have the same length of string and number of washers to make it a fair test. Be sure to test this out first to determine the number of washers you will need to create stability.

Optional demonstration of adjusting the number of washers: Construct single parachute to demonstrate how the time changes with increasing the number of washers.

Optional demonstration adjusting the string length: Construct a at least three parachutes of different string length to demonstrate how string length affects the parachute's fall.

Optional demonstration adjusting the string number: Construct at least three parachutes of different string number to demonstrate how string length affects the parachute's fall. Consider one string in the center, two strings equally placed, and three strings equally placed.

Optional demonstration of adjusting the canopy vents: Construct a few parachutes of having no vents, a few vents, and many vents.

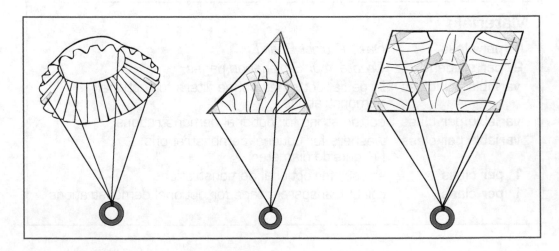

Optional demonstration of adjusting the canopy shape: Construct a few parachutes of in which you fold parts of the coffee filter to create different shapes of the canopy. You may create some shapes of the same surface area and secure them with tape to keep their shape as they fall. For example, circular (*area* = πr^2), rectangular (*area* = *length* × *width*), and triangular (*area* = ½ *base* × *height*).

Homework Options

Reflection

- **Science Content:** What would happen if you dropped a full-scale, open parachute out of an airplane without attaching a person or any other kind of weight to it? *(Students' answers could include: it would not stay open; it would probably invert; and it would fall quickly to the ground.)*

- **Science Process:** You are planning a skydiving adventure using a parachute of your own design. You want to film your entire descent. But you want the camera to wobble as little as possible. Can you identify one or two variables that you should focus your efforts on? How might this parachute be different from a parachute you would design for a drop without a camera? *(The variables students identify might include: the number of strings; the size of the canopy; and the shape of the canopy [vents might help stabilize the parachute]. The design for this parachute might sacrifice a little slowness, with vents, for instance, for the sake of stability.)*

- **Science Content:** The air is thinner at high altitudes, meaning that there are fewer air molecules in a cubic foot of space. What affect do you think altitude has on the speed at which a parachute falls? How do you think a parachute would work in a vacuum? *(Students should recognize that air resistance depends on the presence of air molecules, and that a parachute falls slowly because of air resistance.)*

Preparation for 4.5

- **Science Process:** How do you think you could test your revised recommendations? *(Students should build parachutes according to their revised recommendations and test them. They could also compare these new parachutes to parachutes that deviate from the recommendations slightly.)*

$1\frac{1}{2}$ *class periods* ▶

4.4 Read

How Parachutes Work

5 min.

Guide the class through the science of parachutes.

SECTION 4.4 IMPLEMENTATION

4.4 Read

How Parachutes Work

You have been experimenting with parachutes. You determined the effect different variables have on the way the parachute falls. In previous sections, you have looked at how pulls and pushes can affect how whirligigs fall. In this section, you will see that pulls and pushes affect how your parachute falls as well.

Gravity and Air Resistance...Again

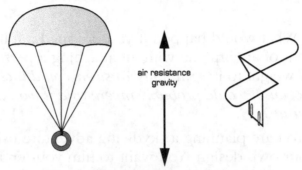

air resistance
gravity

The parachute falls towards the ground because gravitational force is greater than force from air resistance at the time of dropping. As time passes these forces become equal in length.

It is probably obvious to you by now that parachutes work according to the same scientific principles as the whirligig. Gravity pulls the parachute toward the ground. The canopy of the parachute collides with air molecules. These collisions create air resistance. The air pushes up on the parachute. In both the whirligig and the parachute, the pull of gravity is greater than the push up of air resistance. That is why both end up falling toward the ground.

What is different in parachutes and whirligigs are their parts. This affects the kinds of changes you can make in their designs. In turn, the changes affect how quickly the parachute falls toward Earth.

DIV 83

DIVING INTO SCIENCE

◯ Engage

Remind students of the purpose of the challenge and that more knowledge is needed to complete the challenge.

TEACHER TALK

❝Remember that our goal is to recommend to the cereal company how to build a cost-effective, slow-falling parachute, and to do that more knowledge about parachutes is needed.❞

Then remind students that after they wrote their initial explanations for whirligigs, they learned additional whirligig science that they were able to apply to whirligig design. They are going to do the same now. Also they will think about how to apply whirligig science knowledge to the design, build, and test a better parachute before making a recommendation to the cereal company.

TEACHER TALK

"After you wrote explanations for the whirligigs, we studied the science of whirligigs. You are now going to do the same for the parachute. You will also think about how the whirligig science knowledge can be applied to the *Parachute Challenge*. Do you remember the science ideas you used? *(Students should mention gravity, air resistance, and stability.)*"

Next, let students know that they will now learn additional information on how gravity, air resistance, and stability affect the parachute science that will help them with the *Parachute Challenge*. They will have a chance to revise their recommendations and explanations for the cereal company afterwards.

△ Guide

Remind students that the parachute falls to Earth because of the gravitational pull between Earth and the parachute and that objects fall differently to Earth because of the air that surrounds Earth. Use an example of two different objects (like a boulder and a feather) dropped in a place where there is no air to point out they would fall at the same rate, reaching the ground at the same time. Then remind students that air affects the fall so we don't observe two different objects (like a boulder and a feather) dropped reaching the ground at the same time.

Gravity and Air Resistance ... Again
10 min.

Lead a discussion how gravity and air resistance affect the parachute in ways similar to the whirligig.

TEACHER TALK

"All dropped objects fall to Earth because of the force due to gravity between Earth and the object. If we were to drop a boulder and a feather in a place where there was no air, the boulder and the feather would reach the ground at the same time. But here we have air. If we were to drop a boulder and a feather here, the boulder would reach the ground first. Why?"

Make a connection with students' experiences with the whirligig by asking students what they changed about the whirligig to affect how it falls and why. Guide them to understanding that changing the mass and surface area affected the time it took the whirligig to fall through air.

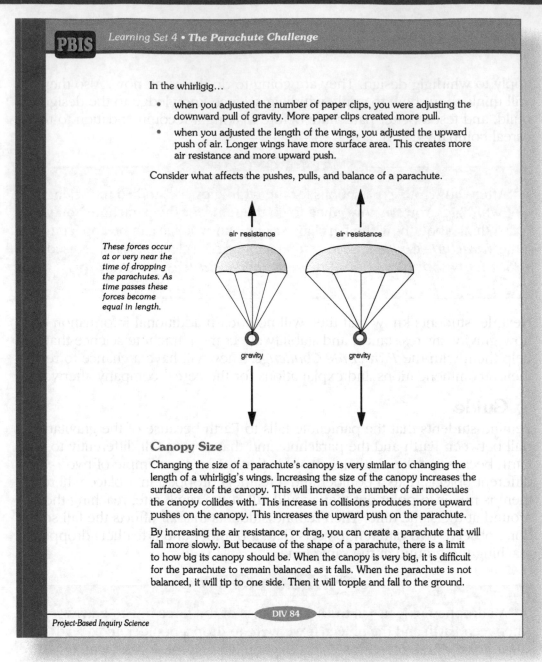

In the whirligig...

- when you adjusted the number of paper clips, you were adjusting the downward pull of gravity. More paper clips created more pull.

- when you adjusted the length of the wings, you adjusted the upward push of air. Longer wings have more surface area. This creates more air resistance and more upward push.

Consider what affects the pushes, pulls, and balance of a parachute.

These forces occur at or very near the time of dropping the parachutes. As time passes these forces become equal in length.

air resistance   air resistance

gravity   gravity

Canopy Size

Changing the size of a parachute's canopy is very similar to changing the length of a whirligig's wings. Increasing the size of the canopy increases the surface area of the canopy. This will increase the number of air molecules the canopy collides with. This increase in collisions produces more upward pushes on the canopy. This increases the upward push on the parachute.

By increasing the air resistance, or drag, you can create a parachute that will fall more slowly. But because of the shape of a parachute, there is a limit to how big its canopy should be. When the canopy is very big, it is difficult for the parachute to remain balanced as it falls. When the parachute is not balanced, it will tip to one side. Then it will topple and fall to the ground.

DIV 84

Project-Based Inquiry Science

NOTE: the two bullets in the student edition on page 84 should state the following:

- when you adjusted the number of paper clips, you were adjusting the downward pull of gravity. More paper clips created more pull due to gravity. This does not directly change the time it takes to fall, rather it affects how big the force due to the air can get, and leads to an increased fall time.

- when you changed the length of the wings, you changed the surface area that air collides with. Longer wings have more surface area. This affects how fast the force due to the air reaches its maximum value and results in the whirligig falling at slower speeds, and taking more time to reach the ground.

Finally, ask students what parts of the parachute are like the whirligig's paper clips and blade length and what affect these will have on how the parachute falls through air. Record students' ideas publicly and let students know that they will be learning about how each part of the parachute affects the way it falls.

△ Guide

Ask students if anyone changed the canopy size during their experiments. If so, ask them to remind the class of their results.

Consider demonstrating the effect of increasing canopy size using a parachute with a single coffee filter for a canopy and a parachute with several coffee filters. First, remind students of the coffee filter demonstration you did at the beginning of the *Whirligig Challenge* and ask them if they can predict what will happen when you drop each of these parachutes.

As you talk about their experiment and the demonstration, point out that increasing the size of the canopy results in a larger surface area, which causes the force due to the air to reach its maximum value much sooner while the parachute is still falling at a slower speed. Thus, the parachute takes a longer time to reach the ground. Tell students this is like increasing the blade length of the whirligig.

Canopy Size
5 min.

Lead a discussion on how the parachute's canopy size, like the whirligig blade length, affects air resistance.

> **TEACHER TALK**
>
> "Look at these parachutes. What did we do when we made the canopy bigger? What else got bigger? *(The surface area.)* What happened to the time it takes a parachute to reach the ground? *(The surface area increases, resulting in the parachute reaching the ground slower.)*"

Note: The student text indicates that the upward push on the canopy increases – it doesn't. The drag force can never be larger than the downward pull due to gravity, rather it grows from zero to its maximum value (which is equal to the downward pull from gravity). As the surface area increases, the maximum value of the drag force is attained more rapidly resulting in slower speeds and longer fall times.)

> **TEACHER TALK**
>
> "What happens is that as we increase the surface area, the force due to the air reaches its maximum value sooner and the parachute falls at a slower speed, taking more time to reach the ground."

META NOTES

A parachute with a very big canopy becomes top heavy and thus unstable. This is the same situation as a whirligig with no paper clips, it also becomes top heavy. The whirligig's center of mass moved up as the lower mass, i.e., paper clips, was removed. The parachute's center of mass moved up as the upper mass, i.e., more canopy material, was increased. Both are cases of instability due to the center of mass being too high. At this point it is O.K. for student to simply recognize that the parachute, like the whirligig, is unstable.

Finally, point out that if the canopy size gets too large then the parachute becomes unstable, taking (on the average) less time to reach the ground and falling inconsistently.

TEACHER TALK

❝Remember the whirligig with no paper clips and how it fell? How is that like what is happening with the parachute that has a very big canopy?❞

NOTES

_____

_____

_____

_____

_____

_____

_____

_____

_____

_____

_____

Number of Washers

A parachute's washers are like paper clips on the whirligig. When you add washers to a parachute, you are increasing the total amount of matter in the parachute. Thus, adding washers to the parachute's load (what it carries) increases the pull of gravity acting on the parachute.

Consider what would happen if you removed all the washers from a parachute. The force of gravity would be greatly reduced. The air resistance would not change. You might think that the parachute would fall really slowly. But something else happens. If you try it, you will see the canopy collapses. The parachute falls quickly. You might also see the canopy (coffee filter) turn itself over. The parachute's load plays an important role in its stability. It is similar to what the paper clips do for the whirligig. They help the parachute stay upright. When the parachute is not upright, the upward push of air on the parachute is uneven. This causes it to turn over or fall quickly to the ground.

String Length

The strings on a parachute support the parachute's load. They keep it connected to the canopy. They also do another important job. The lengths of the strings on a parachute determine the shape of the parachute in two ways:

- They control how far below the canopy the load hangs.
- They control how far right or left of the parachute's center the load hangs.

Suppose the load is close to the canopy. Air resistance pushing up on the canopy can easily flip the parachute over. Increasing the distance between the load and the canopy makes the parachute more stable. But suppose the load hangs too far from the canopy? The canopy will not fully inflate.

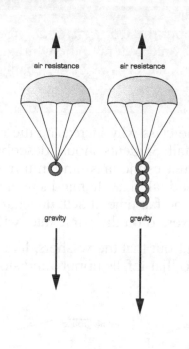

DIVING INTO SCIENCE

Number of Washers
5 min.

Lead a discussion on how the number of washers or load of the parachute, like the whirligig paper clips, results in shorter fall times.

△ Guide

Next, ask students if any group investigated this as a variable and if so to remind the class of their results. Then ask the class if these results are in agreement with the science.

Consider demonstrating the effects of increasing the number of washers on a parachute by dropping a single parachute two or three times, the first time with one washer and adding a couple of washers with each drop.

Then discuss how increasing the number of washers on the parachute increases the mass of the parachute and in turn, the pull of gravity on the parachute. Tell students this is like increasing the number of paper clips on the stem of the whirligig.

META NOTES

If your students are advanced, consider discussing terminal velocity in this section.

META NOTES

The stability of the parachute's fall is more critical to ensure that the parachute design falls consistently and slowly. The stability is affected by several factors that were not variables for the whirligig. These include: string length, number, and placement and canopy vents and shape.

String Length

5 min.

Lead a discussion how string length affects the stability of the parachute as it falls.

TEACHER TALK

❝Think about the *Whirligig Challenge* and changing the number of paper clips on the stem of the whirligig? What happened and why? What do you think happens when we change the number of washers on the parachute? Why? **❞**

Next, ask the class why increasing the number of washers decreases the time of fall. Students should describe how increasing the number of washers increases the mass and in turn, the gravitational pull. This results in a decreased fall time. Remind students that this in and of itself does not change the fall time, it actually changes the maximum amount of air resistance exerted on the parachute, which leads to increased fall times.

Finally, point out that the washers, like the paper clips, add stability to the parachute so that it falls upright and slowly.

turn ove............to the ground.

String Length

The strings on a parachute support the parachute's load. They keep it connected to the canopy. They also do another important job. The lengths of the strings on a parachute determine the shape of the parachute in two ways:

- They control how far below the canopy the load hangs.
- They control how far right or left of the parachute's center the load hangs.

Suppose the load is close to the canopy. Air resistance pushing up on the canopy can easily flip the parachute over. Increasing the distance between the load and the canopy makes the parachute more stable. But suppose the load hangs too far from the canopy? The canopy will not fully inflate.

DIV 85

DIVING INTO SCIENCE

△ Guide

Next, ask students if a group investigated this factor and if so have them remind the class of their results and then discuss the science behind it. Ask the group if they remember what happened to the shape of the canopy when the strings were very short or very long. If no groups investigated string length, consider demonstrating how string length affects the fall of the parachute.

If you did not do the demonstration, draw diagrams or have students draw diagrams of parachutes with very long and very short strings on the board to help students visualize how the shape changes.

Discuss how string length affects the stability of the parachute. Describe how short strings can cause the parachute to flip, and how if the load is too far from the canopy (long strings even when equally spaced) it can cause the load to be off center, leading to decreased stability.

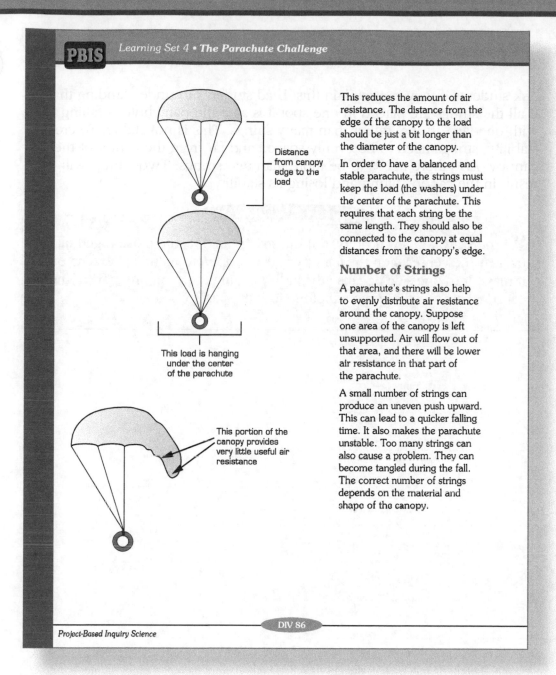

Distance from canopy edge to the load

This load is hanging under the center of the parachute

This portion of the canopy provides very little useful air resistance

This reduces the amount of air resistance. The distance from the edge of the canopy to the load should be just a bit longer than the diameter of the canopy.

In order to have a balanced and stable parachute, the strings must keep the load (the washers) under the center of the parachute. This requires that each string be the same length. They should also be connected to the canopy at equal distances from the canopy's edge.

Number of Strings

A parachute's strings also help to evenly distribute air resistance around the canopy. Suppose one area of the canopy is left unsupported. Air will flow out of that area, and there will be lower air resistance in that part of the parachute.

A small number of strings can produce an uneven push upward. This can lead to a quicker falling time. It also makes the parachute unstable. Too many strings can also cause a problem. They can become tangled during the fall. The correct number of strings depends on the material and shape of the canopy.

Number of Strings

5 min.

Lead a discussion on how the number of strings and placement affects the stability of the parachute as it falls.

Next, discuss with the class how the number of strings affects how the parachute falls. If any groups investigated this, have them remind the class of their results.

TEACHER TALK

"Did anyone investigate how the number of strings or string placement affects how the parachute falls? What were your results? What do you think is the cause for those results? "

Ask students if they can explain this. Lead students to understanding that if all the strings are placed in one spot it is as if the parachute is falling with one large string, rather than many strings. This is not stable. To create stability, strings need to be evenly spaced and far from the center of the canopy. Also there needs to be more than two strings. Two strings will result in the canopy tilting and losing its stability.

TEACHER TALK

"If there are too few strings or if the strings are located close together or near the center then the canopy may not open to its fullest extent, or it may tilt to one side because the air is pushing more on one part of the canopy. This causes the parachute to lose its stability."

NOTES

....

....

....

....

....

....

....

....

....

....

Canopy Vents

Many parachutes have vent holes. Vents control how the air passes through and around the canopy. As air enters and runs into the canopy, it behaves much like water if you were pouring it from one bucket into another. The air strikes the surface of the canopy and is redirected. It will slosh around inside the canopy, especially as new air molecules continue to enter the canopy area.

This new air will push old air over and out of the canopy's edge. This is very similar to how water would move if you were pouring a large amount of it, quickly, into a shallow sink with the stopper closed.

Adding vent holes helps reduce the sloshing of air. This results in a more stable fall. There is, however, a trade-off. Cutting holes in the canopy reduces the amount of air resistance. Vent holes can be useful. However, the number of vent holes has to provide balance between increased stability and decreased air resistance.

Canopy Vents
5 min.

Lead a discussion on how canopy vents change the time it takes the parachute to reach the ground.

△ Guide

Begin by asking students if anyone thought about investigating vents in the canopy. If so, have the group remind the class of their results. If not, ask the class what they think canopy vents are. Then explain how vents are holes in the canopy that allow air to flow through. Ask students why this would be beneficial as it decreases the air resistance. Then describe how it increases stability so there is a trade-off.

Discuss with the class what situations would justify the use of canopy vents, such as, when you are using a very large canopy.

Canopy Shape

5 min.

Lead a discussion on how canopy shape affects the stability of how a parachute falls.

Canopy Shape

You know that the canopy provides air resistance that pushes up on the parachute. The upward push offsets the downward pull of gravity. This causes the parachute to fall slowly. The shape of the canopy can also have an effect. However, it is the size of the canopy and the balance of the canopy that affect this variable. The surface area of the canopy is the key factor, not the shape. It is possible to have a circular canopy and a triangular canopy with equal surface areas. The difference is that it is easier to evenly distribute the strings around a circle. This creates a more balanced upward push of air resistance.

Some parachutes are designed to slice through the air like an airplane wing. The canopies are rectangular. They look like wings. They allow a parachutist to control the path of the parachute.

Review and Revise Explanations and Recommendations

You have just read about how gravity and air resistance are involved in the fall of a parachute. With your group, look at the explanation and recommendation you created after your parachute experiment. Use the science content you read about to support your claims. Edit your claims as needed and rewrite them. Make sure your previous explanation and recommendation are consistent with the science you just learned.

When you are finished, you will once again share your explanations and recommendations with the class.

Finally, discuss the effects of canopy shape on the way a parachute falls. Consider demonstrating how two or three coffee-filter parachutes with roughly the same canopy surface area but very different canopy shapes fall. Emphasize that the shape of the canopy is less significant in how quickly or slowly the parachute falls than the surface area and balance of the canopy. The picture in the student text shows a parachute with a novel shape that provides sufficient air resistance and balance to fall slowly.

○ Get Going

Give groups a time frame and have them review their explanations and recommendations from their recent investigations of the parachute. Distribute new *Create Your Explanation* sheets and have them edit their explanations and recommendations, supporting their claims with the new science content or modifying them where they are inconsistent with the new science content.

TEACHER TALK

❝You probably know a lot more about parachutes now than you did when you wrote your explanations and recommendations. When you look at them now, you may see that you have to change them so they agree with the science we just discussed. Or you may see that what you just learned really backs up what you said. Now you're going to revise your explanations or add new ones and update your recommendations using what you just learned to support them if you can.**❞**

☐ Assess

As groups are editing their explanations and recommendations, walk around and check to make sure that they are using the science knowledge they just learned to support their claims. They should be modifying their claims and recommendations where they see conflict with the science presented, and adding new claims as needed.

NOTES

....

....

....

....

Review and Revise Explanations and Recommendations

10 min.

Guide students to revise their explanations and recommendations and present their revisions to the class.

⬡ Get Going

When groups have finished editing their explanations and recommendations, have each group present theirs to the class. While a group is presenting, the rest of the class should be taking notes on their own *Create Your Explanation* pages.

> **TEACHER TALK**
>
> **"**I don't see how your evidence backs up your claim. Could you clarify that for me? Could you clarify how the science knowledge supports your claim in your explanation? **"**

△ Guide

Encourage students to check that the explanations presented are composed of one or more claims supported by evidence and science knowledge in a logical way. Model for students how they should seek clarification or point out areas they may not understand.

Also, encourage students to point out where they think the group could have used some of the science knowledge they just learned to support their claims.

◇ Evaluate

Make sure students incorporate the appropriate science knowledge introduced today into their explanations. For example, if students investigated the number of strings and location of strings, then their explanations should include a description of how the number and location of strings affects how the air pushes on the canopy, and this in turn affects the stability.

NOTES

....

....

....

....

....

Update the *Project Board*

Now that you've run parachute experiments and learned some of the science of parachutes, you are ready to revise the *Project Board* once again. You will focus on *What are we learning?*, *What is our evidence?*, and *What does it mean for the challenge or question?*

Remember that the claims you record in the *What are we learning?* column come from your investigations. You saw how a variable affects the fall of a parachute. Make sure to include in the *What is our evidence?* column all of the evidence you have (data, trends, science) that supports each claim. In the *What does it mean for the challenge or question?* column, revise your answers to the question, *What affects how an object falls towards Earth?* Revise recommendations about designing a slowly falling parachute. For more advice about what goes in these columns, look back at *Learning Set 3*. Don't forget to update your personal *Project Board*.

Reflect

Think about and answer the following questions. Later, your class will discuss your answers and how they may help you better achieve the *Parachute Challenge*.

1. What are some other objects that use air resistance to change how they fall or travel? What pull or push is air resistance opposing in your example?

2. The book support uses opposing pulls and pushes to keep the book in place. Here, the parachute has opposing pulls and pushes, but it does not stay in one place. What would have to happen to keep the parachute in one place when released?

3. Why do you think it was important to return to your *What are we learning?* and *What does it mean for the challenge or question?* columns? You had filled things in those columns during the *Whirligig Challenge*. Why were you able to revise those columns now?

Update the *Project Board*

10 min.

Update the Project Board *based on what students have learned.*

○ Get Going

After all groups have presented their revised explanations and recommendations, tell students that they will be updating their class *Project Board* to help organize the information and keep track of it. Ask students to take out their class *Project Board* pages so that they can update theirs as you update the class *Project Board* displayed.

△ Guide

Remind students that they will be focusing on column 3 (*What are we learning?*), and column 4 (*What is our evidence?*). Remind students that columns 3 and 4 are linked directly together, and column 5 (*What does it mean for the challenge or question?*) is where they will put a recommendation based on each new claim.

META NOTES

You may wish to review *Introducing the Project Board"* in *Section 3.1* for use of the columns in the *Project Board*. Students will be updating columns 3, 4, and 5.

Begin by asking students what claims they can make about how a parachute falls and the evidence that supports that claim.

As students identify new things they have learned, ask them how it has changed their understanding of the challenge and what recommendation they can make based on the information. Then fill in the recommendation in the column 5 of the *Project Board*, linking it to the information in columns 3 and 4.

TEACHER TALK

❝You used this information in constructing your recommendations. What recommendation can you make based just on this information?❞

☐ Assess

As the class updates the *Project Board*, listen for the following new information:

- **Claim:** Increasing the size of the canopy increases the time it takes the parachute to fall.

- **Evidence:** Experimental observations (students should state the trend in their data), and science knowledge (as the surface area increases the number of collisions with the air increases. This causes the drag force to reach its maximum value sooner resulting in a lower speed and longer time to reach the ground).

- **Recommendation:** To make the parachute fall more slowly, increase its canopy size.

- **Claim:** The load (washers) provides stability, but increases the time it takes the parachute to fall.

- **Evidence:** Experimental observations (when students increased the number of washers from ... to ..., the time it took the parachute to reach the ground decreased from ... to ...; some may note that it increased stability depending on their data) and science knowledge (as the mass increases, gravitational force increases causing a decrease in the time it takes to reach the ground. The maximum drag force increases and so the parachute reaches higher speeds and falls more quickly to the ground. However, decreasing the load may also decrease stability resulting in inconsistent fall times).

- **Recommendation:** To make the parachute fall more slowly, choose the smallest load (number of washers) required to maintain stability.

META NOTES

Increasing the canopy size also increases the mass, but usually there is still an overall increase in the time it takes the parachute to reach the ground.

- **Claim:** Longer strings provide greater stability, but if they're too long, the canopy may not open properly.
- **Evidence:** Experimental observations (during the investigation when they increased the string length they observed...) and science knowledge (when the strings are too short the parachute becomes unstable because the air resistance pushing up on the canopy can make the canopy flip the parachute.)
- **Recommendation:** To increase stability, optimize the string length — not too short or too long.
- **Claim:** The number of strings and their location help to increase stability of the parachute.
- **Evidence:** Experimental observations and science knowledge (the number of strings and their placement affects how much the air resistance pushes a given part of the canopy. If strings are not evenly distributed and far from the center of the canopy, then the push up from the air will not be evenly distributed causing the canopy to sway or flip and the parachute to fall faster.)
- **Recommendation:** To increase the time it takes the parachute to reach the ground and the parachute's stability, use a minimum of three strings evenly placed at the outer edge of the canopy.
- **Claim:** Canopy vents can help stabilize the parachute, but they also decrease the time it takes the parachute to reach the ground.
- **Evidence:** Experimental observations and science knowledge (Vents in the canopy increase stability by allowing the air to flow through the vents in the canopy. However, this decreases the push up from the air, resulting in lower air resistance and hence decreased time of fall.
- **Recommendation:** To increase stability you could use air vents, but these decrease the time it takes the parachute to reach the ground.
- **Claim:** The shape of the canopy affects stability.
- **Evidence:** Experimental observations and science knowledge (the shape of the canopy affects the placement of the strings for stability more than anything else. Shapes that allow symmetric placing of the strings are best.)
- **Recommendation:** To increase stability of the parachute, select a canopy shape that allows for the strings to be places symmetrically.

META NOTES

Increasing the number of strings also increases the overall mass of the parachute, but for the *Parachute Challenge* this change in mass does not affect the parachute's fall time in a significant way.

META NOTES

The surface area affects speed the most, and different shapes can all be made to have the same surface area.

DIVING INTO SCIENCE

△ Guide

After students have addressed each of the ways you might adjust a parachute to affect the time it takes to reach the ground, point out that like in the *Whirligig Challenge* there are basically three things that cause the change in fall time: change in mass (increasing mass results in greater speeds and shorter fall times), change in surface area (increasing surface area results in lower speeds and greater fall times), and change in stability (when unstable, the parachute falls inconsistently and with greater speeds on the average resulting in greater fall times).

Reflect

10 min.

Lead students in reflecting upon how air resistance affects objects and how knowing about air resistance will help them solve the Parachute Challenge.

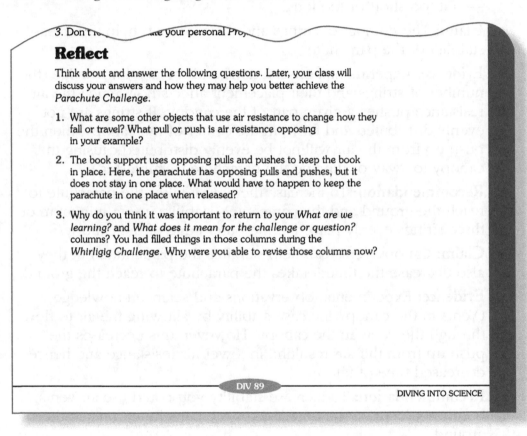

3. Don't ~~~~ ~~~~ your personal Pro~

Reflect

Think about and answer the following questions. Later, your class will discuss your answers and how they may help you better achieve the *Parachute Challenge.*

1. What are some other objects that use air resistance to change how they fall or travel? What pull or push is air resistance opposing in your example?

2. The book support uses opposing pulls and pushes to keep the book in place. Here, the parachute has opposing pulls and pushes, but it does not stay in one place. What would have to happen to keep the parachute in one place when released?

3. Why do you think it was important to return to your *What are we learning?* and *What does it mean for the challenge or question?* columns? You had filled things in those columns during the *Whirligig Challenge.* Why were you able to revise those columns now?

DIV 89

DIVING INTO SCIENCE

△ Guide and Assess

When the class has finished its investigations, use the *Reflect* questions to guide and assess students' understanding of how the parachute parts can affect the force of air resistance that slows down the parachute, and can also affect its stability. Emphasize how this science knowledge increases their understanding of falling and will help them to design a slow-falling parachute.

1. Students might mention a drag car or the space shuttle when it lands — both use a parachute to slow them down. Also, fluffy or bladed seeds use air resistance to slow their fall and be pushed further by the wind.

2. To keep the parachute in one place upon being released would require a force exerted to the parachute the instant it was released that supported its weight. Air resistance is a force that grows from zero to a maximum value. If students are having trouble with this, remind them of holding their hand still and then moving their hand through the air.

META NOTES

Reducing surface area reduces resistance and is used when designing fast cars, rockets, and when birds dive for fish.

3. Students should recognize that what they're learning now builds on what they learned in the *Whirligig Challenge*. In the *Whirligig Challenge*, they learned about how the blades of the whirligig affect the air resistance, and how the other factors in whirligig design related to this. In this section, students learn how the parachute's parts affect and utilize air resistance, and how they affect the stability of the parachute. This information provides further evidence and support to describing how things fall through air in general.

Teacher Reflection Questions

- What kinds of changes did groups make to their explanations and recommendations? How does this show that they understand the science content and are applying it to reach the challenge?

- The goal of this Unit is for students and the teacher to become familiar with the pedagogical tools of PBIS. Do you feel your students understand the purpose and utilization of the *Project Board?* Of the challenge?

- What kinds of issues came up when students were discussing what to put on the *Project Board?* How did you address these issues? What other ideas would you like to try?

NOTES

....

....

....

....

....

SECTION 4.5 INTRODUCTION

4.5 Plan

Design a Slow-Falling Parachute

Overview

Student groups apply their recommendations to plan a design of a slow-falling parachute and get feedback from the class on their design plans. Groups share their parachute design plans and their reasoning for their design plans during a *Plan Briefing*. The class asks questions and gives feedback during presentations, helping the presenting groups to identify weaknesses in their design plans. Using this feedback, and building on ideas from other presentations, groups revise their design plans. Groups will construct their design in the next section.

Targeted Concepts, Skills, and Nature of Science	Performance Expectations
Scientists often work together and then share their findings. Sharing findings makes new information available and helps scientists refine their ideas and build on others' ideas. When another person's or group's idea is used, credit needs to be given.	Groups present their plans to the class and use suggestions and feedback from the class.

Materials	
1 per group	poster paper and markers

Activity Setup and Preparation

Decide where you want students to display their posters and how you want to arrange the room for the *Plan Briefing*. Students should be able to review others' posters before each group presents their parachute design plan to the class.

---

*A class period is considered to be one 40 to 50 minute class.

Homework Options

Reflection

- **Science Content:** Did any of the questions or suggestions you got from classmates surprise you? Summarize what you learned from them. *(Students should draw on feedback from their* Plan Briefings.*)*

- **Science Process:** Do you think the design process would be more or less effective if everyone in the class were in one group? Why? *(Students' should show recognition that getting feedback from other groups was an important part of the design process.)*

Preparation for 4.6

- **Science Process:** After you construct your parachute design, you will need to test it. How will you test it? *(Students should write a clear procedure describing how they will test their parachute.)*

NOTES

_____

_____

_____

_____

_____

_____

_____

_____

$1\frac{1}{2}$ *class periods* ▶

4.5 Plan

Design a Slow-Falling Parachute

Inform students of why it is important to plan a parachute design.

SECTION 4.5 IMPLEMENTATION

4.5 Plan

Design a Slow-Falling Parachute

While working on the *Whirligig Challenge*, you made recommendations. However, you did not have a chance to test them. This time, you are going to use all the recommendations that the class made to design and test a parachute. You are not just giving the cereal company advice about making a better parachute. You are giving them advice about how to design their first one.

Plan

As you read about parachute science, you read about trade-offs. For example, longer strings are good up to a point. However, strings that are too long get tangled. More strings are also good. Yet too many strings make the parachute hard to build. These real-world issues are important to consider along with the science as you work on designing a good parachute for putting inside a cereal box.

You have learned a lot about how a variety of variables affect the fall of a parachute. You have also learned a lot about the science of falling. With your group, design your best parachute. Plan one you think will fall as slowly as possible. Make decisions together about how to set each of the variables in your parachute. How long will your strings be? How much load will your parachute carry? How many coffee filters will you use in the canopy? How will you shape the canopy? What will be the surface area of the canopy? For each design decision you make, know why you are making that decision. Record what evidence you are using to make each decision. Your decisions should be informed by the evidence you have available.

When you are finished, you will have a chance to share your plan with other groups in a *Plan Briefing* before you actually build and test your design. Others in the class might be able to help you with any difficult decisions you need to make as you work on your design plan.

DIV 90

Project-Based Inquiry Science

○ **Engage**

To begin, ask students if they think they are ready to send their recommendations to the cereal company. Remind them of the recommendations they put on their *Project Board*. You might ask them what a design team working on a major project might do before sending off their recommendations.

Students should realize that they need to pull their multiple recommendations together and decide on what they think might be. Then they will need to design it, build a model, and test it before making a recommendation.

Next, let students know that each group will test their recommendations by designing and building a parachute based on them. Before groups build and test their parachutes, they will share their design plans and revise them based on feedback from the class.

△ Guide

Emphasize that groups should use the recommendations the class put on the class's *Project Board* to address each of the variables they identified. Point out that some of these variables need to be optimized. For example, air vents can increase stability but they reduce the amount of air resistance acting on the parachute. It is also important that they meet the criteria and constraints of the cereal company. Post the class's list of criteria and constraints.

Plan

10 min.

Guide students through planning a parachute design.

TEACHER TALK

"You want to plan a design that will meet all the criteria and constraints of the cereal company using all you now know about the parachute before you make your final recommendation to the cereal company. You will get to construct and test your designs later, but first you need to think about what will be the best parachute design. And like you did in the *Book-Support Challenge*, you will get to revise your plan after you share it with the class so you can build on others' ideas."

Let groups know how much time they have to work on their design (10 minutes). As groups are working on their parachute designs, ask students what ideas they have. Also, ask students how they are using the recommendations of the class and what decisions they have had to make.

NOTES

....

....

Communicate Your Plan

40 min.

Lead the class in preparing, giving and discussing their parachute design plans.

Communicate Your Plan

Plan Briefing

As you are finishing your design plan, begin to draw a poster for presentation of your design plan to the class. Your teacher will provide you with a large sheet of paper to create your *Plan-Briefing* poster and possibly a template to follow. You will have 20 minutes to create a *Plan-Briefing* poster and organize your presentation.

Your teacher will then lead your class through a *Plan-Briefing* session.

> **Be a Scientist**
>
> #### Introducing a *Plan Briefing*
> **Preparing a *Plan-Briefing* Poster**
>
> A *Plan Briefing* is very much like the other presentations you have learned to do. In a *Plan Briefing*, you present your design plan. You must present it well enough so that your classmates can appreciate your ideas. They should be able to identify if you have made any mistakes in your reasoning. Then they can provide you with advice before you begin constructing your parachute. As a presenter, you'll learn the most from a *Plan Briefing* if you can be very specific about your design plans and about why you made your design decisions. You'll probably want to draw pictures, maybe providing several views. You certainly want everyone to know why you expect your design to achieve the challenge.
>
> The following guidelines will help you as you decide what to present on your poster:
>
> - Your poster should have a detailed drawing of your design with at least one view. You might consider drawing multiple views so that the audience can see your design from different angles. It is important that the audience can picture what you are planning to build.
>
> - Parts of the design and any special features should all be labeled. The labels should describe how and why you made each of your design decisions. Show the explanations and recommendations that support your decisions. Convincing others that your design choices are quality ones means convincing them that you are making informed decisions backed by scientific evidence.
>
> - Make sure to give credit to groups or students who ran the experiments that inform your design and who gave you ideas.

Plan Briefing: an opportunity during the design process to share plans and get advice from others.

DIV 91

DIVING INTO SCIENCE

META NOTES

Do not allow groups to work more than 10 minutes on their design plans before discussing with the class the *Plan Briefing*, unless most groups are not done. If most groups are not done give them a few more minutes.

○ Get Going

As you see groups nearly finishing their design plans, distribute the materials they will need to create their *Plan-Briefing* poster. Let students know that they will have 20 minutes to complete their posters and that you will hold a class discussion on the posters soon.

△ Guide

After the allotted time for planning their designs, introduce the class to *Plan Briefings*. These are similar to *Solution Briefings*, but in *Plan Briefings* groups present details of their design plans rather than their solutions.

TEACHER TALK

❝Remember in the *Book-Support Challenge* you shared your ideas and your reasoning behind your solutions during a *Solution Briefing.* You will be doing something similar called a *Plan Briefing.* In a *Plan Briefing* you share your design plans. You will be sharing and discussing your parachute design plans and your reasoning behind your design choices. Then you'll be able to revise your plan. This way, you can improve your plan before you actually build your model and test it. To show your plans to the class, you're going to make a *Plan-Briefing* poster. ❞

Tell students that they will make posters with detailed drawings of their plans with all parts labeled, a description of any special features, explanations and recommendations that support the design, and credit to anyone else's ideas used.

Let students know that the class will discuss what criteria the features of the design achieve, what is expected to happen, and any possible problems. Emphasize that *Plan Briefings* should be specific and contain the reasoning behind design choices. Students should use the guide on page 91 for preparing their poster and the guide on page 92 for preparing their presentation for the *Plan Briefings*.

Let students know how much time they have (no more than 20 minutes).

◇ Evaluate

As groups work on their *Plan-Briefing* posters, walk around the room and look at groups' posters to see if their drawings are clear and detailed enough that the class will be able to discuss what criteria the plan will achieve and possible problems with the plan. Also, make sure that students list the explanations and recommendations that support their design plan.

Lead the class in presenting and discussing each group's design plan.

⬡ Get Going

After groups have finished their posters, let them know where they should display them. Then allow the groups to visit each poster for about a minute.

When groups have finished viewing everyone's posters, begin the class presentations.

△ Guide

Remind students that during the presentations they should check if all the criteria and constraints have been met, ask clarifying questions, and give their advice. Then have groups begin their presentations.

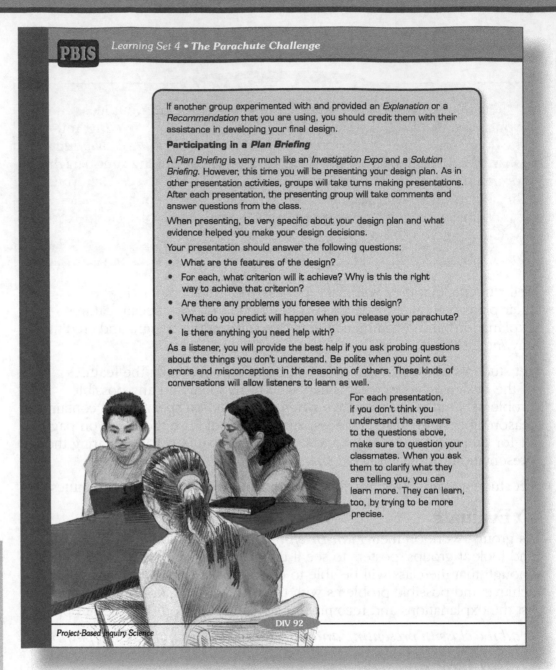

If another group experimented with and provided an *Explanation* or a *Recommendation* that you are using, you should credit them with their assistance in developing your final design.

Participating in a *Plan Briefing*

A *Plan Briefing* is very much like an *Investigation Expo* and a *Solution Briefing*. However, this time you will be presenting your design plan. As in other presentation activities, groups will take turns making presentations. After each presentation, the presenting group will take comments and answer questions from the class.

When presenting, be very specific about your design plan and what evidence helped you make your design decisions.

Your presentation should answer the following questions:

- What are the features of the design?
- For each, what criterion will it achieve? Why is this the right way to achieve that criterion?
- Are there any problems you foresee with this design?
- What do you predict will happen when you release your parachute?
- Is there anything you need help with?

As a listener, you will provide the best help if you ask probing questions about the things you don't understand. Be polite when you point out errors and misconceptions in the reasoning of others. These kinds of conversations will allow listeners to learn as well.

For each presentation, if you don't think you understand the answers to the questions above, make sure to question your classmates. When you ask them to clarify what they are telling you, you can learn more. They can learn, too, by trying to be more precise.

During the presentations, model the participation you expect by asking questions of the presenting group when anything isn't clear and offering suggestions to improve their design.

Also, point out the presenting group can ask for help with a specific aspect of their design from the class.

After each presentation, you may need to ask a question or two to begin the discussion. Then ask a student to ask a question. Questions should be about how they meet the criteria and constraints and why they think their design choices are best. Students should also give ideas on how to improve designs. With the class, summarize the suggested improvements for each group so they can record the ideas.

Revise Your Plan

You may have received some good advice from classmates about how to revise your design plan to make it better. If so, spend some time with your group doing that. Be sure to update the pages you are using to record your plan and to justify your design decisions.

What's the Point?

Do you have a strong opinion about something? Many people do. They assume that their points of view are obvious to others. They tend to think that other people will automatically hold those same views. But often you will be surprised. What was obvious to you looks different to someone else. You struggle with this all the time. What seems to work is to explain why you believe what you believe each time you express an opinion.

Evidence that supports your point of view helps other people to see your point. When people state their opinions without explaining what justifies them, others are more likely to question their viewpoints. Whenever you need to convince someone of something, or when you're trying to decide between several alternatives, presenting evidence that supports a point of view is critical.

The same is true in convincing yourself that you have made a good decision. You should be able to justify a decision with evidence. Then you will be more sure of your decision and more likely to make good decisions.

When you are planning the design of a product or process, it is often useful to hear from others. They can help you see how well your design meets the criteria of the challenge. You need to present reasons for the decisions you made. Then others can help you identify misconceptions you might have. They can also help you be more confident about your decisions. They can help you judge your decisions not simply based on opinion but based on evidence and information.

An important benefit of a *Plan Briefing* is that different teams can learn from each other. A team may have struggled with one aspect of its design. That team may now have good advice for those who haven't yet tackled that problem. They, in turn, may benefit from experiences some other team has had.

Revise Your Plan

10 min.

Have groups revise their plans.

⬡ Get Going

Now that groups have presented their design plans and received feedback from the class, they can use the feedback to revise their plans. Give students a time frame (no more than 10 minutes) and have them revise their plans. Emphasize that they need to record their new plans and justify their revisions.

☐ Assess

As groups are revising their plans, walk around the room and check to see what revisions groups are making. They should be using the feedback they got from the class.

What's the Point?

5 min.

group do... ...re to update the pag... ...ng to record y...
plan and to justify your design decisions.

What's the Point?

Do you have a strong opinion about something? Many people do. They assume that their points of view are obvious to others. They tend to think that other people will automatically hold those same views. But often you will be surprised. What was obvious to you looks different to someone else. You struggle with this all the time. What seems to work is to explain why you believe what you believe each time you express an opinion.

Evidence that supports your point of view helps other people to see your point. When people state their opinions without explaining what justifies them, others are more likely to question their viewpoints. Whenever you need to convince someone of something, or when you're trying to decide between several alternatives, presenting evidence that supports a point of view is critical.

The same is true in convincing yourself that you have made a good decision. You should be able to justify a decision with evidence. Then you will be more sure of your decision and more likely to make good decisions.

When you are planning the design of a product or process, it is often useful to hear from others. They can help you see how well your design meets the criteria of the challenge. You need to present reasons for the decisions you made. Then others can help you identify misconceptions you might have. They can also help you be more confident about your decisions. They can help you judge your decisions not simply based on opinion but based on evidence and information.

An important benefit of a *Plan Briefing* is that different teams can learn from each other. A team may have struggled with one aspect of its design. That team may now have good advice for those who haven't yet tackled that problem. They, in turn, may benefit from experiences some other team has had.

△ Guide

Once students have finished revising their plans, discuss with the class the benefits of using evidence to support your point of view and of getting feedback from others.

NOTES

....

....

....

....

Assessment Options

Targeted Concepts, Skills, and Nature of Science	How do I know if students got it?
Scientists often work together and then share their findings. Sharing findings makes new information available and helps scientists refine their ideas and build on others' ideas. When another persons or group's idea is used, credit needs to be given.	**ASK:** How does presenting your plans to the group help you? **LISTEN:** Students should recognize that the suggestions and feedback they get from their group and their class are useful.

Teacher Reflection Questions

- What types of problems with their designs did groups discover during their *Plan Briefings?* What did they learn from their *Plan Briefings?*

- What types of questions and comments did students make during the presentations? What other kinds of questions and comments do students need to communicate? What else can you do to encourage appropriate student participation in discussion?

- How was managing the *Plan Briefings* different from managing the recommendation and explanation presentations? What would you do differently?

4.6 Build and Test

2 class periods* ▶

Build and Test Your Parachute

Overview

Student groups build parachutes from their design plans, test them, and revise their designs based on the results of their tests. As groups iteratively improve their design plans based on their tests, you may have them briefly present their solution in a *Solution Briefing* to get feedback from the class on difficulties they are having with their design. After student groups build their final design, students present them in *Solution Showcases*, which help students share what they did from the beginning to the end of the design process with the class, allowing students to analyze and evaluate what has worked and what hasn't worked. Then the class tests and compares all of the final parachute designs. Students analyze what works, what does not work and how the design performances are explained by the concepts of gravity and air resistance.

Targeted Concepts, Skills, and Nature of Science	Performance Expectations
Scientists must keep clear, accurate, and descriptive records of what they do so they can share their work with others and consider what they did, why they did it, and what they want to do next.	Students record changes in their design, results of each iteration, and the results of the final test.

Materials

1	per class	class Project Board
1	per class	class list of criteria and constraints
1	per student	*Testing My Design* page
1	per group	stopwatch
5	per group	coffee filters
1	per class	250 ft spool of cotton string
4	per group	washers (outer diameter 1")
1	per group	safety scissors
1	per group	transparent tape

*A class period is considered to be one 40 to 50 minute class.

1	per group	poster paper and markers
1	per group	metric ruler
1	per group	markers, set of 8 colors

Students should be careful not to swing around string with washers attached to it.

Because students will be dropping the parachute at heights greater than 6 ft, take precautions to ensure that the area for which students drop their parachutes will not endanger anyone or any property. Students must be supervised as they drop their parachutes.

Activity Setup and Preparation

- Have a place ready for students to test their parachutes. For this test, a space where the whole class can see the parachutes fall should be cleared. Students will again need to drop their parachutes from a height greater than 6 ft, and they will need an area clear of obstacles that could interfere with the fall of the parachute.

- Have a stopwatch ready. You might also decide on a procedure for testing students' parachutes at the end of the section.

- Have the class's *Project Board* and the class list of criteria and constraints displayed so students can easily refer to them as needed.

Homework Options

Reflection

- **Science Process:** If you had to tell another group of students how to use iteration in designing a parachute, what would you say? What advice would you give them? *(Answers should say something about retaining some features of the original design and building on them.)*

- **Science Content:** You have designed your parachutes and made recommendations to the cereal company. They write back to say that there has been a change of plans, and the parachute has to have a canopy shaped like a long rectangle. What do you do? *(Answers should indicate that some results of the original investigation can be applied to the new design. Students should remember that the shape of the canopy is less important than its area, so a first design for the new parachute should probably have a canopy with the same area as the design they sent to the company.)*

- **Science Process:** Describe how you used the results of your own experiments and the science you learned in *Section 4.5* in your parachute design. *(Students should recognize where their decisions were guided by the results of their experiments and what they read in Section 4.5.)*

DIVING INTO SCIENCE

2 class periods ▶

4.6 Build and Test

Build and Test Your Parachute

5 min.

SECTION 4.6 IMPLEMENTATION

4.6 Build and Test

Build and Test Your Parachute

The moment has arrived. You have planned your best design based on evidence you have available. You have presented it to others. You have received advice from your classmates. You might have even revised your plan based on what your classmates suggested. You are now ready to build your best parachute. You hope to have the parachute that falls the slowest. If you do, it will be included in millions of cereal boxes worldwide!

Build Your Parachute

You will work with your group to create and test your final parachute. You will have the opportunity to revise it up to three times. After you have completed your third or fourth iteration, the class will hold a demonstration and competition. Each group will get to drop their parachute three times. The average of those times will be their score. Each group will also present to the class the changes they made in their parachute design since the *Plan Briefing*. They will explain why they made those changes. They will also explain what were the effects of the changes. When you recommend a parachute design to the cereal company, you'll need to tell them not only how to design the parachute but why you think that design is the best one. On the next page are some hints for you about how to manage iteration to build a better parachute.

Project-Based Inquiry Science

DIV 94

○ **Engage**

Begin by reminding the class that today they will test their parachute design plans so that they can make a good recommendation to the cereal company. They will also test everyone's final design to see which parachute designs fall the slowest.

❝Last time you worked on planning a parachute design that you thought would be good to recommend to the cereal company. Remember the goal is to design the slowest falling parachute possible because that would make the parachute most fun. Now you will have a chance to build your parachute design, test it, and revise it. You'll use the iterative process like you did with the *Book-Support Challenge* and after you come up with your final design we'll test everyone's out and determine which designs might be the best to recommend to the cereal company.❞

△ Guide

Tell the class they will be using the iterative process, the process of improving something over time. They did this in the *Book-Support Challenge*, the *Sandwich-Cookie Challenge* and the *Whirligig Challenge*. They will build and test their parachute, then find ways to improve the design by making small changes. Emphasize that they should not make too many changes at once: if they only make one change at a time, they should be sure what the effect of that change was. Let the class know that if a group is having trouble with their design, they may be asked to get advice from the class by presenting their design in a *Solution Briefing*. Everyone will stop to listen, give advice, and then return to work on building and testing parachute designs. Then tell students that after they have completed three or four iterations, the class will share all their designs in a *Solution Showcase*, and test all the parachutes to see which parachute designs are the slowest-falling.

NOTES

....

....

....

....

Build Your Parachute
10 min.

Describe iteration and its benefits for design work.

Students actually begin building their parachutes under the *Test Your Parachute* segment. Here the goal is to give students an overview of the process they will be using.

The *Solution Briefing* is optional. It is based on your assessment of how much difficulty a group is having during their building and testing process. A *Solution Briefing* will give a group the opportunity to ask the class for advice. These are informal and quick.

DIVING INTO SCIENCE

Test Your Parachute

20 min.

Get students started on their iterative design testing.

Iteration

Iteration is a process of making something better over time. That something may be a product or an understanding. Scientists and student scientists iteratively understand new concepts better over time. Designers iteratively make designs better over time. Each time they test a design, they might find ways to improve it. Recall that each change and new design is called an iteration.

Sometimes your design does not work as well as you expected. Your first feeling may be to throw away those failed plans and begin again. Don't! If you began with a design based on evidence and science, then your parachute will probably work well with some changes.

You saw the power of iteration earlier in this Unit. In the *Sandwich-Cookie Challenge*, you improved the procedure for doing the test. You performed a procedure. Then you reflected on it. You were able to find mistakes and improve your method. During the *Whirligig Challenge*, you iteratively improved your explanations. Now, with your parachute, you will have the opportunity to *iteratively* enhance a design.

There is an important thing to remember as you iterate on your design. Do not make too many changes in a design. Otherwise you will not be able to identify why the new design worked differently. Usually the best way to iterate is to make one revision at a time. Make and test one change at a time. Then you will know the effect of that change.

Test Your Parachute

Below are some suggestions for testing your designs. You can also use a page similar to the one shown on the next page to record your work.

Testing Your Designs

In experiments, it is important to run several trials. Then you can be sure your results are consistent. The same is true in testing a design. Each time you test a design, make sure to drop it enough times. Choose the number of times that will allow you to see how it performs. Be sure, too, to follow the same procedure each time you test it. Otherwise, you will not know if the design is causing the effects you see or if something you did not control in your procedure is responsible for your results.

Recording Your Work

As you test and revise your design, it will be important to record the results

△ Guide

Briefly discuss the importance of procedures with the class. Emphasize that it will be important to test each design the same way as they did the previous design. Each group should decide on a procedure at the beginning, specifying the number of trials, how to use the stopwatch, and the height from which to drop the parachute. Let students know that they should have at least four to five trial measurements for each iteration of their design and they should record their measurements in the *What happened when you tested the design or model?* box. If they are doing a series of iterations of the same variable to optimize it, then they should put all the data on one *Testing My Design* page.

"Remember that it is important that your design is a fair test. What do you need to do to make it a fair test? *(Each iteration should be compared under the same conditions.)* When you test each iteration you'll want to take multiple trials. Why? *(Multiple trials allow you to determine the precision of your results. If they are clustered, your results are consistent and precise and are more likely to be trustworthy.)* For each iteration you should only change one thing at a time so that you can be sure what is causing the change you observe. For example, let's say you've decided you want to increase the surface area of your canopy and you think increasing the number of strings might be useful too. Before you increase the number of strings, first test your design with a canopy of larger surface area, then increase the number of strings, otherwise you won't know if the effect you observed was caused by the surface area or the number of strings. But remember to use what you already know from previous experiments and *Parachute Science* to help you decide what your next iteration should be. It may be that you know enough that you know that changing two things will improve the parachute design based on the evidence you obtained during your investigations and in *Parachute Science*. Remember you are trying to optimize the parachute design to be slowest."

⬡ Get Going

Discuss with the students how to record their results on the *Testing My Design* page. Let students know they should fill out one page for each iteration they test and that they should record all their measurements and observations on this page as well. The measurements and observations should be listed in the *What happened when you tested the design or model?* box. Let students know they will have about 15 minutes to iteratively build and test their parachutes. Tell students that it is also important to record the results of each test and all the changes made.

If students are trying to optimize a variable such as the number of strings, you may want them to do a few iterations for each value of the number of strings, but just use one but list all the data for those iterations on one *Testing My Design* page, listing all the data for those iterations on one page so you can look at the trend in the data.

Have students begin their design iterations.

As students revise their plans, remind them that it is more effective to change one variable in the design for each iteration than to make many changes at once. This allows students to isolate how that change affects the design. If they change multiple variables during an iteration it should be based on reasoning backed by evidence and science knowledge.

The purpose of these *Solution Briefings* is to get the class's advice on how to improve their design.

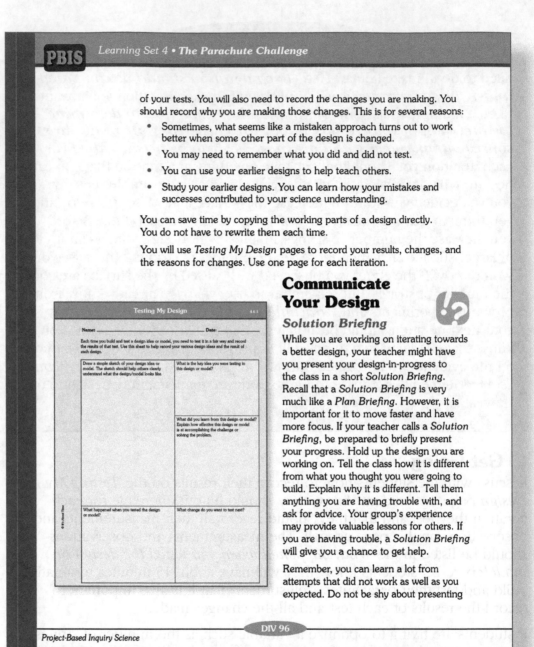

of your tests. You will also need to record the changes you are making. You should record why you are making those changes. This is for several reasons:

- Sometimes, what seems like a mistaken approach turns out to work better when some other part of the design is changed.
- You may need to remember what you did and did not test.
- You can use your earlier designs to help teach others.
- Study your earlier designs. You can learn how your mistakes and successes contributed to your science understanding.

You can save time by copying the working parts of a design directly. You do not have to rewrite them each time.

You will use *Testing My Design* pages to record your results, changes, and the reasons for changes. Use one page for each iteration.

Communicate Your Design

Solution Briefing

While you are working on iterating towards a better design, your teacher might have you present your design-in-progress to the class in a short *Solution Briefing*. Recall that a *Solution Briefing* is very much like a *Plan Briefing*. However, it is important for it to move faster and have more focus. If your teacher calls a *Solution Briefing*, be prepared to briefly present your progress. Hold up the design you are working on. Tell the class how it is different from what you thought you were going to build. Explain why it is different. Tell them anything you are having trouble with, and ask for advice. Your group's experience may provide valuable lessons for others. If you are having trouble, a *Solution Briefing* will give you a chance to get help.

Remember, you can learn a lot from attempts that did not work as well as you expected. Do not be shy about presenting

△ Guide

As groups are building and testing their parachutes, you can ask them what ideas they have tried out. If any groups seem stuck on a design and they don't think they can improve it, you might ask them what evidence they've collected on alternative designs. How do they know that this parachute falls slower than one with slightly longer strings? Or one with fewer strings or washers? You may also want them to present their design to the class, discussing what they think is the problem, dropping their parachute, and then getting feedback from the class on what they should do.

As students are working on their designs, you may choose to have them present *Solution Briefings*, showing the class the designs they are working on and how they have modified their plans. Your decision should be based on how much difficulty the group is having in improving their parachute design. Groups that think they cannot make a better design or whose iterations are not improving their design should be asked to present to the class. The presentations should be very brief summaries of what a group has tried, what changes they've made, and what troubles they are having. The class should then provide advice on how to improve their designs.

△ Guide

Once students have finished iteratively building and testing their parachutes, let them know that they will next present their final designs to the class.

Introduce *Solution Showcases*, highlighting the information a *Solution Showcase* should convey: the original design plan, the history of the group's revisions, the way the group used the *Explanations and Recommendations* of the class, and the final design. Emphasize that groups should describe the changes they made in each iteration and the reasons for the changes.

Also, tell the class that students in the audience should make sure that each design presented meets the criteria and constraints of the challenge and hears answers to the bulleted questions at the end of page 97 of the student text. If they do not hear answers to these or they think the criteria or constraints of the challenge have not been met, then they should ask questions.

Remind students that they will not be altering their designs any more, but what they learn during this *Solution Showcase* will help them achieve the challenge.

Communicate Your Design
30 min.

Lead students in their first Solution Showcase to share their parachute designs.

> ### TEACHER TALK
>
> ❝Remember that you are not going to change your designs any more. These are your final designs. However, you still have not made a recommendation to the cereal company. As you watch all the presentations, pay attention to design features that you think would improve your design. Pay attention to design features that you think would not improve your design. This information will help you to make a good recommendation to the cereal company on how to build a fun, cost-effective, slow-falling parachute. After the presentations you will get to see how well everyone's design works.❞

DIVING INTO SCIENCE

what has not worked as well as you expected. You and others can learn from mistakes. Your peers can give you advice about design, construction, and testing.

Solution Showcase

After every group has a chance to iterate several times on their designs, it will be time to finish this activity. You will present your final design in a *Solution Showcase*. Recall that a *Solution Briefing* is a presentation that allows presenters and audiences to communicate effectively about a design or product. This time, however, you will not get a chance to make your parachute design better. However, after the *Solution Showcase* you might find that these presentations help better you understand the science you are learning.

Explain why you think you might have a very slowly falling design.

Be a Scientist

Introducing a *Solution Showcase*

The goal of a *Solution Showcase* is to have everyone better understand how each group approached the challenge. You get the opportunity to see the variety of solutions that might work. You can also learn what both successful and unsuccessful designs reveal about the way the world works. Be sure to discuss how you included the *Explanations* and *Recommendations* that the class generated in your final design.

A *Solution Showcase* should include the history of your design. Review your original design plan. Then tell the class what happened when you tested it. Talk about how you explained those results. Then report what you did to revise your design. Make sure to present the reasons you made the changes you did. Do this for the whole set of iterations you did. Make sure that the class understands what your final design is. Your teacher will tell you how long you have to present. You will not have a lot of time. Figure out how to present your design's history quickly.

As you listen, it will be important to look at each design carefully. You should ask questions about how the design meets the criteria of the challenge. Be prepared to ask (and answer) questions such as these:

- What techniques were tried and how were they done?
- How well does the design meet the goals of the challenge?
- How did the challenge constraints affect the use or success of this design?
- What problems remain?

DIVING INTO SCIENCE

◯ Get Going

Let students know how long they will have for their *Solution Showcases*, and give them a few minutes to prepare their presentations. Then have each group briefly present their *Solution Showcase*.

△ Guide

As each group presents, the other groups should ask questions about how the design meets the criteria of the challenge. Encourage students to ask questions and model the kinds of questions students should be asking. These should be about what techniques groups tried, what criteria the designs achieve, how the constraints were or were not accounted for in the design, and whether there are any problems with the design.

Some of the questions they might ask are at the bottom of *Introducing a Solution Showcase*.

NOTES

_____

_____

_____

_____

_____

_____

_____

_____

_____

_____

_____

_____

_____

Test Your Final Design

15 min

Test students' parachutes and discuss what made some parachutes perform very well.

Test Your Final Design

After the *Solution Showcase*, it will be time to find out which parachute falls the slowest. Each group will drop their parachute three times. Your class or teacher will decide on a procedure. Different people use stopwatches differently. It will be important to have a procedure that measures time of fall consistently. You will probably find that one or two parachutes perform a lot better than the others. Identify the best parachutes. Discuss with the class why these parachutes performed so well. Think about how each one was designed using the concepts of gravity and air resistance.

Update the *Project Board*

Now that you have completed the *Parachute Challenge* and discussed why the slowest parachutes in the class fell so slowly, it is time to go back to the *Project Board* for one final edit. You will focus mainly on the middle and last columns, filling in what you have learned about how things fall and identifying how what you have learned applies to designing a slowly falling parachute. Add recommendations to the last column based on your discussions about what made the slowly falling parachutes so slow to fall.

What's the Point?

In design, iteration is an important part of the process. The best products are never from the first draft of the design. They are usually the result of several iterations. Early designs are important. They help designers to see weaknesses in the product. They help them to refine criteria. They also give them a chance to specify constraints more carefully. Designers are then able to figure out how to make the product and what materials to use. The result can be a product that is cheaper to produce or that meets users' needs better than the original design. The best products have a history of much iteration.

DIV 98

○ Engage

When all the groups have presented their *Solution Showcases*, ask students which group's parachute they think will fall the slowest and why. Then let them know that they will now test the parachutes and find out which falls the slowest. Again remind students that this information will help them to make the best recommendation to the cereal company.

⬭ Get Going

Discuss with the class the procedure you plan to use for the parachute drops. Each parachute should be dropped three times and the average value calculated. You should be in charge of the stopwatch. You will need to decide on the dropping procedure which should be done consistently for all the parachutes.

Once the class understands the procedure, have each group drop its parachute three times. Publicly record the times of the parachute's fall and then average the three times to come up with the parachute's average fall time. Consider having group members participate in recording the values and figuring out the average.

With the class, identify the best parachutes. Lead a discussion of why those parachutes performed well connecting the design features with the science content on gravity, air resistance, and stability.

TEACHER TALK

"We've just seen that some of these parachutes performed really well. Why? What's different about the way these parachutes are designed? Do the differences affect how air resistance or gravity work on the parachute? What makes (doesn't make) the parachute stable? **"**

△ Guide

Now that students have completed testing their designs, ask them if they have learned anything new about how parachutes fall. Draw their attention to the *Project Board*, and ask them what they can add to the third column (*What are learning?*). Remind students that they must have a claim written in the fourth column (*What is our evidence?*) that supports what they list in the third column.

Next, ask students what they can put in the last column, (*What does it mean for the challenge or question?*) Remind students of what worked in the *Parachute Challenge*, and what knowledge they used to come up with designs that worked. Update the *Project Board* or have a student update it.

Update the Project Board

10 min

NOTES

....

....

DIVING INTO SCIENCE

Assessment Options

Targeted Concepts, Skills, and Nature of Science	How do I know if students got it?
Scientists must keep clear, accurate, and descriptive records of what they do so they can share their work with others and consider what they did, why they did it, and what they want to do next.	**ASK:** What parts of planning your design did you record during the iterative process? **LISTEN:** Students should indicate what changes they made, their observations, what idea they were testing, what they learned from the model, how effective of a design it was, and ideas they had for the next iteration.

Teacher Reflection Questions

- What difficulties did students have in applying the information they obtained about parachutes to their design?

- How well do students understand the iterative process and its usefulness?

- How did you keep the class focused as different groups were testing their final parachutes? What could you do differently next time?

Back to the Challenge

The Parachute Challenge

◄ $1\frac{1}{2}$ *class periods**

Overview

The class discusses what they should tell the cereal company, and students write letters with their recommendations to the cereal company using the evidence and science knowledge they have gathered to support their recommendations.

Targeted Concepts, Skills, and Nature of Science	Performance Expectations
Explanations are claims supported by evidence, accepted ideas, and facts.	Students should be able to write a good recommendation based on their explanations containing claims, evidence from their investigations, and science knowledge.
Scientists make claims (conclusions) based on evidence obtained (trends in data) from reliable investigations.	
The way an object falls through air depends on its mass, surface area, and other factors.	
Earth's gravity pulls objects toward Earth.	
Air resistance is a force opposing the motion of an object moving through air.	

Materials

1 per class   class *Project Board*

*A class period is considered to be one 40 to 50 minute class.

Homework Options

Reflection

- **Science Process:** Were your final recommendations different from the recommendations you made in Section 4.3? What do you understand better now than you did then? *(Answers should reflect an understanding of the science knowledge that went into the final recommendations.)*

NOTES

Back to the Challenge

The Parachute Challenge

Your challenge was to advise the cereal company about the design of a parachute for inside their cereal boxes. The parachute needs to be inexpensive and easy to put together, and it needs to fall slowly. Look back at the last update of the *Project Board* and use the information to decide what advice to give the cereal company.

Address the Challenge

Decide as a class what you should tell the cereal company. Then write a letter to the cereal company president letting him know what kind of parachute to include in cereal boxes. Remember that good advice includes recommendations that are supported with evidence and science knowledge. Your reasoning will be very important to the cereal company.

DIV 99

DIVING INTO SCIENCE

Back to the Challenge

The Parachute Challenge

15 min.

Lead students in writing their recommendations in a letter to the cereal company.

△ Guide

Finally, discuss with the class what the final recommendation for the cereal company should be. As a class, come up with a recommendation for the cereal company. Then ask each student to write a letter explaining their recommendations to the cereal company.

TEACHER TALK

"Remember a recommendation is a type of claim that needs an explanation. Now that we've seen which parachutes fall the slowest, can we say what our recommendations to the cereal company should be? What are some things that should go in the recommendations? What evidence can we use to back those things up? We want the cereal company to follow our recommendations, so they should be persuasive."

Assist the class in how to begin the letter and then have each student complete the letter. For example:

Dear Cereal Company President,

We have investigated parachutes made form the materials you required (coffee filter, string, tape, and washer), and have come up with the following recommendation to build a slow-falling and cost-effective parachute:

☐ Assess

Students' letters should demonstrate the reasoning that connects the recommendations to the evidence and science knowledge. They should also be specific enough that a parachute could be constructed using the letter as a guide.

◇ Evaluate

Make sure students correctly connect their evidence and science knowledge to their claims and that they discuss how gravity, air resistance, and stability affect the parachute.

Teacher Reflection Questions

- What were the biggest changes that you observed in students' thinking about the challenge in the course of the *Parachute Challenge?* Did you observe anything in the class—anything that you did or that students did—that made these changes possible?

- Were students motivated and engaged by the challenges in this Unit? What will you do next time to encourage this?

- How did you manage the discussion of what recommendations to make to the cereal company? How would you, or did you, resolve disagreements at this stage?

META NOTES

Consider having students read their letters of recommendation to the class, trade their letters and give each other feedback, or collecting their letters and providing individual feedback to the students.

Answer the Big Question

How Do Scientists Work Together to Solve Problems?

◀ *1 class period* *

Overview

Students watch a video in which real-life designers meet a design challenge by investigating the effects of the variables involved, identifying criteria and constraints, trying various ideas, and collaborating to arrive at a final design. Students compare what the designers do in the video to what they did in class. Then, discussing the *Stop and Think* questions and writing answers to the *Reflect* questions, they use what they learned through their projects and the video to answer the *Big Question* of the Unit: *How do scientists work together to solve problems?*

Materials

1 per class	DVD player and television
1 per class	IDEO Video, *Deep Dive*

Activity Setup and Preparation

- Have a DVD player and television ready to show the video before class.
- Preview the video before showing it to the class.

Homework Options

- **Science Process:** How do you think the criteria and constraints would be different for a full-size parachute (one that would carry a person)? Be as specific as you can. *(Students' answers may include: the parachute must wrap and fit in a small pack, it must unfurl when it opens, the speed at landing must be low, and it must carry a human-weight load.)*

- **Science Process:** How would the design process have been different if you had skipped the experiments at the beginning? *(Students' answers should reflect a realistic assessment of how the results of the experiments were useful.)*

*A class period is considered to be one 40 to 50 minute class.

329

1 class period ▶

Answer the Big Question

How Do Scientists Work Together to Solve Problems?

Remind students of the Unit question and how they have been working together to solve challenges (i.e., Book Support, Sandwich-Cookie, Whirligig, and Parachute).

Answer the Big Question

How Do Scientists Work Together to Solve Problems?

You began this Unit with the question: *How do scientists work together to solve problems?* You did several small challenges. As you worked on those challenges you learned about how scientists solve problems. You will now watch a video about real-life designers. You will see what the people in the video are doing that is like what you have been doing. Then you will think about all the different things you have been doing during this Unit. Lastly, you will write about what you have learned about doing science and being a scientist.

Watch

IDEO Video

The video you will watch follows a group of designers at IDEO. IDEO is an innovation and design firm. In the video, they face the challenge of designing and building a new kind of shopping cart. These designers are doing many of the same things that you did. They also use other practices that you did not use. As you watch the video, record the interesting things you see.

After watching the video, answer the questions on the next page. You might want to look at them before you watch the video. Answering these questions should help you answer the *Big Question* of this Unit: *How do scientists work together to solve problems?*

Left: A trio IDEO of designers reviews a proposed concept framework together. **Middle:** A project team compares a series of models for a skate park layout. **Right:** The informal atmosphere of a lounge area acts as a backdrop to a group brainstorm.

DIV 100

Project-Based Inquiry Science

○ **Engage**

Initiate a discussion of what the class has learned in *Deep Dive* about working together to solve problems. Students might say that they have learned to share results, to work in small groups to develop ideas or get data and then to get feedback. Connect this with any *Solution Briefing* you conducted during the *Parachute Challenge* since they will be students' most recent experiences of presenting, to get advice from the class. Ask what some real-world applications of these problem-solving strategies might be.

META NOTES

If you remember a specific instance(s) of groups solving a problem by working together this would be a good example to discuss with the class.

❝What are some of the problems you solved by building parachutes? How about in the *Whirligig Challenge?* What are some of the things the class did that helped to solve those problems? What are some real-world challenges where you could use these skills?❞

◯ Get Going

Next, let students know that they will watch a video about a design team that solves these kinds of problems every day. In this video the team is working on the design of a shopping cart. Go over the *Stop and Think* questions with the class before they watch the video so that they know what to look for in the video. Then show the video to the class.

The video is just over 20 minutes. Students should note relevant information to the *Stop and Think* questions while watching the video.

Watch

25 min.

Prepare students to watch the IDEO design team video.

NOTES

....

....

....

....

....

....

....

....

....

Stop and Think

15 min.

Stop and Think

1. List the criteria and constraints that the design team agreed upon. Which criteria and constraints did the team meet? In your opinion, what other criteria and constraints were not included in the team's discussion?

2. Why did the team split into smaller groups? What did the team hope to accomplish by doing this?

3. What types of investigations did you see the teams doing? What information were the teams trying to collect? Discuss how the information they collected helped the team design a better shopping cart.

4. Why do you think team members' ideas were not being criticized during the initial stages of design?

5. Give at least three examples from the video of how this group of people kept themselves on track to reach their goal on time. (How did they keep the project moving along?)

6. Analyze the team's final product. List three advantages and three disadvantages that you see in the new shopping cart.

7. Compare the practices you saw in the video to the practices that you used in the classroom. How are they different? How are they the same?

8. Give examples from the video of collaboration and design practices that you did not use in the classroom.

9. List two aspects of the IDEO work environment that you liked. List two aspects you didn't like.

10. There are additional responsibilities the IDEO workers have to take on in order to maintain their fun, yet productive, work environment. Identify and discuss at least three of these responsibilities.

11. Relate the responsibilities you have identified to working with a group in the classroom. Justify your choices using evidence.

DIV 101

DIVING INTO SCIENCE

△ Guide and Assess

After the class has seen the video, have students write their answers to the *Stop and Think* questions and then meet with their groups to come up with the best answers.

Once groups have had time to write their answers, discuss them with the class. You can use the following points to guide the discussion.

1. Students should be able to identify most of the criteria and constraints discussed in the video during the interview stage and the initial design discussion called *Deep Dive*. The criteria and constraints mentioned in the video are:

- Criteria: the design must be buildable and it must cost about the same as a traditional shopping cart.

- Constraints: it must be safe for children, it should discourage theft, carts must fit together (nest), groceries should be easy to find, and
it shouldn't be likely to coast away in the wind.

Students should be able to pick out the criteria and constraints met by the final design. The design team met the criteria for child safety, discouraging theft, nesting carts, easily finding groceries, not likely to move in the wind, and easy to move (wheels turned in all directions). They also met the constraint of costing the same as a traditional shopping cart.

Students should come up with other criteria or constraints. These will most likely come from their own experiences with shopping carts. Other possible criteria and constraints not mentioned: They should be durable in all weather conditions; they should not require much cleaning; and that they should have high capacity.

2. Students should demonstrate understanding that smaller groups can obtain background information faster and can focus on one aspect of the larger challenge. This keeps the designers focused, allows each group to optimize just one idea and tends to be a more efficient use of time. The design team determined four focus areas to work on (safety, ease of checkout, ease of finding groceries in cart, ease of shopping) and decided to break into small groups, each one focusing on a specific feature.

3. Students should note that the first investigation the designers did was researching the problem.

Student responses should describe how design teams investigated what problems shopping carts had and how people used them: the team members observed and interviewed shoppers using shopping carts, and they interviewed store employees who worked with the shopping carts about what kinds of issues they had.

Student responses should include how they used the information obtained to plan designs addressing the problems they heard about.

4. Student responses may include how ideas that don't seem to work may become useful when combined with other ideas, how ideas that don't work may lead to ideas that do work, and how critiquing rather than criticizing ideas encourages open brainstorming.

5. Examples might include: the team broke into small groups that each focused one of the issues; team leaders occasionally orchestrated the efforts of the group; and the group voted on ideas to work with, narrowing its focus.

6. Some advantages students might point out are: since it has no components with a lot of surface area (once the baskets are removed), it is unlikely to coast away in the wind; it allows you to leave the cart somewhere and take only the basket with you as you shop; it has a safety seat for children with a work area, the wheels move in all directions. Some disadvantages students might point out are: the plastic baskets may not be durable and may need to be replaced often, and the storage and cleaning of all the components may be tedious and time consuming, the cart may support paper bags to be hung from the hooks when leaving the store.

7. Some of the similarities students may describe are: the class and the design team both did a lot of brainstorming; they both thought about what the criteria and constraints were; they both shared mockups after smaller groups had tackled individual design problems; they both built on everyone's ideas to get the best solution. Some of the differences students may describe are: IDEO started out with the whole group brainstorming general ideas, while the class only brainstormed as a group when it was identifying criteria and constraints and when groups presented their work to the class for feedback.

8. Student responses may include: IDEO's team posted ideas on the walls and then voted on them.

9. Look for areas students liked that might be useful principles. Look for areas students did not like that might be things that could be changed or that were not essential to the design process.

10. Students may point out: team members had to refrain from criticizing one another's ideas; team members had to stay focused — "one conversation at a time"; and team members had to collaborate and build on each other's ideas.

11. Possible ways of relating these to working with a group in the classroom are: brainstorming in a classroom was most effective when students proposed ideas without fear of criticism; when groups focused on investigating one variable, it kept their conversations focused; and the presentations the class gave— including *Investigation Expos* and *Solution Showcases*—allowed groups to build on one another's ideas.

PBIS

Reflect

The following questions review the concepts you have learned in this Unit. Your goal was to understand how scientists solve problems. You should start thinking about yourself as a student scientist. The things you are learning about how scientists solve problems will help you solve problems in the classroom and outside of school too.

Write a brief answer to each question. Use examples from class to justify your answers. Be prepared to discuss your answers in class.

1. *Teamwork* – Scientists and designers often work in teams. Think about your teamwork. Record the ways you helped your team. What things made working together difficult? What did you learn about working as a team?

2. *Learning from other groups* – What did you learn from other groups? What did you help other groups learn? What does it take to learn from another group or help another group learn? How can you make *Plan* and *Solution Briefings* work better?

3. *Informed decision-making* – What is an informed decision? What kinds of informed decisions have you had to make recently? What do you know now about making informed decisions that you didn't know before this Unit? What role do experimental results play in making informed decisions? Provide an example of using experimental results from this Unit.

4. *Iteration* – If at first you don't succeed, try, try again. But simply trying again isn't enough. What else do you need to do to be successful? What happens if your design doesn't work well enough the second time?

5. *Achieving criteria* – What's a criterion? How do you know which criteria are important? What if you can't achieve all of them? How did you generate criteria? On which challenges were you able to achieve the whole set of criteria? How did you have to decide which ones to achieve?

DIV 102

Project-Based Inquiry Science

Reflect
20 min.

Lead students in a discussion that reflects on the main goals of this Unit and answers the Big Question — How do scientists work together to solve problems?

△ Guide and Assess

Next, use the *Reflect* questions to assess students' understanding of the *Big Challenge*. Have students write their answers to the *Reflect* questions, and then lead a class discussion of students' responses. Use the points below to guide the discussion and assess students' answers.

1. Student responses should include the contribution of ideas, whether they were used in the end or not, and choices that students made. Students might describe a difficulty as when they have opposing ideas, when they don't understand a group member's idea, or when they misunderstand each other's ideas. Students may mention that they learned the usefulness of brainstorming with their group, that even ideas is that don't work have value, and building on each other's ideas.

2. Make sure student responses contain the idea of building on each other's ideas and the usefulness of getting advice from the class, particularly in *Plan* and *Solution Briefings*. Students should also describe their ideas on how to improve these briefings. Remind students of the importance of giving credit if they do not bring it up. Students may describe how using information from each other's experiments helped to save time so they didn't have to investigate everything on their own.

3. Students should describe an informed decision as one being based on evidence from experiments and science knowledge. In making recent informed decisions, students should describe decisions they made in the challenges (*Parachute, Whirligig, and Book Support*) to improve the design. Students used the results of their own experiments and science knowledge in the *Parachute Challenge*.

4. Students should describe how using the iterative process helped them to improve their designs. They should mention the process changing one small thing in their design during each iteration as the most effective way of using iteration. If they change many things at once, they won't know which of those things made a difference. Similarly, students should realize that, even if their design doesn't work on the second try, they should not scrap it, but instead they should keep modifying it in small ways.

5. Students should know that a criterion is something that must be achieved to satisfy the requirements of the challenge. Students may mention constraints as well. If they do not, bring up the constraints as being the limitations, such as the materials.

6. Students' answers should say something about fair tests being things that are tested under the same conditions (so procedures must be consistent, only the manipulated and responding variables are allowed to change and all other variables must be held constant), and a test that provides an answer to the investigative question being asked.

7. Students, should understand that when they are investigating something they cannot determine what causes a change if more than one thing is varying. That is why they should only intentionally change one variable, measure how the responding variable changes, and keep all other variables constant if possible. If they cannot keep other variables constant then they should make sure their change is insignificant to their results. Students should describe examples of from the *Whirligig Challenge* and the *Parachute Challenge*.

6. *Running experiments* – What does it mean to do a fair test? What's hard about doing a fair test? What did you learn about running experiments successfully that you didn't know before? Use examples from class to illustrate your answer.

7. *Controlling variables* – What does it mean to control variables? What happens if you don't control important variables? Some variables are more important to control than others. Why? Use examples from class to illustrate.

8. *Using cases to reason* – Scientists and engineers build on each other's work. Sometimes they build on the completed work. Sometimes they build on the ideas of others. You did that as well. What are the benefits of using the ideas and solutions of others? What does it take to understand what other students in your class present?

8. Students should discuss ways that they built on the ideas and solutions of others, and the benefits. They should describe how building on each other's ideas helps to achieve a better solution, and it requires students to be attentive to other students as they present their ideas in class and aware of the goals. Students should include connections of what they did during any of the challenges of this Unit

Then, ask students what the answer is to the *Big Question*: *How do scientists work together to solve problems?*

◇ Evaluate

Students' responses should include all eight of these items: Teamwork; Learning from other groups; Informed decision-making; Iteration; Achieving criteria; Running experiments; Controlling variables; Using cases to reason.

Teacher Reflection Questions

- Did students see the connection between how the IDEO design team solves a design challenge and how they have been solving challenges in this Unit?

- The *Reflect* questions are designed to guide students in putting together ideas they have been introduced to. These questions were for the entire Unit. How could you further guide students to put together these big ideas?

- How did you engage students in watching the video closely and actively, rather than passively?

References

AAAS Project 2061. (1993). Benchmarks for science literacy. New York, New York: Oxford University Press, Inc.

Aikenhead, G.S. (1987). High school graduates' beliefs about science-technology-society III. Characteristics and limitations of scientific knowledge. *Science Education*, 71, 459-487.

Allen, R.D., Statkiewitz, W.R., & Donovan, M. (1983). Student perceptions of evidence and interpretations. In J. Novak (Ed.), *Proceedings of the international seminar: Misconceptions in science and mathematics* (pp. 79-83). Ithaca, NY: Cornell University.

Carey, S., Evans, R., Honda, M., Jay, E., & Unger, C. (1989). An experiment is when you try it and see if it works: A study of grade 7 students' understanding of the construction of scientific knowledge. *International Journal of Science Education*, 11, 514-529.

Dykstra, D., Boyle, C., & Monarch, I. (1992). Studying conceptual change in learning physics. *Science Education*, 76, 615-652.

Jung, W., Pfundt, H., & Rhoeneck, C. von. (Eds.). (1981). *Proceedings of the international workshop on "problems concerning students' representations of physics and chemistry knowledge."* Ludwigsburg: Paedagogische Hochschule.

Kuhn, D. (1991). *The skills of argument*. Cambridge: Cambridge University Press.

Kuhn, D. (1992). Thinking as argument. *Harvard Educational Review*, 62, 155-178

Kuhn, D., Amsel, E., & O'Loughlin, M. (1988). *The Development of Scientific Thinking Skills*. San Diego, CA: Academic Press.

Lederman, N., & O'Malley, M. (1990). Students' perceptions of the tentativeness in science: Development, use, and sources of change. *Science Education*, 74, 225-239.

Linn, M., Clement, C., & Pulos, S. (1983). Is it formal if it's not physics? The influence of content on formal reasoning. *Journal of Research in Science Teaching*, 20, 755-776.

Linn, M. & Swiney, J. (1981). Individual differences in formal thought: Role of cognitions and aptitudes. *Journal of Educational Psychology*, 73, 274-286.

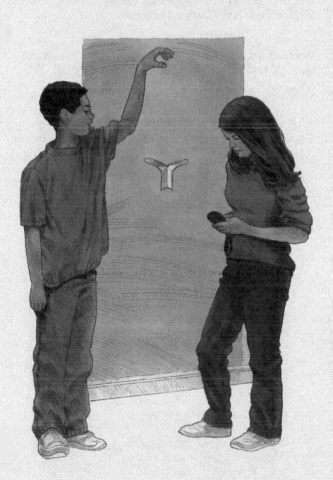

References

McCormick, R., Hennessy, S. & Murphy, P. (1993, April). Problem-solving processes in technology education. Paper presented at the 55th annual conference of the ITEA, Charlotte, NC.

Mead, M., & Metraux, R. (1957). Image of the scientist among high-school students: A pilot study. *Science*, 26, 384-390.

Osborne, R. (1985). Building on children's intuitive ideas. In R. Osborne & P. Freyberg (Eds.), *Learning in Science* (pp. 41-50). Auckland, NZ: Heinemann.

Roseberry, A., Warren, B., & Conant, F. (1992). Appropriating scientific discourse: Findings from language minority classrooms (Working paper 1-92). Cambridge, MA: TERC.

Schauble, L. (1990). Belief revision in children: The role of prior knowledge and strategies for generating evidence. *Journal of Experimental Child Psychology*, 49, 31-57.

Schauble, L., Klopfer, L.E., & Raghavan, K. (1991). Students' transition from an engineering model to a science model of experimentation. *Journal of Research in Science Teaching*, 28, 859-882.

Solomon, J. (1992). Images of physics: How students are influenced by social aspects of science. In R. Duit, F. Goldberg, & H. Niedderer (Eds.), *Research in physics learning: Theoretical issues and empirical studies* (pp. 141-154). Kiel, Germany: Institute for Science Education at the University of Kiel.

Waterman, M. (1983). Alternative conceptions of the tentative nature of scientific knowledge. In J. Novak (Ed.), *Proceedings of the international seminar misconceptions in science and mathematics* (pp. 282-291). Ithaca, NY: Cornell University.

Wollman, W. (1977a). Controlling variables: Assessing levels of understanding. *Science Education*, 61, 371-383.

Wollman, W. (1977b). Controlling variables: A neo-Piagetian developmental sequence. *Science Education*, 61, 385-391.

Wollman, W., & Lawson, A. (1977). Teaching the procedure of controlled experimentation: A Piagetian approach. *Science Education*, 61, 57-70.

Blackline Masters

Diving Into Science Blackline Masters

* Number indicates Learning Set.section.sequence within section

Name: _____ **Date:** _____

Design #	Note cards used	Paper clips used	Rubber bands used	View of design from above	What happened?

Name: _____ **Date:** _____

Design or group	How well it works	What I learned and useful ideas		
		Design ideas	Construction ideas	Science ideas

Plans for our next iteration

Drops on a Penny Data

Name: _____ **Date:** _____

Make a line plot showing each group's results.

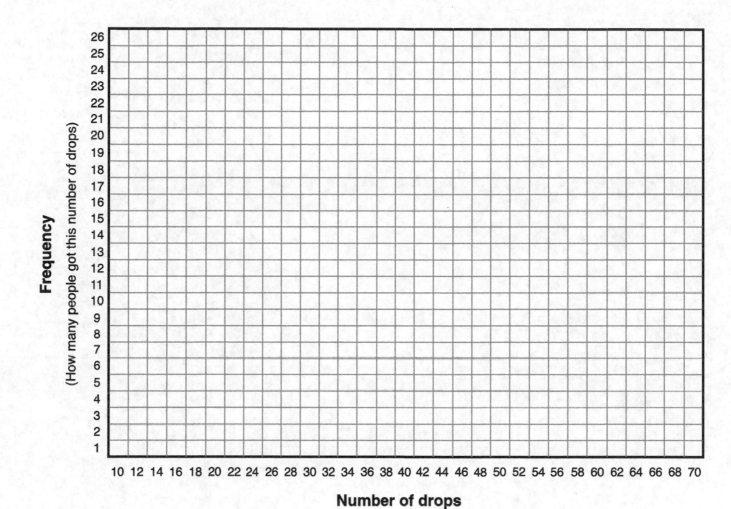

Frequency
(How many people got this number of drops)

Number of drops

Name: _____ **Date:** _____

Demonstration	Predict	Observe	Compare
#1 Describe the event here			
#2 Describe the event here			
#3 Describe the event here			

Name:_____ **Date:**_____

What do we think we know?	What do we need to investigate?	What are we learning?	What is our evidence?	What does it mean for the challenge or question?

Name: _____ Date: _____

Top view	Description (structure, behavior, mechanism)
Side view	**What happened?**

Name: _____ **Date:** _____

Question

What question are you investigating and answering with this experiment?

Prediction

What do you think the answer is and why do you think that?

Variable Identification

- Which part of the whirligig will you be changing in your experiment?

- Which variable will you manipulate (change) in your experiment to test the effects of that whirligig part?

- What conditions and procedures will you keep the same (hold constant or control) in your experiment?

- What will you measure?

- How many trials will you do for each value of your manipulated variable?

Procedure and Data

Write detailed instructions for how to conduct the experiment. Include the following:

- how you will set up the whirligig

- how you drop it

- how you measure its performance

- how you record the data

- how many trials will you do

Name:_____ **Date:**_____

Question

> What question are you investigating and answering with this experiment?

Prediction

> What do you think the answer is and why do you think that?

Variable Identification

> Part of the whirligig you will be changing
>
> Variable you will manipulate
>
> Conditions and procedures you will keep
> the same
>
> What you will measure
>
> Number of trials you will do

Procedure and Data

> Write detailed instructions for how to conduct the experiment.

Name: _____ Date: _____

Data

- Record the results for each trial in a table to keep it organized.

Analyze the data to look for a trend between the variable you changed and the variable you measured. **Hint:** Calculating an average mean or finding the median are two common ways to analyze data.

Quality of Experiment

- How well did your procedure test the effects of the variable you manipulated?

- How well did you control the variables you needed to hold constant?

- How consistently did you follow your procedure each time you ran it?

- How much variation does your data show for each value of your manipulated variable?

If you think you could have done better at any of these, you might need to redesign or re-do your experiment.

Meaning of Experiment

Based on your data analysis, write a statement that could be read or spoken as an answer to your research question. Use the trends you see in the data to show how the variable you changed affected the variable you measured. Also, use any science knowledge you have to support or explain the answer to your research question.

Name:_____ **Date:**_____

Data

Record the results for each trial in a table to keep it organized.

Analyze the data. Show your analysis in this space.

Quality of Experiment

How well did your procedure test the effects of the variable you manipulated?

If you think you could have done better at any of these, you might need to redesign or re-do your experiment.

Meaning of Experiment

Use the trends in your data and your science knowledge to write a statement that answers your research question.

Create Your Explanation

Name: _____ **Date:** _____

Use this page to explain the lesson of your recent investigations.

Write a brief summary of the results from your investigation. You will use this summary to help you write your explanation.

Claim – a statement of what you understand or a conclusion that you have reached from an investigation or a set of investigations.

Evidence – data collected during investigations and trends in that data.

Science knowledge – knowledge about how things work. You may have learned this through reading, talking to an expert, discussion, or other experiences.

Write your explanation using the *Claim*, *Evidence*, and *Science knowledge*.

Name: _____ **Date:** _____

Question

What question are you investigating and answering with this experiment?

Prediction

What do you think the answer is and why do you think that?

Variable Identification

- Which part of the parachute will you be changing in your experiment?

- Which variable will you manipulate (change) in your experiment to test the effects of that parachute part?

- What conditions and procedures will you keep the same (hold constant or control) in your experiment?

- What will you measure?

- How many trials will you do for each value of your manipulated variable?

Procedure and Data

Write detailed instructions for how to conduct the experiment. Include the following:

- how you will set up the parachute

- how you drop it

- how you measure its performance

- how you record the data

- how many trials will you do

Name: _____ **Date:** _____

Data

Record the results for each trial in a table to keep it organized.

Analyze the data to look for a trend between the variable you changed and the variable you measured. **Hint:** Calculating an average mean or finding the median are two common ways to analyze data.

Quality of Experiment

- How well did your procedure test the effects of the variable you manipulated?

- How well did you control the variables you needed to hold constant?

- How consistently did you follow your procedure each time you ran it?

- How much variation does your data show for each value of your manipulated variable?

If you think you could have done better at any of these, you might need to redesign or re-do your experiment.

Meaning of Experiment

Based on your data analysis write a statement that could be read or spoken as an answer to your research question. Use the trends you see in the data to show how the variable you changed affected the variable you measured. Also use any science knowledge you have to support or explain the answer to your research question.

Name:_____ **Date:**_____

Question

> What question are you investigating and answering with this experiment?

Prediction

> What do you think the answer is, and why do you think that?

Variable identification

> Part of the parachute you will be changing
>
> Variable you will manipulate
>
> Conditions and procedures you will keep the same
>
> What you will measure
>
> Number of trials you will do

Procedure and Data

> Write detailed instructions for how to conduct the experiment.

Name:_____ **Date:**_____

Data

> • Record the results for each trial in a table to keep it organized.

Quality of Experiment

> • How well did your procedure test the effects of the variable you manipulated?
>
> • How well did you control the variables?
>
> • How consistently did you follow your procedure?
>
> • How much variation does your data show for each value?

Meaning of Experiment

> Write a statement that could be read or spoken as an answer to your research question.

Name: _____ **Date:** _____

Each time you build and test a design idea or model, you need to test it in a fair way and record the results of that test. Use this sheet to help record your various design ideas and the result of each design.

Draw a simple sketch of your design idea or model. The sketch should help others clearly understand what the design/model looks like.	What is the key idea you were testing in this design or model?
	What did you learn from this design or model? Explain how *effective* this design or model is at accomplishing the challenge or solving the problem.
What happened when you tested the design or model?	What change do you want to test next?

Project Board

Name: _____ **Date:** _____

What do we think we know?	What do we need to investigate?	What are we learning?	What is our evidence?	What does it mean for the challenge or question?

NOTES

NOTES

NOTES

NOTES

NOTES

NOTES